Medical Zoology

Parasites and Vectors for Life Science and Allied Health Students

Prof Fazal Ahmad (Msc, DHAP Ireland)

Made with ❤ on the Notion Press Platform

Dedication

This book is dedicated to the Almighty,
the source of all knowledge, wisdom, and guidance.
Whatever understanding I possess is by his grace alone.

I humbly dedicate this work to the loving memory of my late mother and father.
Their prayers, sacrifices, and moral values shaped my character and education.
Their blessings continue to guide me in every step of my life.

May this work stand as a sincere expression of gratitude, faith, and remembrance.

CONTENTS

Author Notes

Life science is the branch of science that deals with living organisms. It helps us understand how living things grow, function, and interact with their environment. Among all branches of life science, zoology holds a very important place.

Zoology is not limited only to the study of animals. It is the basic foundation from which many medical subjects have developed. Several concepts used in medicine were first explained through zoological studies. Therefore, zoology acts as a bridge between basic biology and medical science.

In medicine, pathology is the subject that explains disease processes. Most of the principles of pathology are strongly connected with zoology and its allied branches. Subjects like biochemistry, biotechnology, medical microbiology, parasitology, mycology, and virology have originated from fundamental zoological concepts.

These subjects help us understand how diseases begin, how they spread in the body, and how the body responds to them. Knowledge of parasites, microbes, and host responses is essential for understanding infection, inflammation, and tissue damage. Without a clear understanding of zoology and life science, pathology becomes difficult to understand properly.

This book, Medical Zoology, is written to highlight that zoology and its subdivisions are core subjects for medical education. Many disease mechanisms taught in pathology and clinical medicine are based on biological principles first studied in zoology.

Readers are encouraged to view zoology as a practical and useful subject. It helps medical students to understand diseases in a better way, improve diagnostic thinking, and support proper treatment. Thus, life science and zoology together form a strong foundation for pathology and modern medicine.

SCAN ME

Scan this code to access pronunciation support for important medical zoology terms. This resource is designed to help students improve clarity in scientific terminology.

Preface

Medical Zoology occupies an important position among the life sciences as it deals with animals that influence human health and disease. Parasites and vectors are responsible for a large number of infections worldwide and continue to pose significant public health challenges, especially in developing regions. A clear understanding of their biology, life cycles, and modes of transmission is essential for students pursuing careers in life science and allied health disciplines.

This book has been written with the objective of providing a systematic and concept oriented approach to medical zoology, with special emphasis on parasites and vectors of medical importance. The content has been developed from a zoological perspective, focusing on morphology, classification, life cycles, host parasite relationships, and transmission pathways. The subject matter has been presented in a simplified and structured manner to facilitate easy understanding without compromising academic standards.

The book is primarily intended for undergraduate and postgraduate students of zoology, paramedical sciences, and allied health courses, including medical laboratory technology and public health programs. It is also expected to serve as a useful reference for teachers and learners seeking a concise yet comprehensive resource in medical zoology.

Care has been taken to maintain academic safety by limiting the scope to biological and laboratory aspects of parasitic infections. Clinical treatment protocols and drug dosage details have been intentionally excluded, as they fall outside the domain of zoology based education. Wherever necessary, standard terminology related to pathogenesis, clinical features, and laboratory diagnosis has been used strictly for educational purposes.

The chapters have been organized logically, beginning with fundamental concepts of medical zoology and parasitology, followed by detailed discussions on protozoa, helminths, and arthropod vectors. Each topic has been arranged to support conceptual clarity and syllabus alignment, particularly for allied health and paramedical courses.

It is hoped that this book will help students develop a strong foundation in medical zoology and enable them to understand the biological basis of parasitic diseases and their prevention. Suggestions for improvement are always welcome, as they will help enhance the quality and usefulness of future editions.

Fazal Ahmad

Acknowledgement

I express my sincere gratitude to all those who have directly or indirectly supported and inspired me in the completion of this book.

First, I respectfully remember and offer my heartfelt thanks to Late Prof Dr U K Singh, Founder of Dr Zakir Husain Institute, whose vision, dedication, and academic leadership deeply inspired me. His commitment to education continues to guide my professional journey.

I am deeply grateful to Late Prof Dr R N Trivedi, former Director and Dean of Indian Institute of Bioinformatics and Biotechnology, who guided me academically and provided me the opportunity to teach Parasitology in the Biotechnology Department. His encouragement and trust allowed me to serve as a faculty member in the year 2004 and strengthened my academic foundation in medical sciences.

I would like to express my sincere thanks to Prof Zeeshan Ahmad, Senior Faculty of Life Science at a Government College. I am highly inspired by his dynamic teaching style and his continuous academic support. His dedication to teaching and mentoring has been a source of motivation in my academic journey.

I also express my deep gratitude to Prof Dr A K Singh, Pathologist at Government Medical College, SKMCH, Muzaffarpur, for his valuable guidance and professional inspiration in the field of pathology and medical sciences.

I sincerely appreciate Prof Gauri Shankar Pandey, Director, Dr Zakir Husain Institute, Patna, for his academic guidance, institutional support, and encouragement, which have significantly contributed to my professional growth.

I also acknowledge with gratitude Prof Dr Rohit Singh, Group Director, and Prof Dr A K Nayak, Advisor of Dr Zakir Husain Institute and IIBM Group. Both have consistently appreciated and supported my academic efforts, for which I remain thankful.

I would like to express my appreciation to Prof Dr S N Pandey, my colleague, for professional interaction and academic association, and to Prof Rajpati Ram, faculty member of Laboratory Technology, for his cooperation and support in academic activities.

Finally, I acknowledge all my teachers, colleagues, students, and well wishers whose support, encouragement, and motivation have helped me complete this academic work successfully.

Introduction

Medical zoology is a specialized branch of zoology that deals with animals which are directly or indirectly related to human health and disease. It mainly focuses on parasites and vectors that play an important role in the causation and transmission of various diseases affecting humans. The subject forms a vital link between basic biological sciences and health related disciplines.

Parasites such as protozoa and helminths have adapted to survive within the human body, often producing significant pathological effects. Arthropods like mosquitoes, flies, lice, ticks, and fleas act as vectors by transmitting disease causing organisms from one host to another. Together, parasites and vectors contribute substantially to the global burden of infectious diseases, particularly in tropical and subtropical regions.

Medical zoology emphasizes the study of morphology, life cycles, host parasite relationships, and modes of transmission of parasitic organisms. Understanding these aspects is essential for accurate laboratory diagnosis, effective prevention, and control of parasitic diseases. Knowledge of medical zoology also helps students appreciate the biological basis of disease transmission and the ecological factors influencing the spread of infections.

For students of life science and allied health disciplines, medical zoology provides a strong conceptual foundation. It supports learning in subjects such as medical laboratory technology, public health, nursing, radiology, and other paramedical courses where an understanding of parasites and vectors is essential. The subject is primarily educational and biological in nature and does not involve clinical treatment or drug prescription.

This book has been designed to present medical zoology in a clear, systematic, and student friendly manner. Emphasis has been placed on core zoological principles, simplified explanations, and logical organization of topics. The content aims to strengthen conceptual understanding while remaining relevant to health science education.

By studying medical zoology, students develop the ability to recognize medically important parasites and vectors, understand their life cycles, and appreciate their role in disease transmission and prevention. This knowledge is fundamental for building competence and confidence in allied health and life science professions.

1. Medical Zoology

Conceptual Framework Based on Organ Localization of Parasites

Medical zoology deals with animals that are directly or indirectly related to human health and disease. In this chapter, the organ wise distribution of protozoan and helminth parasites is presented in tabulated form to explain their relationship with different tissues and organ systems of the human body. These tables are not merely descriptive but provide a conceptual framework for understanding why medical zoology depends on classification, terminology, and systematic organization.

Parasites do not infect the human body in a random manner. Each parasite shows a specific preference for certain tissues or organs. This phenomenon is known as tissue tropism and it forms the biological basis for the classification of parasites and the terminology used in medical zoology.

Organ Name	Protozoa Name	Disease Caused
Intestine	Entamoeba histolytica	Amoebiasis
Intestine	Giardia lamblia	Giardiasis
Intestine	Balantidium coli	Balantidiasis
Intestine	Cryptosporidium species	Cryptosporidiosis
Intestine	Isospora species	Isosporiasis
Blood	Plasmodium species	Malaria
Blood	Trypanosoma species	Trypanosomiasis
Blood	Babesia species	Babesiosis
Brain	Toxoplasma gondii	Toxoplasmosis
Brain	Naegleria fowleri	Primary amoebic meningoencephalitis

Organ Name	Protozoa Name	Disease Caused
Brain	Acanthamoeba species	Granulomatous amoebic encephalitis
Brain	Trypanosoma brucei	African sleeping sickness
Liver	Entamoeba histolytica	Amoebic liver abscess
Liver	Leishmania donovani	Visceral leishmaniasis
Spleen	Leishmania donovani	Visceral leishmaniasis
Lymph nodes	Trypanosoma brucei	African trypanosomiasis
Skin	Leishmania tropica	Cutaneous leishmaniasis
Urogenital tract	Trichomonas vaginalis	Trichomoniasis
Oral cavity	Entamoeba gingivalis	Gingivitis
Oral cavity	Trichomonas tenax	Oral trichomoniasis

Organ wise Localization of Helminths of Medical Importance

Organ Name	Helminth Name	Disease Caused
Intestinal tract	Ascaris lumbricoides	Ascariasis
Intestinal tract	Ancylostoma duodenale	Hookworm disease
Intestinal tract	Necator americanus	Hookworm disease
Intestinal tract	Enterobius vermicularis	Enterobiasis

Organ Name	Helminth Name	Disease Caused
Intestinal tract	Taenia solium	Taeniasis
Intestinal tract	Taenia saginata	Taeniasis
Intestinal tract	Hymenolepis nana	Hymenolepiasis
Intestinal tract	Strongyloides stercoralis	Strongyloidiasis
Liver	Fasciola hepatica	Fascioliasis
Liver	Echinococcus granulosus	Hydatid disease
Liver	Schistosoma species	Hepatic schistosomiasis
Lungs	Paragonimus westermani	Paragonimiasis
Lungs	Ascaris lumbricoides larva	Loeffler syndrome
Brain	Taenia solium larva	Neurocysticercosis
Brain	Echinococcus granulosus	Cerebral hydatid disease
Muscles	Trichinella spiralis	Trichinellosis
Lymphatic system	Wuchereria bancrofti	Lymphatic filariasis
Lymphatic system	Brugia malayi	Lymphatic filariasis
Skin	Dracunculus medinensis	Dracunculiasis
Skin	Onchocerca volvulus	Onchocerciasis
Urinary bladder	Schistosoma haematobium	Urinary schistosomiasis
Blood vessels	Schistosoma species	Schistosomiasis

Why Classification Is Necessary in Medical Zoology

From the tables , it is evident that different parasites localize in specific organs such as the intestine, liver, blood, brain, lungs, skin, lymph nodes, and muscles. Without classification, it would be impossible to study, identify, or communicate information about such a vast diversity of organisms.

Classification helps to group similar organisms together and also helps in understanding biological relationships. These relationships allow prediction of life cycles and modes of transmission and help correlate organ involvement with disease patterns.

For example, intestinal parasites are studied separately from blood parasites. Protozoa are distinguished from helminths based on cellular organization.

Thus, classification is not artificial. It is a biological necessity.

Basis of Classification of Parasites

Parasites are classified primarily on the basis of their cellular organization, body structure, mode of reproduction, life cycle pattern, and site of localization within the host. These biological characteristics help in grouping parasites systematically and in understanding their behavior, transmission, and disease producing potential. On the basis of these criteria, medically important parasites are broadly divided into protozoa and helminths.

Protozoa and Their Organ Specificity

Protozoa are unicellular, eukaryotic organisms belonging to the kingdom Protista. The term protozoa is derived from Greek words meaning first animals, and it was coined because these organisms show animal like characteristics such as motility, ingestion of food, and lack of a rigid cell wall. Protozoa possess a true nucleus and membrane bound organelles, which clearly distinguishes them from bacteria. Bacteria are prokaryotic organisms that lack a true nucleus and cellular organelles, while viruses are acellular entities that can survive and multiply only inside living host cells. Thus, protozoa are fundamentally different from both bacteria and viruses in structure, organization, and mode of life.

Despite being microscopic in size, protozoa show remarkable biological specialization for survival in specific organs of the human body. As illustrated in the figure, some protozoa localize in the intestine, some circulate in the blood, and others invade tissues such as the brain, liver, and lymph nodes. This organ specificity forms the basis for their classification into intestinal protozoa, blood protozoa, and tissue protozoa

Helminths and Tissue Adaptation

Helminths are multicellular parasitic worms belonging to the animal kingdom. The term helminth is derived from a Greek word meaning worm. Unlike protozoa, which are unicellular and microscopic, helminths are multicellular organisms that are usually visible to the naked eye in their adult stage. Helminths possess well differentiated tissues and organ systems adapted for parasitic life. This multicellular organization clearly distinguishes helminths from protozoa, bacteria, and viruses.

Helminths are true animals and show complex structural features such as a body covering, digestive system, reproductive organs, and in some cases specialized attachment structures. Bacteria and viruses lack such organization, and protozoa do not show tissue level differentiation. Because of their larger size and complex body structure, helminths exhibit a different pattern of interaction with the human host compared to protozoa.

One of the most important characteristics of helminths is their ability to adapt to specific tissues and organs of the human body. This phenomenon is known as tissue adaptation. Different helminths show preference for different sites such as the intestine, liver, lungs, blood vessels, lymphatic system, muscles, and subcutaneous tissues. This adaptation is not accidental but results from evolutionary changes that allow the parasite to survive, obtain nutrition, and complete its life cycle within the host.

The tissue adaptation of helminths explains why they are broadly classified into different groups. Intestinal helminths inhabit the gastrointestinal tract and derive nutrition from host food or tissues. Tissue helminths migrate through or reside in organs such as muscles, lungs, or brain, often producing localized pathological effects. Some helminths inhabit blood vessels or lymphatic channels, where they cause systemic manifestations.

This organ specific adaptation plays a crucial role in determining the clinical manifestations, diagnostic methods, and epidemiological patterns of helminthic infections. Therefore, understanding helminths and their tissue adaptation is essential in medical zoology, as it provides the biological basis for classification, disease manifestation, and prevention strategies.

Arthropods as Vectors and Their Adaptation

Arthropods are a large group of invertebrate animals belonging to the phylum Arthropoda. The term arthropod is derived from Greek words meaning jointed legs, reflecting one of their most characteristic features. Arthropods are multicellular animals with a segmented body, jointed appendages, and a hard outer covering called an exoskeleton. These features clearly distinguish arthropods from protozoa and helminths and place them firmly within the animal kingdom.

In medical zoology, certain arthropods are of special importance because they act as vectors of disease. A vector is an organism that transmits disease causing agents from an infected host to a healthy host. Arthropods such as mosquitoes, flies, lice, fleas, ticks, and mites serve as vectors because of their close association with humans and their blood feeding or body contact habits. Unlike parasites that live permanently within the host, vectors usually transmit infection during feeding or contact and then move on to other hosts.

Arthropods are not bacteria or viruses, nor do they directly cause disease by multiplying inside the human body in most cases. Instead, they act as carriers or transmitters of pathogens such as protozoa, helminths, bacteria, and viruses. This role makes arthropods a crucial link between the infectious agent and the human host.

One of the key reasons arthropods are efficient vectors is their remarkable adaptation for survival and transmission. Many arthropods have piercing and sucking mouthparts that allow them to feed on blood without killing the host. Blood feeding provides nutrition for reproduction and simultaneously allows the uptake and transmission of infectious agents. Their small size and ability to fly or crawl enable them to reach multiple hosts within a short period.

Arthropods also show behavioral adaptations that enhance disease transmission. Many vectors are active during specific times of the day or night, which increases contact with humans. Some prefer indoor environments, while others thrive in outdoor habitats close to human settlements. Their breeding habits are well adapted to environmental conditions such as stagnant water, soil, or organic waste, allowing rapid multiplication.

In addition to structural and behavioral adaptations, some arthropods provide a suitable environment for the development of parasites within their bodies. In such cases, the parasite undergoes part of its life cycle inside the vector before being transmitted to humans. This type of transmission is known as biological transmission and highlights the intimate relationship between the arthropod and the pathogen.

The adaptation of arthropods as vectors explains why they are classified separately from parasites in medical zoology. Understanding their structure, behavior, and life cycle is essential for controlling vector borne diseases. Effective prevention strategies such as vector control, environmental management, and personal protection are based on knowledge of these adaptations.

Thus, arthropods as vectors represent a critical component of medical zoology, as they serve as the connecting link between parasites, the environment, and human hosts.

Life Cycle Concepts in Medical Zoology

The life cycle of a parasite refers to the complete sequence of developmental stages through which the organism passes from its origin to maturity and reproduction. In medical zoology, understanding life cycle concepts is fundamental because the survival, transmission, and pathogenicity of parasites depend directly on their life cycles. Each stage of the life cycle is biologically designed to ensure continuation of the species under specific environmental and host conditions.

Life cycles in medical zoology are not random events. They are the result of long evolutionary adaptation that allows parasites to utilize one or more hosts for nourishment, growth, and reproduction. By studying life cycles, it becomes possible to understand how parasites enter the human body, migrate to specific organs, multiply, and exit the host to infect new individuals.

Parasites may complete their life cycle in a single host or may require more than one host. When a parasite completes its entire life cycle in only one host, the life cycle is described as a direct life cycle. In such cases, the parasite is transmitted from one host to another without the involvement of an intermediate host. This type of life cycle is commonly seen in several intestinal parasites and ectoparasites.

In contrast, many parasites require two or more hosts to complete their life cycle. This is known as an indirect life cycle. In these cases, different developmental stages occur in different hosts. The definitive host is the host in which the parasite attains sexual maturity, while the intermediate host harbors larval or developmental stages. This division of life cycle stages among hosts increases the chances of survival and transmission of the parasite.

Life cycle concepts also explain why certain parasites show organ specificity. The migration of parasites through various tissues during different stages of their life cycle determines the organs they inhabit. For example, some parasites enter through the skin, migrate via the bloodstream, and finally settle in specific organs such as the intestine, liver, or lymphatic system. These migratory patterns are essential for diagnosis and classification.

Understanding life cycles is crucial for disease prevention and control. Each stage of the life cycle offers a potential point where transmission can be interrupted. Measures such as sanitation, vector control, safe food practices, and environmental management are designed based on knowledge of parasite life cycles. Without this understanding, effective control strategies cannot be developed.

From a laboratory and public health perspective, life cycle concepts help in selecting appropriate specimens for diagnosis and in predicting the spread of infection within a community. They also provide the biological basis for explaining epidemiological patterns of parasitic diseases.

Thus, life cycle concepts form the core of medical zoology. They integrate classification, host parasite relationships, tissue adaptation, and transmission dynamics into a single biological framework. A clear understanding of life cycles enables students of life science and allied health disciplines to appreciate how parasites survive, spread, and cause disease, making this concept central to the study of medical zoology.

Biological Consequences of Incomplete Life Cycles and Host Transition

Parasites are biologically programmed to complete their life cycles through specific hosts and environments. Each developmental stage is adapted to occur in a particular host, tissue, or external condition. When a parasite fails to reach the required host or vector, its normal development is disrupted. This interruption produces important biological consequences that directly influence morphology, growth, survival, and disease production.

If a parasite does not gain access to the next required host, it usually cannot complete its development. In many cases, the parasite remains in an immature or arrested stage and eventually dies because essential conditions for further growth are absent. Certain developmental changes such as sexual maturation, reproduction, or transformation into adult forms occur only in the appropriate host. Without these conditions, the parasite cannot continue its life cycle.

In some situations, even an incomplete or abnormal developmental stage can cause disease. Large parasites generally do not enter the human body in their adult form. Instead, eggs, cysts, or larval stages enter the host through contaminated food, water, skin penetration, or vectors. Once inside the human body, these immature stages may migrate through tissues and organs, causing mechanical damage, inflammation, or immune reactions. Thus, disease can occur even when the parasite does not complete its full life cycle.

Host transition through vectors represents another important biological concept. Many parasites move from one host to another with the help of vectors such as mosquitoes, flies, ticks, or other arthropods. During this transition, the parasite may undergo developmental changes inside the vector before entering the next host. Each host involved in the life cycle serves a different biological role, and the infection produced in each host may differ in nature and severity.

It is biologically possible for a parasite to exist harmlessly or with minimal effect in one host, such as an animal or plant, while causing significant disease in another host such as humans. In such cases, the first host acts as a reservoir, maintaining the parasite in nature, while humans may become accidental or secondary hosts. Because humans are often not the natural host, the parasite may show abnormal migration or incomplete development, leading to more severe pathological effects.

These concepts explain why parasites show strict host specificity, why vectors are essential for transmission, and why disease patterns differ between hosts. Understanding the biological consequences of incomplete life cycles and host transition helps students appreciate the importance of life cycle studies in medical zoology and provides a strong conceptual foundation for all subsequent chapters.

Definitive Host, Intermediate Host, and Accidental Host Concept

Parasites depend on one or more hosts to complete their life cycle. Each host involved plays a specific biological role. Understanding the concepts of definitive host, intermediate host, and accidental host is essential in medical zoology because these terms explain how parasites grow, reproduce, and cause disease.

A **definitive host** is the host in which the parasite attains sexual maturity or undergoes sexual reproduction. This host is essential for the completion of the parasite life cycle. Without reaching the definitive host, the parasite cannot reproduce sexually and therefore cannot continue its species. In many parasitic infections, humans act as the definitive host, especially for intestinal parasites.

An **intermediate host** is the host in which the parasite undergoes larval development or asexual multiplication. The parasite does not reach sexual maturity in this host. The intermediate host provides suitable biological conditions for growth and transformation of immature stages. In many parasitic diseases, insects or animals act as intermediate hosts and play a crucial role in transmission.

An **accidental host** is a host that is not normally part of the parasite life cycle. When a parasite enters an accidental host, it is usually unable to complete its normal development. However, even in an accidental host, the parasite may migrate through tissues and cause disease. Humans often become accidental hosts for parasites that naturally infect animals.

The biological behavior of a parasite differs depending on the type of host involved. In the definitive host, the parasite follows its normal developmental pattern. In the intermediate host, the parasite develops only partially. In the accidental host, development is abnormal or incomplete, often leading to severe tissue damage or inflammatory reactions.

These host concepts help explain why the same parasite may produce different effects in different hosts. They also clarify why some infections are self limiting while others lead to serious disease. Understanding definitive, intermediate, and accidental hosts is fundamental for studying parasite life cycles, disease transmission, and prevention strategies in medical zoology.

Relationship Between Organ Localization and Disease

Parasites do not infect the human body in a random manner. Each parasite shows a specific preference for certain organs or tissues. This preference is known as organ localization and it plays a decisive role in determining the type of disease produced. The biological characteristics of the parasite and the environment of the host tissue together decide where the parasite survives and multiplies.

Organ localization is closely related to the life cycle and mode of entry of the parasite. Parasites entering through contaminated food or water usually localize in the intestinal tract. Those entering through insect bites or direct penetration often circulate in the blood or migrate to internal organs. Some parasites are capable of crossing tissue barriers and invading organs such as the liver, lungs, brain, lymph nodes, or muscles.

The site of localization directly influences the clinical manifestations of disease. Intestinal parasites mainly cause digestive disturbances and nutritional deficiencies. Blood parasites produce systemic effects such as fever and anemia. Tissue parasites may lead to localized inflammation, organ dysfunction, or neurological symptoms depending on the affected site. Thus, the same biological organism can produce different disease patterns based on where it localizes in the body.

Organ localization also determines the methods used for laboratory diagnosis. Stool examination is useful for intestinal parasites, blood examination is required for blood parasites, and tissue or fluid samples are needed for parasites affecting internal organs. Therefore, knowledge of organ localization guides the selection of appropriate diagnostic specimens.

From a public health perspective, understanding organ localization helps in predicting disease severity, transmission patterns, and preventive strategies. It also explains why certain infections are mild while others are severe or life threatening. Organ specific adaptation reflects the evolutionary success of parasites and highlights the importance of biological specialization in disease causation.

Thus, the relationship between organ localization and disease provides a unifying concept that links parasite biology, classification, life cycle, host interaction, diagnosis, and prevention. This understanding forms a strong conceptual foundation for the detailed study of parasites and vectors in subsequent chapters

Sub branches of Medical Zoology

Medical Zoology is the applied study of animals that directly or indirectly affect human health. It is traditionally divided into the following sub branches.

1. **Medical Parasitology**
   Study of animal parasites of humans, including protozoa and helminths, their life cycle, transmission, pathology, diagnosis, treatment, and prevention.
2. **Medical Entomology**
   Study of insects and arthropods of medical importance such as mosquitoes, flies, lice, fleas, ticks, and mites, with emphasis on vector borne diseases.
3. **Medical Malacology**
   Study of molluscs, mainly snails and slugs, which act as intermediate hosts in diseases like schistosomiasis and fascioliasis.
4. **Medical Arachnology**
   Study of arachnids such as ticks, mites, spiders, and scorpions that cause disease, infestation, envenomation, or allergic reactions.
5. **Medical Helminthology**
   Study of parasitic worms including nematodes, cestodes, and trematodes affecting humans, often treated as a focused subdivision within parasitology.
6. **Medical Protozoology**
   Study of disease causing protozoa such as Plasmodium, Entamoeba, Leishmania, and Trypanosoma, also commonly treated as a subdivision of parasitology.
7. **Venomous and Poisonous Animals in Medicine**
   Study of snakes, scorpions, spiders, jellyfish, and other animals producing venom or toxins, including mechanisms of toxicity and clinical management.
8. **Zoonoses and Reservoir Hosts**
   Study of animals that act as natural reservoirs of human diseases, focusing on transmission from animals to humans.

- **Forensic and Applied Medical Zoology**
  Application of zoological knowledge in medico legal cases, forensic entomology, and public health investigations.

- In most undergraduate and allied health science syllabi, Medical Parasitology and Medical Entomology form the core, while the other branches are introduced as applied or extension topics to strengthen clinical relevance.

Role of Radiology in Medical Zoology

Medical zoology primarily deals with the biological aspects of parasites and vectors, including their morphology, life cycles, and organ localization. Radiology plays a supportive role in medical zoology by helping to visualize the effects of parasitic infections within the human body. While radiology does not identify parasites directly, it provides valuable information about organ involvement, tissue damage, and disease progression.

Many parasites localize in specific organs such as the liver, lungs, brain, muscles, and lymphatic system. Imaging techniques such as ultrasonography, X ray, computed tomography, and magnetic resonance imaging help in detecting structural changes produced by these parasites. These changes may include cyst formation, organ enlargement, calcification, obstruction, or tissue destruction.

Radiology is especially useful in identifying tissue and organ involvement in parasitic diseases. For example, cystic lesions in organs, space occupying lesions in the brain, enlargement of lymphatic channels, or changes in abdominal organs can suggest parasitic etiology when correlated with clinical and laboratory findings. Thus, radiological imaging supports the understanding of organ localization discussed in medical zoology.

From an educational perspective, radiology helps students of life science and allied health disciplines visualize the biological concepts they study in medical zoology. It reinforces the relationship between parasite localization and disease manifestation without entering into clinical treatment protocols. Radiology therefore acts as a bridge between biological knowledge and applied health sciences.

In medical zoology, radiology is not used as a diagnostic replacement but as a complementary tool that enhances understanding of parasite behavior within the host. Its role highlights the interdisciplinary nature of health sciences and strengthens the conceptual framework of organ localization and disease.

Role of Medical Laboratory Technology in Medical Zoology

Medical zoology provides the biological foundation for understanding parasites and vectors, while medical laboratory technology plays a crucial role in the practical detection and identification of these organisms. Laboratory techniques transform theoretical knowledge of parasites into observable and measurable evidence, making medical zoology applicable in health sciences.

Parasites often produce characteristic forms such as cysts, eggs, larvae, or trophozoites that can be identified through laboratory examination. Medical laboratory technology enables the collection, processing, and microscopic examination of appropriate specimens such as stool, blood, urine, sputum, and tissue samples. The selection of specimens is guided by the knowledge of organ localization and life cycle patterns studied in medical zoology.

Microscopy remains one of the most important tools in medical zoology. Through direct wet mounts, stained preparations, and concentration techniques, laboratory professionals can visualize parasitic stages and correlate them with their biological characteristics. This visual confirmation reinforces concepts such as morphology, developmental stages, and host parasite interaction.

Medical laboratory technology also supports epidemiological understanding by helping to identify the prevalence and distribution of parasitic infections in communities. Routine laboratory screening contributes to surveillance programs and public health planning by providing data on parasitic disease burden.

From an educational perspective, medical laboratory technology helps students connect zoological concepts with real world application. Observing parasites under the microscope strengthens conceptual clarity and builds confidence in understanding medical zoology. It also highlights the importance of accuracy, standard procedures, and scientific discipline in parasitic identification.

In medical zoology, medical laboratory technology does not replace biological understanding but complements it. Together, they form a complete framework that links parasite biology, organ localization, disease manifestation, and public health relevance.

2. Basic Concepts of Parasitology

Introduction to Parasitology

Parasitology is a fundamental discipline in medical science that deals with the study of parasites, their biology, their interaction with the host, and the diseases they produce. Although parasites are often described simply as organisms that live at the expense of another organism, this definition alone is insufficient to explain their medical importance.

Parasites represent a highly evolved group of organisms that have developed complex survival strategies over millions of years. Through the process of evolution, parasites have adapted themselves to live within or on the surface of the host, often causing disease while ensuring their own continuation. This delicate balance between parasite survival and host damage forms the core subject matter of parasitology.

In medical practice, parasitology is critically important because parasitic infections remain a major cause of morbidity and mortality, especially in developing countries. These infections affect millions of people worldwide and contribute significantly to malnutrition, anemia, organ damage, impaired growth in children, and reduced quality of life._Many parasitic diseases are chronic in nature and may remain undiagnosed for long periods due to their slow progression and nonspecific symptoms.

Parasitology is not limited to the study of the parasite alone. It also includes the study of the host response, the environment, and the factors that influence transmission. The outcome of parasitic infection depends on multiple variables such as the type of parasite, the infective dose, the route of entry, the immune status of the host, and environmental conditions. Therefore, parasitology provides an integrated understanding of disease rather than an isolated description of organisms.

Another important aspect of parasitology is the study of life cycles. Parasites do not infect humans randomly. Each parasite follows a specific life cycle that involves one or more hosts and distinct developmental stages. Knowledge of these life cycles is essential for understanding how infections occur, how they spread in the community, and how they can be prevented or controlled. Many public health interventions are based directly on breaking the life cycle of parasites.

Parasitology also has a strong connection with other medical disciplines such as pathology, microbiology, immunology, public health, and clinical medicine. In pathology, parasitology helps explain tissue damage and disease mechanisms. In public health, it guides preventive strategies and control programs. For clinicians, a sound understanding of parasitology is essential for accurate diagnosis, appropriate treatment, and effective patient counseling.

Thus, parasitology is not merely the study of parasites. It is the study of host parasite relationships, disease mechanisms, transmission dynamics, and preventive strategies. A clear understanding of basic concepts of parasitology forms the foundation for learning medical zoology and for managing parasitic diseases effectively in clinical and community settings.

Basic Concepts of Parasitology

A parasite is a living organism that lives on or inside another living organism, known as the host, and derives nutrition, shelter, and support from the host while causing harm to it.

In zoology, the term parasite is used in a **specific biological sense**. Parasitism represents a stable and well defined mode of life in which the organism is adapted to depend on the host for survival. This relationship is not accidental or temporary. It is the result of long evolutionary processes that allow the parasite to live, grow, and reproduce within the host environment.

From a zoological perspective, a parasite is identified mainly by its **degree of dependence on the host**. True parasites are biologically dependent on the host to complete their normal life cycle. They show special structural and physiological adaptations such as organs of attachment, protective coverings, and mechanisms to evade host immunity. Protozoa and helminths are classical examples of such parasites, and both belong to the animal kingdom. Therefore, they are studied under zoology and parasitology.

A common doubt is why **pathogenic bacteria**, even though they live inside the human body and cause disease, are not called parasites. In zoology, parasitism is not defined merely by disease production. Bacteria are excluded because they do not belong to the animal kingdom. They are prokaryotic organisms and lack a true nucleus and membrane bound organelles. Due to this fundamental difference in cellular organization, bacteria are studied under microbiology and not under zoology.

Another important distinction is biological dependence. Most pathogenic bacteria are **not obligatorily dependent on the host**. They can survive and multiply outside the human body in soil, water, air, or food. Their presence inside the host is often temporary and opportunistic rather than an essential requirement for completion of a fixed life cycle. In contrast, true parasites require the host for growth, development, or reproduction.

Moreover, bacterial infections are usually **acute infective processes**, whereas parasitism represents a long term biological association. Parasitic infections are often chronic and involve continuous interaction between the parasite and host tissues over extended periods.

Thus, in zoology, an organism is termed a parasite only when it shows evolutionary adaptation to parasitic life, biological dependence on the host, a stable host parasite relationship, and belongs to the animal kingdom. This clear distinction forms the foundation of parasitology as a branch of medical zoology.

Types of Parasites

Parasites can be classified in different ways based on their **site of living**, **dependence on the host**, and **duration of association with the host**. This classification helps in understanding their biology, life cycle, and disease producing ability.

Based on Site of Living

Ectoparasites

Ectoparasites live on the surface of the host body. They usually infest skin, hair, or external body surfaces.
Examples include lice, ticks, mites, and fleas.
They mainly cause irritation, blood loss, allergic reactions, and may act as vectors for disease transmission.

Endoparasites

Endoparasites live inside the body of the host. They may inhabit the intestine, blood, tissues, or organs.

Examples include protozoa and helminths.
Endoparasites are responsible for many systemic and chronic diseases.

Based on Dependence on the Host

Obligate parasites
Obligate parasites are completely dependent on the host for survival. They cannot complete their life cycle without the host.
Most protozoa and helminths fall under this category.

Facultative parasites
Facultative parasites are organisms that normally live freely in the environment but may become parasitic under certain conditions.They do not require the host for their normal life cycle but can cause disease if they enter the host.

Based on Duration of Association

Permanent parasites
Permanent parasites remain in or on the host for most or all of their life cycle.
Examples include tapeworms and lice.

Temporary parasites
Temporary parasites visit the host only for feeding and then leave.
Examples include mosquitoes and bed bugs.

Based on Occurrence in the Host

Accidental parasites
Accidental parasites infect a host in which they do not normally live. In such hosts, they may not complete their life cycle and often cause severe disease.

Erratic parasites

Erratic parasites are parasites that reach an **abnormal or unusual site** within the host body instead of their normal habitat. This abnormal migration is **accidental** and does not occur because the target organ is weak, damaged, or diseased.

Parasites do not possess the ability to identify or select weak organs. Erratic migration usually occurs when the parasite enters an incorrect pathway, is carried passively by blood or lymphatic circulation, or fails to reach its normal site during development. Factors such as abnormal route of entry, high parasite load, host immune response, or mechanical disturbances may contribute to this misplaced localization.

The organs involved in erratic parasitism are generally **normal and healthy initially**. Tissue damage occurs only after the parasite lodges in the abnormal site. Since the parasite is not adapted to survive in that organ, it produces marked inflammatory reactions, mechanical obstruction, or destruction of tissue, often resulting in severe clinical manifestations.

Thus, erratic parasitism refers to **wrong localization of the parasite**, not weakness of the organ, and is associated with increased tissue damage due to abnormal host parasite interaction.

Monoxenous parasites
These parasites complete their life cycle in a single host.

Heteroxenous parasites
These parasites require more than one host to complete their life cycle.

Host

A host is an organism that harbors the parasite and provides nutrition and shelter.

Types of host

1. **Definitive host**
   The host in which the parasite attains sexual maturity or undergoes sexual reproduction.
2. **Intermediate host**
   The host in which the parasite undergoes larval development or asexual reproduction.
3. **Reservoir host**
   An animal host that maintains the parasite in nature and acts as a source of infection for humans.
4. **Accidental host**
   A host in which the parasite does not normally complete its life cycle.

Revision in short Types of Parasites

1. **Ectoparasite**
   Parasites that live on the surface of the host.
2. **Endoparasite**
   Parasites that live inside the body of the host.
3. **Obligate parasite**
   Parasites that cannot survive without a host.
4. **Facultative parasite**
   Organisms that can live freely but may become parasitic under certain conditions.
5. **Permanent parasite**
   Parasites that remain in the host for most of their life cycle.
6. **Temporary parasite**
   Parasites that visit the host only for feeding.

Types of Hosts Based on Life Cycle

Definitive host
The host in which the parasite attains sexual maturity and undergoes sexual reproduction.

Intermediate host
The host in which the parasite undergoes larval development or asexual multiplication.

Paratenic host
A parasite present in a **paratenic host** usually causes **little or no disease**, because it does not undergo development or multiplication in that host. The paratenic host mainly serves as a **transport or carrier host**, allowing the parasite to survive until it reaches the definitive host.

In contrast, the **definitive host** is the host in which the parasite completes its development or sexual reproduction. In the definitive host, the parasite becomes biologically active, multiplies, and produces **significant pathological effects**.

Vector host
The host that transmits the parasite from one host to another and may support part of its development.

Life Cycle of Parasites

The life cycle of a parasite refers to the **sequence of developmental stages** that the parasite passes through from one generation to the next. These stages occur in a **definite and fixed order** and are the result of long evolutionary adaptation. The life cycle of a parasite is not random. It is biologically programmed and essential for the survival, multiplication, and transmission of the parasite.

In parasitology, understanding the life cycle is extremely important because it explains **how infection begins, how the parasite spreads, and how disease can be prevented or controlled**. Each parasite has its own characteristic life cycle, which determines the host involved, the route of transmission, and the site of infection in the human body.

A parasite may complete its life cycle in **one host or more than one host**. Based on this, life cycles are broadly classified into two types.

Direct life cycle
In a direct life cycle, the parasite completes its entire development in a single host. There is no requirement for an intermediate host. Transmission usually occurs directly from one host to another through ingestion, contact, or penetration of the skin. Such parasites are commonly transmitted by contaminated food, water, or soil.

Indirect life cycle
In an indirect life cycle, the parasite requires **two or more hosts** to complete its development. One host acts as the definitive host, while the other acts as the intermediate host. Sometimes vectors are also involved. Developmental stages occur in different hosts, and transmission depends on the completion of these stages.

The life cycle of parasites is closely related to **pathogenicity**. Disease occurs when the parasite enters the human body at a particular stage of its life cycle. Some stages are infective, while others are diagnostic. Knowledge of these stages helps in laboratory diagnosis and treatment planning.

Life cycle study also plays a vital role in **prevention and control**. Many public health measures are designed to interrupt the life cycle of parasites by eliminating intermediate hosts, controlling vectors, improving sanitation, and promoting personal hygiene.Thus, the life cycle of parasites forms the **foundation of parasitology**, linking parasite biology with clinical disease, diagnosis, treatment, and public health control strategies.

Understanding life cycle is essential for

Diagnosis
Treatment
Prevention
Control strategies

Mode of Transmission

Parasites are transmitted by
Ingestion of contaminated food or water
Skin penetration
Insect bite
Vertical transmission
Autoinfection

Pathogenicity of Parasites

Pathogenicity refers to the ability of a parasite to cause disease. Disease may occur due to
Mechanical damage
Toxic substances
Immune reactions
Nutritional deprivation

Importance of Parasitology in Medicine

Parasitology helps in
Understanding cause of parasitic diseases
Planning treatment
Preventing transmission
Controlling community spread

3. Host Parasite Relationship

Introduction

Parasitic diseases are not caused by parasites alone. The development, severity, and outcome of a parasitic infection depend on the **interaction between the host and the parasite**. This interaction is known as the **host parasite relationship**.

The same parasite may produce severe disease in one individual while causing mild infection or no symptoms in another. This variation occurs due to differences in host factors such as immunity, nutrition, age, and general health, as well as parasite factors like virulence and number of organisms.

The host parasite relationship is a **dynamic and continuous process**. The parasite attempts to survive and multiply within the host, while the host activates defense mechanisms to eliminate or control the parasite. Disease occurs when this balance is disturbed.

Understanding the host parasite relationship is essential in medical science because it explains the pathogenesis of parasitic diseases, variations in clinical presentation, and the basis of prevention and control strategies.

Nature of Host Parasite Relationship

The host parasite relationship is a **dynamic biological interaction** in which both the host and the parasite influence each other. It is not a fixed or static relationship and may change with time, immune status of the host, and environmental conditions.

In this relationship, the parasite attempts to survive, multiply, and complete its life cycle within the host. At the same time, the host activates various defense mechanisms to eliminate or control the parasite. The outcome of this interaction determines whether the infection remains mild, becomes severe, or stays asymptomatic.

The host parasite relationship may lead to different outcomes depending on the balance between host defense mechanisms and parasitic activity. In some cases, the host successfully eliminates the parasite through effective immune responses, resulting in complete recovery without long term effects. In other situations, the parasite may persist within the host without producing any clinical symptoms, leading to an asymptomatic or carrier state. Sometimes, the parasite survives for a long period and causes chronic infection characterized by intermittent or periodic exacerbations of symptoms. In severe cases, when the parasite multiplies unchecked due to high virulence or compromised host immunity, it may result in serious disease with extensive tissue damage and systemic involvement.

In many parasitic infections, a **balance is established** between the host and the parasite. The parasite survives without causing serious damage, and the host tolerates its presence. Disease occurs when this balance is disturbed due to factors like reduced immunity, increased parasite load, or increased virulence of the parasite.

Thus, the nature of host parasite relationship explains the variation in clinical manifestations and the course of parasitic diseases in different individuals.

Factors Related to the Parasite

The severity and outcome of parasitic infection depend largely on characteristics of the parasite itself. Certain biological properties of parasites determine their ability to invade the host, survive within tissues, multiply, and produce disease. These parasite related factors play a key role in shaping the host parasite relationship.

1. Virulence of the parasite

Virulence refers to the ability of a parasite to cause damage and produce disease in the host. Highly virulent parasites invade tissues aggressively, cause extensive cellular injury, and lead to severe clinical manifestations. Parasites with low virulence may produce mild symptoms or remain asymptomatic.

2. Number of parasites entering the host

The severity of infection is directly related to the parasite load. A small number of parasites may be controlled effectively by the host immune system, whereas a large number can overwhelm host defenses and result in severe disease.

3. Site of localization

The organ or tissue in which the parasite resides greatly influences disease outcome. Parasites located in vital organs such as brain, liver, lungs, or blood produce more serious clinical effects compared to those residing in less critical tissues.

4. Duration of infection

Long standing parasitic infections often lead to chronic inflammation, tissue destruction, and long term complications. Persistence of parasites within the host increases the likelihood of chronic disease.

5. Ability to evade host immune response

Some parasites possess mechanisms that help them escape or suppress host immune defenses. This ability allows parasites to survive for long periods within the host and contributes to recurrent or persistent infections.

Factors Related to the Host

The outcome of a parasitic infection is not determined by the parasite alone. Characteristics of the host play an equally important role in deciding whether the infection will be mild, severe, or asymptomatic. Host related factors influence susceptibility, immune response, and the overall course of disease.

1. Age of the host

Age significantly affects host response to parasitic infections. Infants and elderly individuals usually have weaker immune defenses and are more susceptible to severe infections. Adults with a mature immune system often show better resistance.

2. Nutritional status

Good nutrition strengthens host immunity, whereas malnutrition reduces resistance to infection. Deficiency of proteins, vitamins, and minerals impairs immune responses and allows parasites to multiply more easily.

3. Immune status of the host

Immunity is one of the most important host factors. Individuals with compromised immunity due to disease, drugs, or other conditions are more prone to severe and prolonged parasitic infections. A strong immune system can limit parasite growth and reduce disease severity.

4. Genetic factors

Genetic makeup of the host influences susceptibility or resistance to certain parasitic infections. Some individuals are naturally more resistant, while others are more prone to severe disease due to inherited traits.

5. Presence of associated diseases

Coexisting illnesses such as chronic infections or systemic diseases weaken host defenses. These conditions reduce the ability of the host to control parasitic infections and increase the risk of complications.

Balance Between Host and Parasite

In many parasitic infections, a state of balance is established between the host and the parasite. In this condition, the parasite survives and multiplies within the host without causing severe damage, while the host tolerates the presence of the parasite without developing serious disease. This balanced relationship allows both the host and the parasite to coexist for a long period.

The parasite adapts to the host environment by limiting tissue damage and avoiding strong immune reactions. At the same time, the host immune system controls parasite multiplication without completely eliminating it. As a result, the infection may remain mild, chronic, or asymptomatic.

Disease develops when this balance is disturbed. Factors such as reduced host immunity, poor nutrition, stress, aging, or increased virulence and parasite load can shift the balance in favor of the parasite. When this happens, uncontrolled multiplication of the parasite leads to tissue damage, inflammation, and clinical symptoms.

Thus, the concept of balance between host and parasite explains why many parasitic infections remain silent for long periods and why sudden worsening of disease may occur when host defenses are weakened.

Effects of Parasite on the Host

Parasites produce disease in the host by various mechanisms. The effects produced by parasites depend on their location, number, duration of infection, and interaction with host tissues. These effects may be local or systemic and are responsible for the clinical manifestations of parasitic diseases.

1. Mechanical damage

Parasites may cause direct physical damage to host tissues by their size, movement, or attachment to organs. This can result in obstruction, pressure effects, tissue injury, and impairment of normal organ function.

2. Nutritional deprivation

Parasites compete with the host for nutrients such as proteins, vitamins, and minerals. This leads to nutritional deficiencies, weight loss, anemia, and general weakness, especially in chronic infections.

3. Toxic and metabolic effects

Some parasites release toxic substances or metabolic byproducts that damage host tissues. These substances may cause fever, inflammation, and systemic illness.

4. Inflammatory reaction

The presence of parasites triggers inflammatory responses in host tissues. Persistent inflammation can lead to tissue swelling, pain, fibrosis, and long term organ damage.

5. Immunological effects

Parasitic infections may alter host immune responses, leading to hypersensitivity reactions, allergic manifestations, or immune mediated tissue injury. In some cases, immune responses contribute more to disease severity than the parasite itself.

Host Response to Parasitic Infection

When a parasite enters the body, the host activates various defense mechanisms to prevent infection or limit its effects. The host response may be immediate or delayed and plays a crucial role in determining the severity and outcome of parasitic diseases.

1. Local tissue response

At the site of parasite entry or localization, the host may show tissue reactions such as redness, swelling, and cellular infiltration. These local responses attempt to restrict parasite spread and reduce tissue damage.

2. Inflammatory response

Parasitic infections commonly induce inflammation characterized by accumulation of immune cells and release of inflammatory mediators. While inflammation helps in controlling the parasite, prolonged inflammation may contribute to tissue injury.

3. Immune response

The host immune system produces antibodies and activates immune cells to recognize and destroy parasites. Both innate and acquired immune responses are involved in controlling parasitic infections.

4. Hypersensitivity reactions

In some individuals, parasitic antigens trigger exaggerated immune responses leading to allergic or hypersensitivity reactions. These reactions may cause itching, rashes, respiratory symptoms, or tissue damage.

Here is the section written in the **same academic tone and structure**, consistent with the rest of Chapter 3.

Adaptations of Parasites in the Host

Parasites have developed several structural, functional, and biological adaptations that enable them to survive, multiply, and complete their life cycle within the host. These adaptations help parasites overcome host defense mechanisms and establish long term infections.

1. Structural adaptations

Many parasites possess specialized structures such as hooks, suckers, spines, or adhesive organs that help them attach firmly to host tissues. These structures prevent their removal by normal physiological processes like peristalsis or blood flow.

2. Physiological adaptations

Parasites are adapted to survive in low oxygen environments and hostile conditions within the host. Some parasites can resist digestive enzymes, bile salts, or acidic environments, allowing them to live in organs such as the intestine or stomach.

3. Immune evasion mechanisms

Parasites have the ability to evade or suppress host immune responses. They may alter their surface antigens, hide within host cells, or release substances that reduce immune activity. These mechanisms allow parasites to survive for long periods within the host.

4. High reproductive capacity

Many parasites produce a large number of offspring to ensure survival and continuation of their species. This compensates for losses during transmission and increases the chances of successful infection of new hosts.

5. Life cycle adaptations

Parasites often have complex life cycles involving multiple hosts or developmental stages. These adaptations help them survive in different environments and increase the efficiency of transmission from one host to another.

Understanding the host parasite relationship is of great importance in medical science. It explains why parasitic infections vary in severity from person to person and why the same parasite may produce different clinical manifestations in different individuals.

Knowledge of this relationship helps clinicians understand the **pathogenesis of disease**, including tissue damage, immune reactions, and systemic effects produced during parasitic infections. It also aids in identifying individuals who are at higher risk of severe disease, such as those with poor immunity or nutritional deficiencies.

The concept of host parasite relationship is essential for **accurate diagnosis**, as clinical features depend not only on the parasite but also on host response. It also plays a key role in **planning treatment**, since immune status and parasite load influence therapeutic outcome.

In public health, understanding host parasite interaction helps in designing **preventive and control measures**, including sanitation, vector control, health education, and early detection of infections.

Thus, knowledge of host parasite relationship forms the foundation for effective diagnosis, treatment, prevention, and control of parasitic diseases.

4. Classification of Parasites

Introduction

Parasites include a wide variety of organisms that differ in size, structure, cellular organization, and complexity. Some parasites are unicellular and microscopic, while others are multicellular and visible to the naked eye. Because of this diversity, a proper system of classification is necessary to study parasites in a systematic and scientific manner.Classification helps in understanding the biological nature of parasites, their relationship with the host, their life cycles, and the diseases they cause. In medical zoology, parasites are broadly classified based on their **cellular organization and body structure**, which also aligns with modern biological classification systems.

Kingdom is the **highest major taxonomic category** in biological classification, placed just below domain. It includes a **large group of organisms** that share **fundamental structural, cellular, and functional characteristics**.

In simple terms, a kingdom groups together organisms that are **basically similar in their overall body organization and life processes.**

In **Animal Kingdom classification**, a **kingdom** is defined as

A large group of living organisms that share common features such as

1. Type of cell organization
2. Mode of nutrition
3. Level of body complexity
4. Method of reproduction
5. Pattern of development

Based on these basic characters, all animals are placed together in **Kingdom Animalia.**

Kingdom Animalia includes **all multicellular, eukaryotic organisms** that

1. Do not have a cell wall
2. Are heterotrophic in nutrition
3. Usually show active movement at some stage of life
4. Have tissues and organs for specific functions

This common foundation allows further classification into **phylum, class, order, family, genus, and species**, which is essential for understanding medically important parasites.

Five Kingdom System of Classification

Living organisms are classified into five major kingdoms based on cellular organization, mode of nutrition, and level of complexity. This system was proposed to bring uniformity and clarity in biological classification.

The five kingdoms are

1. Monera
2. Protista
3. Fungi
4. Plantae
5. Animalia

From a medical zoology and parasitology point of view, parasites mainly belong to **two kingdoms**, namely **Kingdom Protista** and **Kingdom Animalia**. Protozoan parasites are placed under Kingdom Protista, while multicellular parasitic worms known as helminths are placed under Kingdom Animalia.

Parasites in Five Kingdom System

Kingdom Monera

This kingdom includes bacteria. Bacteria are unicellular organisms without a true nucleus. Although many bacteria are pathogenic, they are **not considered animal parasites** and are studied under microbiology, not medical zoology.

Kingdom Protista

Protozoan parasites belong to this kingdom. They are unicellular organisms with a true nucleus and cellular organelles. Despite being single celled, protozoa perform all vital life functions and are considered the **simplest form of animals**.

Protozoan parasites are of major medical importance and cause diseases such as amoebiasis and malaria.

Kingdom Fungi

Some fungi are parasitic and cause infections in humans. However, fungal infections are studied under medical mycology and are not included in medical zoology.

Kingdom Plantae

Plants do not include medically important parasites affecting humans directly. Hence, they are not relevant in medical parasitology.

Kingdom Animalia

Most multicellular parasites belong to this kingdom. These parasites are known as **metazoan parasites** or **helminths**. They possess well developed body organization and complex life cycles.Helminths are further classified into flatworms and roundworms based on body structure.

Relevance to Medical Zoology

Thus, in medical zoology
Protozoa are studied under Kingdom Protista
Helminths are studied under Kingdom Animalia

This classification forms the foundation for further detailed classification of parasites into protozoa and helminths, as shown in the diagram.

Classification of Parasites

Parasites are broadly classified into **Protozoa** and **Helminths** based on cellular organization and body structure.

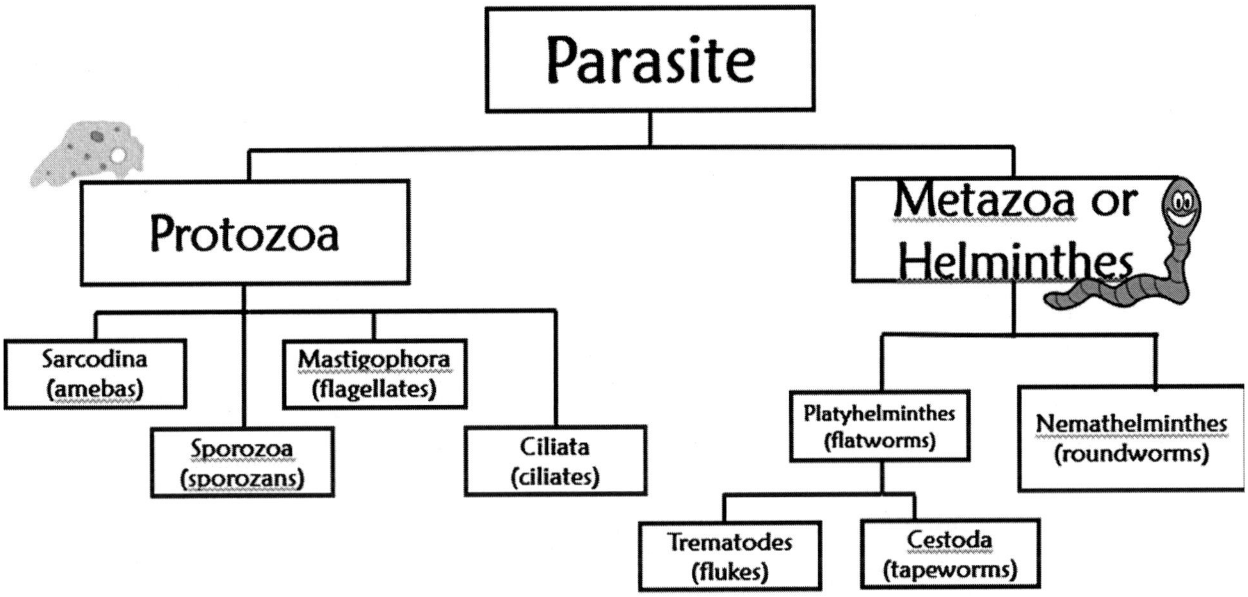

A. Protozoa

.

Protozoa are unicellular organisms possessing a true nucleus and cellular organelles. Although they consist of a single cell, protozoa are capable of performing all vital life functions such as nutrition, respiration, reproduction, and excretion. Many protozoa are parasitic and cause important diseases in humans. Because of their medical significance, protozoa form a major part of medical zoology and parasitology.

Protozoan infections are common in tropical and subtropical regions and are responsible for significant morbidity and mortality. Understanding protozoa of medical importance helps in diagnosis, treatment, and prevention of parasitic diseases.

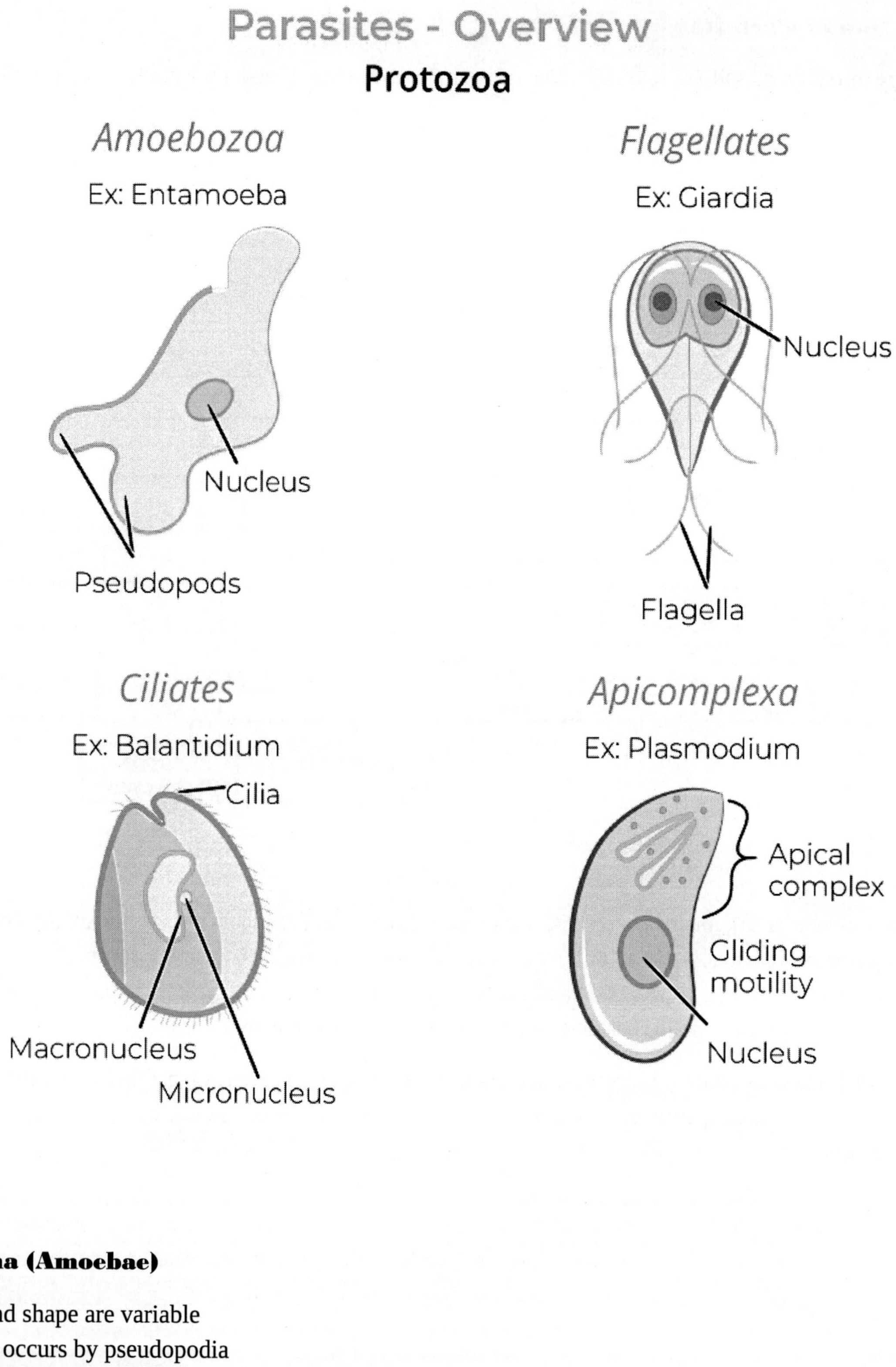

1. Sarcodina (Amoebae)

- Body size and shape are variable
- Locomotion occurs by pseudopodia
- They multiply by binary fission

Examples include
Entamoeba
Naegleria

2. Mastigophora (Flagellates)

- Possess one or more flagella for locomotion
- Flagella help in movement and attachment
- Include intestinal and blood flagellates

Examples include
Leishmania
Giardia
Trichomonas

3. Phylum Apicomplexa

Formerly known as Sporozoa

- Adult forms lack locomotory organs
- Reproduction occurs through spore like stages called oocysts
- Alternation of sexual and asexual generations is present
- All members are obligate parasites

Examples

- Plasmodium
- Toxoplasma

This format is scientifically correct, simple for students, and acceptable in medical zoology examinations and textbooks.

4. Ciliata (Ciliates)

- Locomotion occurs with the help of cilia
- Cilia are present all over the body surface
- They possess two nuclei

Example includes
Balantidium

B. Helminths

Helminths are multicellular organisms.
Different cells perform different functions.
They belong to Kingdom Animalia.

1. Trematodes (Flukes)

- Body is leaf like and unsegmented
- Sexes are not separate in most species
- They are hermaphrodite
- Alimentary canal is incomplete
- Body cavity is absent

Exception
Schistosoma has separate sexes

Example includes

Fasciola
Schistosom

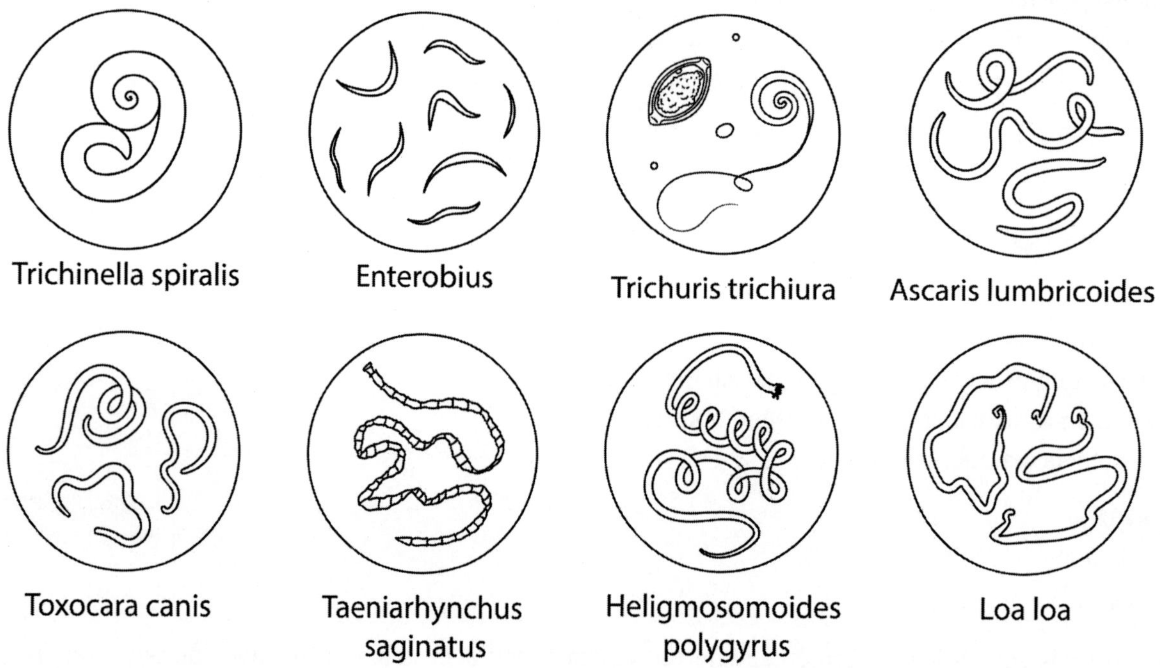

2. Nematodes (Roundworms)

- Body is elongated and cylindrical , Body is unsegmented
- Sexes are separate
- Male and female worms are distinct
- Body cavity is present

Examples include
Hookworm
Roundworm
Threadworm

3. Cestodes (Tapeworms)

- Body is long, flat, and segmented
- Sexes are not separate
- They are hermaphrodite
- Alimentary canal is absent
- Body cavity is absent

Examples include
Taenia
Echinococcus

Table Classification of Parasites

Comparison of Protozoa and Helminths

Feature	Protozoa	Helminths
Cellular organization	Unicellular organisms	Multicellular organisms
Body structure	Single cell performs all functions	Different cells perform different functions
Kingdom	Protista	Animalia
Size	Microscopic	Usually macroscopic
Reproduction	Mostly asexual	Mostly sexual
Examples	Amoebae Flagellates Sporozoa Ciliates	Trematodes Nematodes Cestodes

Classification of Protozoa

Group	Locomotory organ	Key features	Examples
Sarcodina Amoebae	Pseudopodia	Variable shape Movement by pseudopodia	Entamoeba Naegleria
Mastigophora Flagellates	Flagella	One or more flagella present	Leishmania Giardia Trichomonas
Sporozoa Sporozoans	Absent in adult stage	Spore formation Obligatory parasites	Plasmodium Toxoplasma
Ciliata Ciliates	Cilia	Cilia all over body surface Two nuclei	Balantidium

Classification of Helminths

Group	Body shape	Sex	Alimentary canal	Examples
Trematodes Flukes	Leaf like Unsegmented	Not separate Hermaphrodite	Incomplete	Fasciola Schistosoma
Nematodes Roundworms	Cylindrical Unsegmented	Separate	Complete	Hookworm Roundworm Threadworm
Cestodes Tapeworms	Flat Segmented	Not separate Hermaphrodite	Absent	Taenia Echinococcus

5. Protozoa of Medical Importance

Introduction

Protozoa are unicellular organisms possessing a true nucleus and cellular organelles. Although they consist of a single cell, protozoa are capable of performing all vital life functions such as nutrition, respiration, reproduction, and excretion. Many protozoa are parasitic and cause important diseases in humans. Because of their medical significance, protozoa form a major part of medical zoology and parasitology.

Protozoan infections are common in tropical and subtropical regions and are responsible for significant morbidity and mortality. Understanding protozoa of medical importance helps in diagnosis, treatment, and prevention of parasitic diseases.

General Characteristics of Medically Important Protozoa

Protozoa of medical importance share certain common features.

- They are unicellular organisms
- They possess a true nucleus
- Reproduction is mainly asexual
- Many have complex life cycles
- They may live inside or outside host cells
- Transmission occurs through food, water, vectors, or direct contact

Classification of Medically Important Protozoa

Medically important protozoa are classified into the following groups.

1. Sarcodina (Amoebae)

These protozoa move with the help of pseudopodia.
They cause diseases mainly in the intestine and central nervous system.

Important examples	**Diseases caused**
a. Entamoeba histolytica	Amoebiasis
b. Naegleria fowleri	Primary amoebic meningoencephalitis

a. Entamoeba histolytica

Disease Amoebiasis

Amoebiasis is an intestinal infection caused by Entamoeba histolytica.
The parasite mainly affects the **large intestine**.

What happens in this disease

- The parasite invades the intestinal wall
- It causes **ulceration of the intestine**
- Patient may develop diarrhea, abdominal pain, and dysentery
- In severe cases, the parasite may spread to the **liver**, causing liver abscess

Final statement

Entamoeba histolytica causes amoebiasis, an intestinal disease characterized by ulceration of the colon and dysentery.

b. Naegleria fowleri

Disease Primary amoebic meningoencephalitis

Primary amoebic meningoencephalitis is a **severe and rapidly progressive infection of the brain** caused by Naegleria fowleri.

What happens in this disease

- The amoeba enters the body through the **nasal cavity**
- It reaches the brain through the **olfactory nerve**
- It causes **acute inflammation of the brain and meninges**
- Symptoms include severe headache, fever, vomiting, altered consciousness
- The disease progresses rapidly and is **usually fatal**

This infection is commonly associated with **swimming or bathing in warm contaminated water**.

Clinical Notes

Naegleria fowleri causes primary amoebic meningoencephalitis, a rapidly fatal infection of the brain and meninges.

2. Mastigophora (Flagellates)

These protozoa move with the help of flagella.
They may live in the intestine, blood, or urogenital tract.

Important examples	**Diseases caused**
a. Giardia lamblia	Giardiasis
b.Leishmania donovani	Kala azar
c.Trichomonas vaginalis	Trichomoniasis

a. Giardia lamblia

Disease Giardiasis

Giardiasis is an **intestinal infection** caused by Giardia lamblia. The parasite mainly inhabits the **upper part of the small intestine**. Infection occurs by ingestion of cysts through **contaminated food or water**. The parasite interferes with normal absorption of nutrients, leading to **diarrhea, abdominal cramps, bloating, and malabsorption**. Chronic infection may result in **weight loss and nutritional deficiencies**.

b.Leishmania donovani

Disease Kala azar

Kala azar, also known as **visceral leishmaniasis**, is a systemic infection caused by Leishmania donovani. The parasite is transmitted to humans through the bite of an **infected sandfly**. It primarily affects the **reticuloendothelial system**, involving organs such as the spleen, liver, and bone marrow. The disease is characterized by **prolonged fever, enlargement of spleen and liver, anemia, weight loss, and general weakness**. If untreated, kala azar may become **fatal** due to progressive organ involvement and immune suppression.

c. Trichomonas vaginalis

Disease Trichomoniasis

Trichomoniasis is a **urogenital infection** caused by Trichomonas vaginalis. The parasite mainly infects the **urogenital tract** and is transmitted primarily through **sexual contact**. In females, it commonly causes **vaginitis** with symptoms such as vaginal discharge, itching, burning sensation, and discomfort during urination. In males, infection is often **asymptomatic** but may cause urethritis and irritation. Trichomoniasis is an important sexually transmitted infection and requires treatment of **both partners** to prevent reinfection.

3. Sporozoa (Sporozoans)

These protozoa do not possess locomotory organs in the adult stage.
They are obligate intracellular parasites and show alternation of sexual and asexual reproduction.

Important examples	**Diseases caused**
a. Plasmodium species	Malaria
b. Toxoplasma gondii	Toxoplasmosis

a.Plasmodium species

Disease Malaria

Malaria is a **parasitic disease of the blood** caused by Plasmodium species. The infection is transmitted to humans through the bite of an **infected female Anopheles mosquito**. After entering the body, the parasite first multiplies in the **liver cells** and then infects **red blood cells**. Destruction of red blood cells leads to

intermittent fever with chills and rigors, anemia, weakness, and enlargement of spleen. Severe forms of malaria may cause complications involving the brain, kidneys, and other organs and can be life threatening if not treated promptly.

b.Toxoplasma gondii

Disease Toxoplasmosis

Toxoplasmosis is an infection caused by Toxoplasma gondii. The parasite is commonly transmitted by ingestion of **oocysts from contaminated food or water** or by consumption of **undercooked meat** containing tissue cysts. In healthy individuals, the infection is usually mild or asymptomatic. In **pregnant women**, the parasite may cross the placenta and cause **congenital toxoplasmosis**, leading to serious fetal complications. In **immunocompromised patients**, toxoplasmosis may involve the **brain, eyes, and other organs**, producing severe disease.

4. Ciliata (Ciliates)

These protozoa move with the help of cilia.
They are less common as human parasites.

Important examples	**Diseases caused**
a. Balantidium coli	Balantidiasis

a.Balantidium coli

Disease Balantidiasis

Balantidiasis is an **intestinal infection** caused by Balantidium coli. It is the **only ciliate protozoan** known to infect humans. The infection is acquired by ingestion of cysts through **contaminated food or water**, often associated with close contact with **pigs**, which act as reservoir hosts. The parasite primarily affects the **large intestine**, producing symptoms such as **diarrhea, abdominal pain, and dysentery**. In severe cases, ulceration of the intestinal wall may occur, resembling amoebic dysentery.

Mode of Transmission of Protozoan Infections

Protozoan infections are transmitted by different routes.

- Ingestion of contaminated food or water
- Bite of infected vectors such as mosquitoes and sandflies
- Sexual contact
- Congenital transmission in some cases

Pathogenic Effects of Protozoa

Protozoa cause disease by various mechanisms.

- Tissue invasion and destruction
- Production of toxins
- Nutritional deprivation
- Immune mediated damage

Clinical manifestations depend on
Species of protozoa
Parasite load
Host immunity

Diagnosis of Protozoan Infections

Diagnosis is based on

- Microscopic examination of stool, blood, or tissue samples
- Serological tests
- Molecular techniques in advanced laboratories

Prevention and Control

Protozoan infections can be prevented by

- Safe drinking water
- Proper sanitation
- Personal hygiene
- Vector control
- Early diagnosis and treatment

Table Pathogenic Amoebae Causing Human Disease

Name of Amoeba	Disease Caused	Reason of Disease	Mode of Transmission	Infection Control	Drugs Used
Entamoeba histolytica	Amoebiasis	Invasion and destruction of intestinal mucosa	Contaminated food and water containing cysts	Safe drinking water Proper sanitation Personal hygiene	Metronidazole Tinidazole
Naegleria fowleri	Primary amoebic meningoencephalitis	Acute inflammation and destruction of brain tissue	Entry through nose during swimming in warm contaminated water	Avoid swimming in contaminated water Proper chlorination	Amphotericin B
Acanthamoeba species	Granulomatous amoebic encephalitis Keratitis	Tissue invasion and immune mediated damage	Contaminated water Contact lens contamination	Proper contact lens hygiene Avoid contaminated water	Pentamidine Azoles
Balamuthia mandrillaris	Granulomatous amoebic encephalitis	Progressive destruction of brain tissue	Soil exposure Entry through skin or respiratory tract	Avoid soil contamination Proper wound care	Combination therapy limited response

Important Notes

- Entamoeba histolytica is the **most common intestinal pathogenic amoeba**
- Naegleria fowleri causes **rapidly fatal brain infection**
- Acanthamoeba and Balamuthia cause **chronic brain infections**
- Water hygiene and sanitation are key preventive measures

Conclusion

Protozoa of medical importance are responsible for a wide range of human diseases. A clear understanding of their classification, mode of transmission, and pathogenic effects is essential for effective diagnosis, treatment, and prevention of protozoan infections.

6. Intestinal Amoebae

Introduction

Intestinal amoebae are **unicellular protozoan parasites** that inhabit the **human intestine**, particularly the large intestine. Several species of amoebae are found in humans, of which some are **pathogenic** and capable of producing disease, while others are **non pathogenic** and live harmlessly as commensals.

The medical importance of intestinal amoebae lies in their ability to cause intestinal infections that may range from **asymptomatic colonization to severe dysentery and extra intestinal complications**. Accurate identification of intestinal amoebae is essential, as pathogenic and non pathogenic species may appear similar on microscopic examination but differ greatly in clinical significance.

Understanding intestinal amoebae helps medical and allied health students in proper diagnosis, treatment, and prevention of amoebic infections, and prevents unnecessary therapy in cases involving non pathogenic species.

General Characteristics of Intestinal Amoebae

Intestinal amoebae are **unicellular protozoan organisms** that inhabit the **human intestine**, mainly the large intestine. They belong to the group Sarcodina and show amoeboid movement with the help of pseudopodia. These organisms may exist either as **pathogenic parasites** or as **non pathogenic commensals**.

The life cycle of intestinal amoebae is simple and consists of **two stages**, the trophozoite and the cyst. The trophozoite is the active, motile, and feeding stage found inside the intestine, while the cyst is the **infective and resistant stage** responsible for transmission from one host to another.

Intestinal amoebae are usually transmitted through **ingestion of cysts** present in contaminated food or water. Poor sanitation, unhygienic conditions, and inadequate personal hygiene play a major role in their spread.

Most intestinal amoebae reside in the lumen of the intestine and do not cause disease. However, Entamoeba histolytica has the ability to invade the intestinal wall and produce tissue damage, leading to clinical disease.

Accurate identification of intestinal amoebae is important in medical practice, as treatment is required only for **pathogenic species**, while non pathogenic amoebae do not require therapy.

Classification of Intestinal Amoebae

Intestinal amoebae are classified into **pathogenic** and **non pathogenic** forms.

A. Pathogenic Intestinal Amoeba

Entamoeba histolytica

Entamoeba histolytica is the **most important pathogenic intestinal amoeba**. It causes **amoebiasis**, an intestinal disease characterized by ulceration of the colon and dysentery. In severe cases, it may spread to extra intestinal sites such as the liver.

B. Non Pathogenic Intestinal Amoebae

These amoebae do not cause disease but may be found in stool examination.

Important non pathogenic intestinal amoebae include

- Entamoeba coli
- Entamoeba hartmanni
- Endolimax nana
- Iodamoeba butschlii

Presence of these amoebae indicates **fecal contamination**, not disease.

Life Cycle Forms of Intestinal Amoebae

The life cycle of intestinal amoebae is simple and consists of **two distinct forms**, the **trophozoite** and the **cyst**. These two forms play different roles in survival, multiplication, and transmission of the parasite.

1. Trophozoite

The trophozoite is the **active, motile, and feeding form** of intestinal amoebae. It lives in the intestinal lumen and moves with the help of **pseudopodia**. In pathogenic species, the trophozoite has the ability to **invade the intestinal wall** and cause tissue damage.

This form multiplies by **binary fission** and is responsible for producing clinical manifestations in diseases such as amoebiasis. Trophozoites are usually found in **fresh stool samples** but do not survive for long outside the host.

2. Cyst

The cyst is the **infective and resistant form** of intestinal amoebae. It is spherical in shape and possesses a **thick protective wall** that enables it to survive in unfavorable environmental conditions. The cyst is passed in the feces and remains viable in soil, water, and food.

Infection occurs when a person **ingests mature cysts** through contaminated food or water. Inside the intestine, the cyst undergoes **excystation**, releasing trophozoites that initiate infection.

Morphology of Entamoeba histolytica

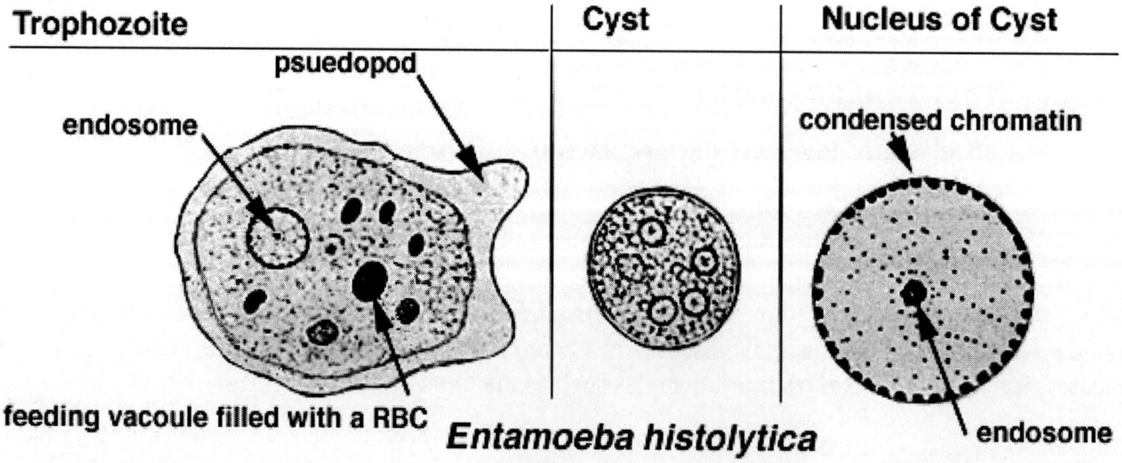

Entamoeba histolytica exists in **two morphological forms**, the **trophozoite** and the **cyst**. Each form has distinct structural features that are important for diagnosis.

1. Trophozoite

The trophozoite is the **active and motile form** of the parasite.

- Size usually ranges from 15 to 30 micrometers
- Shape is variable due to formation of pseudopodia
- Cytoplasm is differentiated into ectoplasm and endoplasm
- Nucleus is single, round, and contains a **central karyosome**
- Nuclear membrane has **fine and evenly distributed chromatin**
- Actively motile with finger like pseudopodia
- In pathogenic infections, trophozoites may contain **ingested red blood cells**, which is a diagnostic feature

The trophozoite is responsible for **tissue invasion and disease production**.

2. Cyst

The cyst is the **infective and resistant form** of the parasite.

- Shape is spherical
- Size ranges from 10 to 15 micrometers
- Mature cyst contains **four nuclei**
- Each nucleus has a central karyosome
- Chromatoid bodies may be present and are cigar shaped
- Glycogen mass may be seen in immature cysts
- Cyst wall is thick and protective

The cyst enables survival outside the host and plays a key role in **transmission of infection**.

Life Cycle of Entamoeba histolytica

The life cycle of Entamoeba histolytica is **simple and direct**, involving **only one host**, the human being. It consists of **two stages**, the cyst and the trophozoite.

Notes

1. Ingestion of Cyst

Infection begins when a person ingests **mature cysts** of Entamoeba histolytica through **contaminated food or water**. The cyst is the **infective stage** and is resistant to adverse environmental conditions.

2. Excystation

After ingestion, the cyst reaches the **small intestine**, where it undergoes **excystation**. During this process, the cyst wall breaks and releases **trophozoites**.

3. Trophozoite Stage

The released trophozoites move to the **large intestine**, where they become active. They multiply by **binary fission** and live in the intestinal lumen. In pathogenic infections, trophozoites **invade the intestinal wall**, causing ulceration and tissue damage.

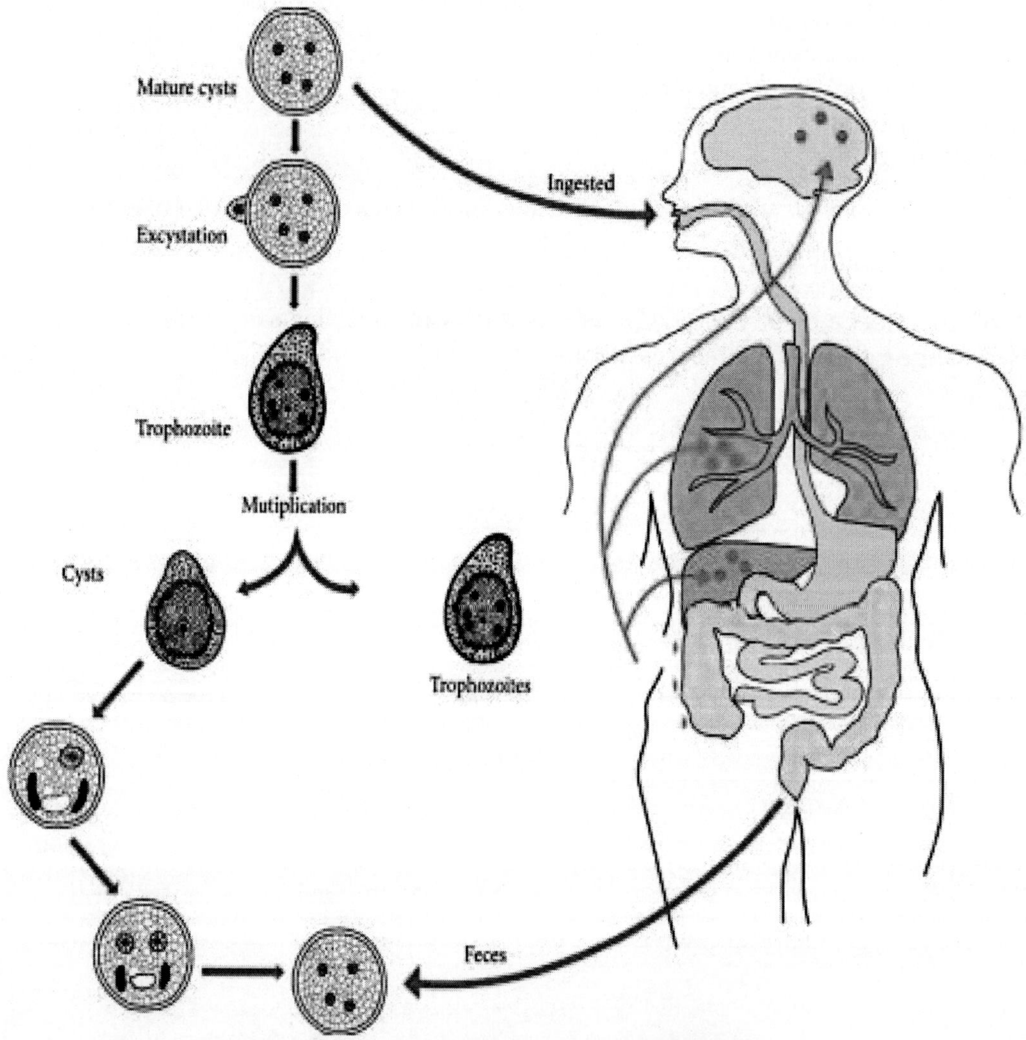

Life cycle of *Entamoeba histolytica*

Some trophozoites may enter the bloodstream and reach extra intestinal sites such as the **liver**, leading to liver abscess.

4. Encystation

As trophozoites move towards the lower part of the intestine, they undergo **encystation**. During this process, trophozoites transform into cysts by developing a protective wall.

5. Passage of Cysts in Feces

The mature cysts are passed out in the **feces**. These cysts can survive in the external environment and serve as a source of infection to new hosts.

Important Points to Remember

- **Cyst is the infective stage**
- **Trophozoite is the pathogenic stage**
- Transmission occurs through contaminated food and water
- Human is the only host

Pathogenesis of Amoebiasis

The disease caused by Entamoeba histolytica occurs due to the **invasive ability of trophozoites** to penetrate and destroy the intestinal mucosa. Not all infections result in disease; pathogenicity depends on **virulence of the parasite and host immunity**.

After excystation, trophozoites reach the **large intestine**, where they adhere to the intestinal epithelium. In pathogenic strains, trophozoites invade the mucosal lining, producing **flask shaped ulcers** in the intestinal wall. These ulcers may extend deep into the submucosa, leading to bleeding and tissue necrosis.

The parasite may also spread through the bloodstream to **extra intestinal organs**, particularly the liver, causing **amoebic liver abscess.**

Role of Secretory Enzymes

The pathogenicity of Entamoeba histolytica is largely due to the production of **secretory enzymes and cytotoxic substances**.

Important secretory enzymes include:

- **Proteolytic enzymes**, which digest host tissue and facilitate invasion
- **Cysteine proteases**, which destroy intestinal mucosa and immune cells
- **Phospholipases**, which damage host cell membranes

These enzymes help the parasite to
Break down tissue barriers
Destroy epithelial cells
Evade host immune response

As a result, extensive tissue damage occurs, leading to **ulceration, hemorrhage, and inflammation**.

Amoebiasis and AIDS

Amoebiasis shows a **more severe course** in patients suffering from **AIDS**, due to impairment of the immune system. Human immunodeficiency virus infection reduces cell mediated immunity, which plays a crucial role in controlling Entamoeba histolytica infection.

In patients with AIDS, amoebic infection is more likely to become **invasive**, leading to severe intestinal disease. Such patients may develop **extensive ulceration of the colon**, severe diarrhea, dehydration, and weight loss. Extra intestinal complications such as **amoebic liver abscess** are also more common and may progress rapidly.

The response to infection in AIDS patients is poor because trophozoites can multiply unchecked due to reduced immune surveillance. Secondary bacterial infections may further complicate the clinical picture.

Early diagnosis and prompt treatment are essential in AIDS patients to reduce morbidity and prevent life threatening complications.

Clinical Importance

• Amoebiasis is more severe in immunocompromised patients
• Higher risk of invasive and extra intestinal disease
• Early treatment improves prognosis
• Preventive measures are especially important in AIDS patients

Clinical Features of Amoebiasis

The clinical manifestations of amoebiasis vary widely depending on the **severity of infection**, **virulence of the parasite**, and **immune status of the host**. Infection may be asymptomatic or may produce severe intestinal and extra intestinal disease.

1. Asymptomatic Amoebiasis

Many individuals infected with Entamoeba histolytica remain **asymptomatic carriers**.

• No obvious clinical symptoms
• Cysts are passed in stool
• Individual acts as a source of infection to others

2. Intestinal Amoebiasis

Intestinal amoebiasis is the most common clinical form.

Common symptoms include

• Diarrhea
• Abdominal pain
• Passage of mucus and blood in stool
• Tenesmus
• Weakness and fatigue

In severe cases
• Ulceration of the colon occurs
• Profuse bleeding may be present
• Risk of intestinal perforation increases

3. Amoebic Dysentery

This is a severe form of intestinal amoebiasis.

- Frequent stools with blood and mucus
- Severe abdominal cramps
- Fever may be present
- Rapid deterioration in general condition

4. Extra Intestinal Amoebiasis

The parasite may spread from the intestine to other organs.

Common extra intestinal manifestations

- Amoebic liver abscess
- Right upper abdominal pain
- Fever
- Tender hepatomegaly

Less commonly, involvement of
- Lungs
- Brain
- Skin

may occur.

Amoebic Appendicitis

Amoebic appendicitis occurs when Entamoeba histolytica involves the **appendix** either as a primary infection or as an extension of caecal amoebiasis. The parasite invades the mucosa of the appendix, producing inflammation similar to acute appendicitis.

Clinical features

- Right lower abdominal pain
- Fever
- Nausea and vomiting
- Tenderness in right iliac fossa

Amoebic appendicitis is often **misdiagnosed as bacterial appendicitis** and may be detected only after surgical removal of the appendix and histopathological examination.

Amoebic Granuloma

Amoebic granuloma is a **localized mass lesion** produced by chronic infection with Entamoeba histolytica. It is also known as **amoeboma**. It commonly occurs in the **caecum or ascending colon**.

The lesion is formed due to prolonged inflammatory response, fibrosis, and granulation tissue formation.

Clinical importance

- Mimics carcinoma of colon
- Produces intestinal obstruction
- May present as an abdominal mass

Correct diagnosis is essential to avoid unnecessary surgical intervention.

Complications of Intestinal Amoebiasis

If untreated or inadequately treated, intestinal amoebiasis may lead to several complications.

Common complications include

- Severe intestinal hemorrhage
- Intestinal perforation
- Peritonitis
- Toxic megacolon
- Amoebic appendicitis
- Amoebic granuloma

These complications increase morbidity and may be life threatening.

Sequelae of Intestinal Amoebiasis

Sequelae refer to **long term consequences** that persist after the acute infection has subsided.

Important sequelae include

- Chronic colitis
- Stricture formation in colon
- Recurrent abdominal pain
- Malabsorption
- Nutritional deficiencies

These conditions significantly affect quality of life and require long term medical follow up.

Hepatic Amoebiasis

Hepatic amoebiasis is the **most common extra intestinal manifestation** of infection caused by Entamoeba histolytica. It occurs when trophozoites spread from the intestine to the **liver through the portal circulation**.

The condition commonly presents as an **amoebic liver abscess**, which is a localized collection of necrotic tissue within the liver.

Pathogenesis

After invading the intestinal wall, trophozoites enter the portal vein and reach the liver. In the liver, they destroy hepatocytes through **direct tissue invasion and action of secretory enzymes**, leading to abscess formation.The abscess content is classically described as **thick brownish fluid**, often referred to as anchovy sauce like material.

Clinical Features

Common clinical features include

- Fever
- Right upper abdominal pain
- Tender hepatomegaly
- Malaise and weakness
- Loss of appetite

Jaundice is uncommon but may occur in severe cases.

Complications

If untreated, hepatic amoebiasis may lead to serious complications.

- Rupture of liver abscess into peritoneal cavity
- Rupture into pleural cavity or lungs
- Pericardial involvement
- Secondary bacterial infection

These complications can be life threatening.

Diagnosis

Diagnosis is based on

- Clinical features and history
- Imaging studies such as ultrasonography or CT scan
- Serological tests
- Stool examination may be negative in many cases

Treatment

Treatment includes

- Anti amoebic drugs such as metronidazole or tinidazole
- Luminal amoebicides to eliminate intestinal infection
- Drainage of abscess in selected cases

Laboratory Diagnosis of Amoebiasis

Laboratory diagnosis of amoebiasis is based on **demonstration of the parasite**, **serological tests**, and **supporting investigations**, along with clinical correlation. Accurate diagnosis is important to differentiate pathogenic amoebiasis from non pathogenic amoebic infection.

1. Stool Examination

Stool examination is the most commonly used diagnostic method.

- Microscopic examination of fresh stool may reveal **trophozoites**
- Formed stool samples usually show **cysts**
- Presence of trophozoites containing **ingested red blood cells** confirms Entamoeba histolytica
- Multiple stool samples increase diagnostic yield

2. Microscopy with Staining Techniques

Special staining methods improve identification.

- Iodine staining helps in visualization of cysts
- Permanent stained smears help differentiate Entamoeba histolytica from non pathogenic amoebae

3. Serological Tests

Serological tests detect antibodies against Entamoeba histolytica.

• Useful in extra intestinal amoebiasis
• High sensitivity in amoebic liver abscess
• Antibodies may remain positive even after treatment

4. Antigen Detection Tests

Antigen detection tests identify amoebic antigens in stool samples.

• Useful in differentiating pathogenic species
• Helpful in cases where microscopy is inconclusive

5. Imaging Techniques

Imaging studies support diagnosis in extra intestinal disease.

• Ultrasonography is useful in hepatic amoebiasis
• CT scan helps in detection of liver abscess and complications

6. Other Investigations

• Liver function tests may be altered in hepatic involvement
• Stool culture is not useful for amoebiasis

Treatment and Prevention of Amoebiasis

Treatment of Amoebiasis

Treatment of amoebiasis depends on the **clinical presentation** and whether the infection is **intestinal or extra intestinal**. The aim of treatment is to eliminate both the **tissue invading trophozoites** and the **luminal cysts**.

Intestinal amoebiasis

• Metronidazole is the drug of choice
• Tinidazole may be used as an alternative
• Treatment should be followed by a **luminal amoebicide** to eradicate cysts from the intestine

Extra intestinal amoebiasis

• Metronidazole or tinidazole is used for hepatic amoebiasis
• Luminal amoebicide is added after completion of therapy
• Drainage of liver abscess may be required in selected cases

Asymptomatic cyst passers

• Treated with luminal amoebicides only
• Prevents spread of infection

Early diagnosis and complete treatment are essential to prevent complications and recurrence.

Prevention of Amoebiasis

Prevention of amoebiasis is based on **interrupting transmission** and improving **sanitation and hygiene**.

Preventive measures include

- Safe drinking water
- Proper disposal of human waste
- Washing hands before meals and after defecation
- Proper washing and cooking of food
- Health education and awareness

Identification and treatment of asymptomatic carriers also play an important role in controlling the spread of amoebiasis.

7. Flagellates of Medical Importance

Introduction

Flagellates are an important group of protozoa characterized by the presence of one or more flagella, which serve as organs of locomotion. These organisms belong to the group Mastigophora and include several species that are of great medical importance. Flagellates infect humans by localizing in the intestine, urogenital tract, blood, or internal tissues, where they produce a wide range of diseases.

From a medical zoology perspective, flagellates are significant because they show clear adaptation to parasitic life. Some flagellates live freely in the lumen of organs, while others invade host tissues or circulate in body fluids. Their pathogenicity depends on factors such as site of localization, mode of transmission, and interaction with host cells.

Flagellates are unicellular eukaryotic organisms possessing a true nucleus and membrane bound organelles. Despite being single celled, they are capable of performing all essential life functions, including nutrition, respiration, excretion, and reproduction. Reproduction in flagellates occurs mainly by longitudinal binary fission.

Medically important flagellates are transmitted through different routes. Intestinal flagellates are commonly transmitted through contaminated food and water. Urogenital flagellates are transmitted mainly through sexual contact. Blood and tissue flagellates are transmitted through insect vectors, making them important agents of vector borne diseases.

The study of flagellates of medical importance helps students understand the biological basis of several common and serious human diseases. Knowledge of their morphology, life cycle, habitat, and pathogenic effects is essential for accurate laboratory diagnosis and for planning effective preventive measures. This chapter focuses on the major flagellates affecting humans and presents them in a systematic and simplified manner suitable for life science and allied health students.

General Characteristics of Flagellates of Medical Importance

Flagellates of medical importance share several common biological and structural features that distinguish them from other groups of protozoa. These characteristics are closely related to their mode of locomotion, survival within the host, and disease producing ability.

Flagellates are **unicellular eukaryotic organisms**. Each organism consists of a single cell that performs all vital life functions such as nutrition, respiration, excretion, growth, and reproduction. They possess a **true nucleus** enclosed by a nuclear membrane and contain membrane bound organelles.

The most distinctive feature of flagellates is the presence of **one or more flagella**. Flagella are long, whip like structures that arise from the body of the organism and are responsible for locomotion. In some species, flagella also help in attachment to host tissues and in maintaining position within body fluids.

Most medically important flagellates reproduce by **longitudinal binary fission**, in which the organism divides along its long axis. Sexual reproduction is generally absent or rare in this group. This simple mode of reproduction allows rapid multiplication within the host.

Flagellates show **definite habitat specificity** within the human body. Some species inhabit the intestinal lumen, others localize in the urogenital tract, while certain flagellates circulate in blood or invade internal organs such as the liver, spleen, and lymph nodes. This site specificity plays an important role in determining the type of disease produced.

Depending on the species, flagellates may exist in **trophozoite stage** alone or in both trophozoite and cyst stages. The trophozoite is the active, motile, and feeding form, while the cyst is a resistant form adapted for survival outside the host and for transmission.

Transmission of flagellates occurs through **multiple routes**. Intestinal flagellates are commonly transmitted through ingestion of cysts in contaminated food or water. Urogenital flagellates are transmitted mainly through sexual contact. Blood and tissue flagellates are transmitted by insect vectors, making them important agents of vector borne diseases.

Because of their medical importance, flagellates are studied in detail in medical zoology. Understanding their general characteristics provides a foundation for the study of individual flagellate parasites, their life cycles, pathogenic effects, laboratory diagnosis, and prevention.

Classification of Flagellates of Medical Importance

Flagellates of medical importance are classified mainly on the basis of their **habitat in the human body** and their **mode of transmission**. This classification helps in understanding their biological behavior, disease producing potential, and laboratory diagnosis.

From a medical zoology point of view, flagellates are broadly divided into three major groups.

1. Intestinal Flagellates

These flagellates live in the **intestinal tract** of humans, mainly in the small intestine. Infection usually occurs through ingestion of cysts present in contaminated food or water. Poor sanitation and inadequate personal hygiene play an important role in their transmission.

Important example
Giardia lamblia

Disease caused
Giardiasis

Intestinal flagellates mainly interfere with digestion and absorption, leading to gastrointestinal symptoms and nutritional deficiencies.

2. Urogenital Flagellates

These flagellates inhabit the **urogenital tract**. Transmission occurs primarily through **sexual contact**. Unlike intestinal flagellates, cyst stage is usually absent in this group.

Important example
Trichomonas vaginalis

Disease caused
Trichomoniasis

Urogenital flagellates produce local inflammation and irritation of mucosal surfaces.

3. Blood and Tissue Flagellates

These flagellates circulate in the **blood or lymph** or invade internal organs such as liver, spleen, bone marrow, and central nervous system. Transmission occurs through **insect vectors**, making them important agents of vector borne diseases.

Important examples
Leishmania species
Trypanosoma species

Diseases caused
Visceral leishmaniasis
African trypanosomiasis

Blood and tissue flagellates are responsible for serious systemic diseases and often produce chronic and progressive infections.

Classification in Table Format

Group of Flagellates	Habitat in Human Body	Mode of Transmission	Important Example	Disease Caused
Intestinal flagellates	Small intestine	Contaminated food and water	Giardia lamblia	Giardiasis
Urogenital flagellates	Urogenital tract	Sexual contact	Trichomonas vaginalis	Trichomoniasis
Blood and tissue flagellates	Blood and internal organs	Insect vector	Leishmania donovani	Kala azar
Blood flagellates	Blood and lymph	Insect vector	Trypanosoma species	Trypanosomiasis

Importance of This Classification

This classification is not artificial but is based on sound biological principles. It reflects the site of localization of the parasite in the human body, the mode of transmission, the pathogenic behavior, and the diagnostic approach required for identification. Intestinal flagellates are mainly diagnosed by examination of stool samples because they inhabit the intestinal lumen and are shed through feces. Urogenital flagellates are identified in genital secretions as they localize in the urogenital tract and produce local infections. Blood and tissue flagellates are detected in blood or tissue samples since they circulate in body fluids or invade internal organs. Thus, the classification of flagellates of medical importance provides a logical and systematic framework for understanding their morphology, life cycle, disease manifestations, laboratory diagnosis, and prevention.

Giardia lamblia

The name Giardia lamblia has both historical and descriptive significance. The genus name **Giardia** is derived from the name of the French scientist **Alfred Mathieu Giard**, who made important contributions to the study of protozoa and parasitology. The species name **lamblia** is derived from **Vilém Dušan Lambl**, a Czech physician who first provided a clear microscopic description of this organism in human intestinal samples.

Thus, the name Giardia lamblia honors two scientists associated with the discovery and study of this parasite. In older literature, the organism may also be referred to as Lamblia intestinalis or Giardia intestinalis, but Giardia lamblia is the commonly accepted and widely used name in medical zoology.

The name does not describe a disease or body part but reflects the historical development of parasitology and recognition of the scientists who identified and characterized the organism.

Intestinal flagellates are protozoan parasites that inhabit the intestinal tract of humans, mainly the small intestine. These organisms are transmitted through ingestion of contaminated food or water and are closely associated with poor sanitation and inadequate hygiene. Intestinal flagellates interfere with normal digestive and absorptive functions of the intestine and are an important cause of gastrointestinal illness, especially in children and immunocompromised individuals.

Among the intestinal flagellates, **Giardia lamblia** is the most important species of medical significance. It is widely distributed throughout the world and is a common cause of protozoal diarrhea.

Morphology

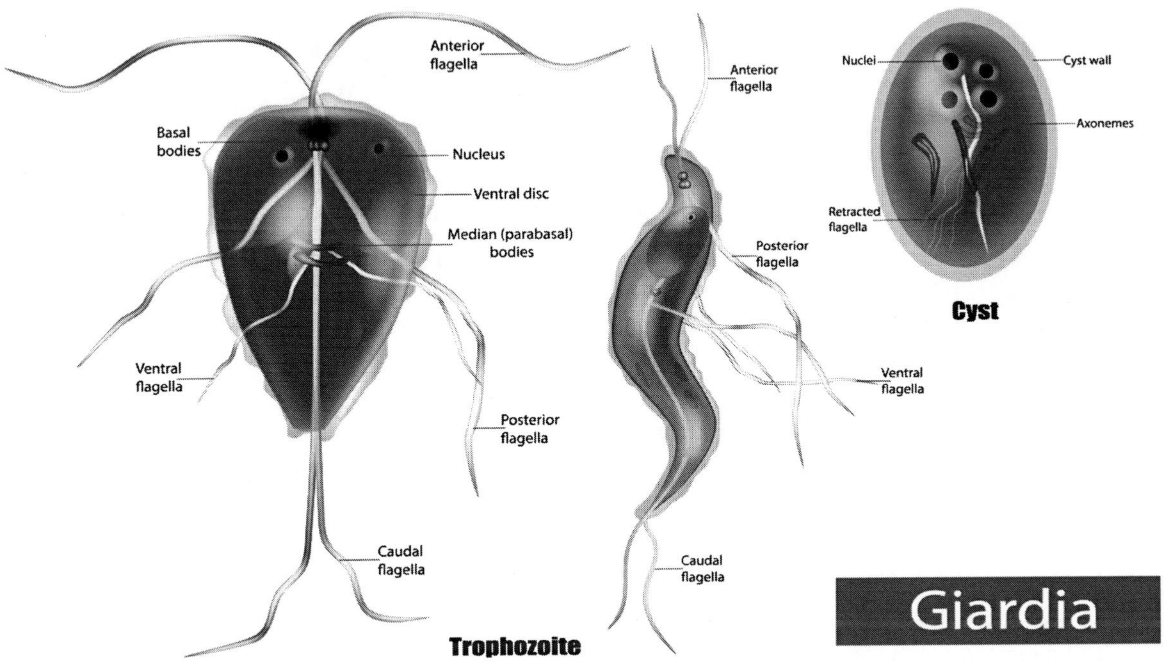

Morphology

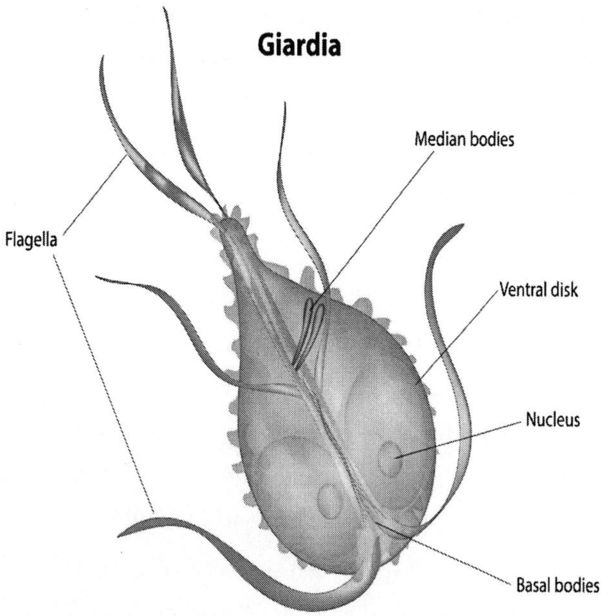

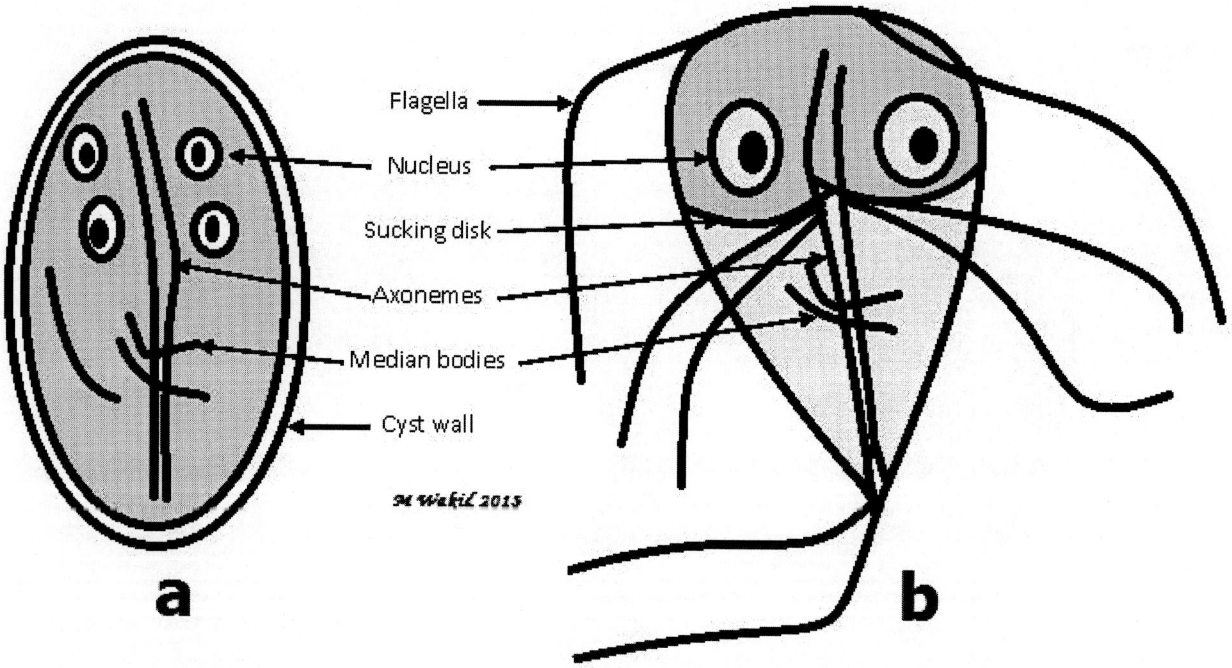

Fig. a. Cyst of Giardia lamblia b. Trophozoite of Giardia lamblia

Cyst

The cyst is the **resistant and infective stage** of Giardia lamblia. It is **oval or ellipsoidal in shape** and measures approximately **8 to 12 micrometers in length**. The cyst is surrounded by a **thick protective wall**, which allows it to survive outside the host in water and moist environments.

A mature cyst contains **four nuclei**, usually clustered toward one end. Remnants of axonemes and median bodies may be seen within the cyst as fibrillar structures. The cytoplasm is compact, and metabolic activity is minimal in this stage.

The cyst is highly resistant to environmental conditions and is responsible for transmission of infection. On ingestion by humans, the cyst undergoes **excystation** in the small intestine, releasing trophozoites that multiply and colonize the intestinal mucosa.

Trophozoite

The trophozoite is the **active, motile, and feeding stage** of Giardia lamblia. It is **pear shaped** and shows **perfect bilateral symmetry**. The average size of the trophozoite is **10 to 20 micrometers in length and 5 to 15 micrometers in width**. The body is **dorsoventrally flattened**, with a **convex dorsal surface** and a **concave ventral surface**.

A prominent **ventral sucking disc** is present on the ventral surface. This disc functions as an organ of attachment and enables the parasite to adhere firmly to the mucosal surface of the small intestine.

The trophozoite contains **two large nuclei**, situated anteriorly. Each nucleus has a central karyosome and lacks peripheral chromatin. The paired nuclei give the organism a characteristic **face like appearance** under light microscopy, which is a useful diagnostic feature.

There are **eight flagella**, arranged in **four pairs**. These include anterior, posterior, caudal, and ventral flagella. The flagella arise from basal bodies and are responsible for active motility.

Axonemes are present as internal microtubular structures that extend longitudinally through the body. They form the structural core of the flagella and also help in maintaining body shape. **Median bodies** are present as curved rod like structures near the center of the trophozoite and are considered characteristic morphological features.

The cytoplasm is finely granular and lacks mitochondria. Instead, energy metabolism occurs through anaerobic pathways, reflecting adaptation to the intestinal environment.

Morphological Significance

The trophozoite is responsible for **pathogenic effects** and clinical manifestations, while the cyst plays a key role in **transmission and survival** of the parasite. Clear understanding of both forms is essential for accurate microscopic identification and diagnosis.

Life Cycle of Giardia lamblia

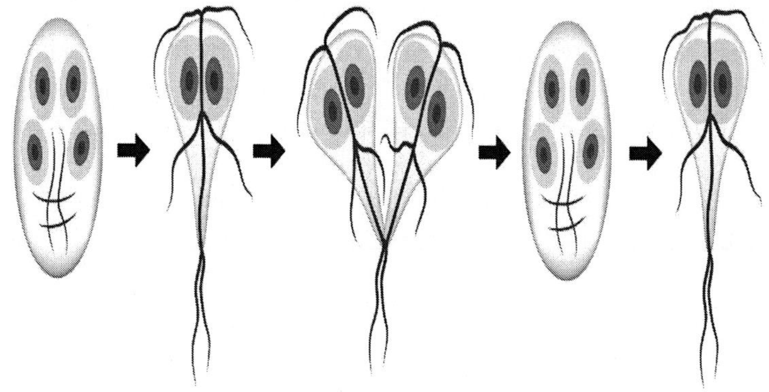

The life cycle of Giardia lamblia is **simple, direct, and monoxenous**, meaning it is completed in a single host, the human being. There is **no intermediate host**. The parasite exists in two forms, the cyst and the trophozoite, each having a specific role in transmission and disease production.

The **cyst is the infective stage** of Giardia lamblia. Infection begins when a person ingests mature cysts through contaminated drinking water, food, or by poor personal hygiene. The cysts are resistant to environmental conditions and can survive for long periods outside the host, especially in water.

After ingestion, the cysts pass through the stomach. Exposure to gastric acid and digestive enzymes initiates the process of **excystation** in the upper part of the small intestine. Each cyst releases **two trophozoites**, which become active and motile.

The **trophozoites** move to the duodenum and jejunum, where they attach to the intestinal mucosa by means of the ventral sucking disc. They do not invade the intestinal wall but remain on the surface of the mucosa. The trophozoites multiply rapidly by **longitudinal binary fission**, leading to heavy colonization of the intestinal lining.

As the intestinal contents move toward the lower intestine, conditions become unfavorable for trophozoites. This leads to the process of **encystation**, during which trophozoites transform into cysts. The cyst wall is formed, nuclear division occurs, and mature cysts containing four nuclei are produced.

The **mature cysts are passed in the feces** of the infected individual. These cysts contaminate water sources and food, thereby continuing the cycle of transmission. Trophozoites may also be passed in diarrheal stools, but they do not survive outside the host and are not infective.

Thus, the life cycle of Giardia lamblia is completed through ingestion of cysts, excystation in the small intestine, multiplication of trophozoites, encystation, and excretion of cysts. Understanding this life cycle is essential for explaining the pathogenicity, laboratory diagnosis, and prevention of giardiasis.

Pathogenicity and Disease Caused by Giardia lamblia

Giardia lamblia causes a disease known as **giardiasis**, which is primarily an infection of the small intestine. The pathogenicity of the parasite is mainly related to its **attachment to the intestinal mucosa**, rapid multiplication, and interference with normal digestive and absorptive processes.

After excystation, the trophozoites attach to the mucosal surface of the duodenum and jejunum by means of the ventral sucking disc. Although the parasite does not invade the intestinal wall, its firm attachment causes **mechanical irritation** and damage to the epithelial surface. This results in blunting of intestinal villi and disruption of the normal absorptive surface.

The presence of large numbers of trophozoites interferes with the absorption of fats, carbohydrates, and fat soluble vitamins. This leads to **malabsorption syndrome**, which is a key feature of giardiasis. Enzymatic activity of the intestinal mucosa may also be reduced due to epithelial damage.

Giardia lamblia produces disease through several mechanisms, including mechanical obstruction of the intestinal surface, alteration of intestinal permeability, and induction of local inflammatory responses. The parasite may also produce metabolic byproducts that contribute to mucosal irritation.

The severity of disease depends on factors such as the number of parasites, duration of infection, and immune status of the host. In some individuals, especially children and immunocompromised persons, infection may become chronic and lead to significant nutritional deficiencies.

Thus, Giardia lamblia causes disease by disrupting the normal structure and function of the small intestinal mucosa, resulting in gastrointestinal symptoms and malabsorption. This understanding of pathogenicity forms the basis for recognizing the clinical features and planning preventive measures.

Clinical Features of Giardiasis

The clinical manifestations of giardiasis vary widely and depend on factors such as the number of parasites present, duration of infection, and immune status of the host. The infection may be **asymptomatic** or may produce **acute or chronic illness**.

In many individuals, especially adults, infection with Giardia lamblia may remain asymptomatic. Such individuals act as carriers and continue to shed cysts in feces, contributing to the spread of infection without showing obvious symptoms.

When symptoms are present, giardiasis commonly produces **gastrointestinal disturbances**. The most frequent clinical feature is **diarrhea**, which is usually foul smelling and may be greasy due to fat malabsorption. Stools are typically bulky and frothy.

Patients often complain of **abdominal pain and cramps**, particularly in the upper abdomen. **Bloating, flatulence, and abdominal distension** are common due to impaired digestion and fermentation of unabsorbed nutrients.

Because the parasite interferes with absorption in the small intestine, **malabsorption syndrome** may develop. This leads to **weight loss**, **weakness**, and **nutritional deficiencies**, especially in chronic infections. Deficiency of fat soluble vitamins may also occur.

In children, chronic giardiasis can result in **failure to thrive**, delayed growth, and poor weight gain. Recurrent or prolonged infection may affect physical and cognitive development due to persistent nutritional deficiency.

Systemic symptoms such as **fatigue and malaise** may be present. Fever is usually absent or mild, which helps differentiate giardiasis from invasive intestinal infections.

Thus, the clinical features of giardiasis range from asymptomatic carriage to chronic gastrointestinal illness with malabsorption. Recognition of these features is important for correlating clinical presentation with laboratory diagnosis and for understanding the public health significance of the disease.

Pathology of Giardiasis

The pathology of giardiasis is mainly confined to the **small intestine**, particularly the duodenum and jejunum. The disease is characterized by **functional and structural changes** in the intestinal mucosa rather than deep tissue invasion.

After excystation, the trophozoites attach firmly to the epithelial surface of the intestinal mucosa by means of the ventral sucking disc. Although Giardia lamblia does not invade the intestinal wall, its persistent attachment causes **mechanical irritation and epithelial damage**.

One of the most important pathological changes is **blunting and shortening of intestinal villi**. This reduces the effective absorptive surface area of the intestine. In addition, there may be **loss of brush border enzymes**, leading to impaired digestion of carbohydrates and fats.

Mild to moderate **inflammatory changes** may be seen in the mucosa, including infiltration of lymphocytes and plasma cells. The inflammation is usually superficial and does not produce ulceration, which helps differentiate giardiasis from invasive intestinal protozoal infections.

The pathological changes result in **malabsorption**, especially of fats, leading to steatorrhea and nutritional deficiencies. Prolonged infection may cause generalized mucosal dysfunction, contributing to chronic diarrhea and weight loss.

In children, repeated or chronic infection can produce more pronounced pathological effects, leading to growth retardation and poor nutritional status. The severity of pathological changes depends on the parasite load, duration of infection, and immune response of the host.

Thus, the pathology of giardiasis is primarily functional, involving damage to the intestinal mucosa and disruption of absorptive mechanisms, which forms the biological basis of the clinical manifestations of the disease.

Epidemiology and Susceptibility of Giardiasis

Giardiasis is a **cosmopolitan infection** and occurs worldwide, affecting both developed and developing countries. The disease is particularly common in regions with **poor sanitation, unsafe drinking water, and inadequate hygiene practices**. It is one of the most frequent protozoal causes of waterborne diarrhea.

The infection is more prevalent in **children**, especially those living in crowded conditions such as hostels, daycare centers, and institutions. Travelers to endemic areas are also at increased risk due to exposure to contaminated water and food. Outbreaks of giardiasis are commonly associated with **contaminated water supplies**, including rivers, lakes, and improperly treated municipal water.

Humans are the primary reservoir of infection, although the parasite may also infect animals such as dogs and cattle, which can contribute to environmental contamination. Transmission occurs mainly through the **fecal oral route**, with ingestion of cysts present in contaminated water or food.

Susceptibility to giardiasis varies among individuals. Persons with **poor personal hygiene**, malnutrition, or **compromised immunity** are more susceptible to infection and may develop more severe or prolonged disease. Children are particularly vulnerable due to immature immune defenses and frequent exposure to contaminated environments.

Chronic infection is more likely to occur in individuals with reduced immune response, leading to persistent symptoms and nutritional deficiencies. Asymptomatic carriers play an important role in maintaining transmission within the community by continuously shedding cysts.

Thus, the epidemiology and susceptibility of giardiasis are closely linked to environmental sanitation, water quality, personal hygiene, and host immune status. Understanding these factors is essential for planning effective diagnostic, preventive, and control strategies.

Laboratory Diagnosis of Giardiasis

Laboratory diagnosis of giardiasis is based on **demonstration of the parasite or its stages** in appropriate clinical specimens. The choice of specimen depends on the site of localization and stage of infection.

The most commonly used specimen is **stool**. Stool examination aims to detect **cysts or trophozoites** of Giardia lamblia. In formed stools, cysts are more commonly found, whereas in loose or diarrheal stools, trophozoites may be present. Because cyst excretion may be intermittent, **examination of multiple stool samples on different days** increases diagnostic accuracy.

Direct microscopic examination of stool using **saline and iodine wet mounts** is the simplest and most commonly used method. Cysts appear oval with multiple nuclei, while trophozoites show characteristic pear shaped bodies with two nuclei and flagella.

In cases where stool examination is negative but clinical suspicion remains high, **duodenal aspirate or duodenal biopsy** may be examined to demonstrate trophozoites. This method is more invasive and is reserved for selected cases.

Concentration techniques such as sedimentation methods may be used to increase the chances of detecting cysts in stool samples. These techniques are particularly useful in low intensity infections.

From a laboratory perspective, proper collection, preservation, and prompt examination of specimens are essential for accurate diagnosis. Repeated examination and correlation with clinical features improve reliability.

Prevention and Control of Giardiasis

Prevention and control of giardiasis are based on **interruption of transmission**, improvement of environmental sanitation, and promotion of personal hygiene. Since the infection is transmitted mainly through ingestion of cysts, preventive measures focus on avoiding contamination of food and water.

Safe drinking water is the most important preventive measure. Drinking water should be properly treated by filtration and adequate disinfection. Boiling of water before consumption is an effective method for destroying cysts, especially in areas where safe water supply is not assured.

Personal hygiene plays a crucial role in preventing infection. Regular hand washing with soap after using the toilet and before handling food reduces fecal oral transmission. Children should be educated about basic hygiene practices at an early age.

Food hygiene is equally important. Fruits and vegetables should be thoroughly washed before consumption. Uncooked or improperly handled food should be avoided, particularly in endemic areas.

Proper sanitation and safe disposal of human feces help prevent contamination of water sources and the environment. Overcrowding and poor sanitation increase the risk of transmission and should be addressed through public health measures.

Early detection and treatment of infected individuals, including asymptomatic carriers, help reduce spread of infection within the community. In institutional settings such as hostels and daycare centers, screening and treatment of contacts may be necessary during outbreaks.

Public health education regarding modes of transmission, safe water practices, and hygiene is essential for long term control of giardiasis. Control measures are most effective when combined with improvements in water supply, sanitation, and health awareness.

Thus, prevention and control of giardiasis depend on integrated efforts involving personal hygiene, environmental sanitation, safe water supply, and community level health education.

Treatment of Giardiasis

Treatment

For educational purpose only

Drug name	Dose in adults	Dose in children	Duration
Metronidazole	250 mg three times per day	5 mg per kg body weight three times per day	5 to 7 days
Tinidazole	2 g once per day	50 mg per kg body weight single dose	1 day
Nitazoxanide	500 mg two times per day	Dose adjusted according to age and body weight	3 days

Supportive care

Adequate hydration is essential, especially in patients with diarrhea. Nutritional support may be required in chronic cases associated with malabsorption. Temporary lactose intolerance may persist after treatment due to intestinal mucosal damage.

Academic note

The above drug names, doses, and duration are provided **only for educational completeness** and understanding of disease management. This book does not recommend self medication or replace clinical guidelines. Treatment must always be prescribed by a qualified medical practitioner.

Trichomonas vaginalis

Introduction

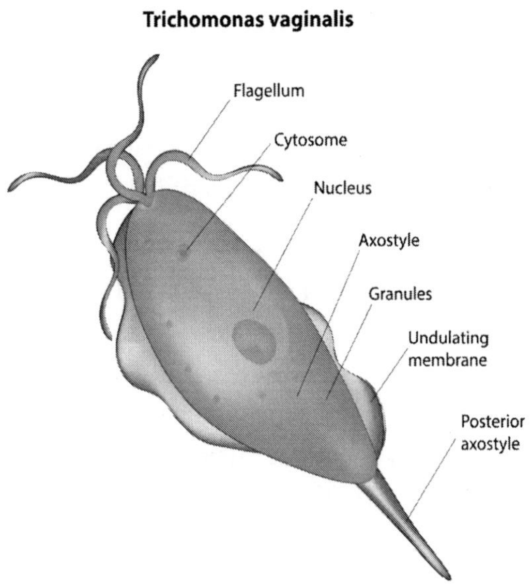

Trichomonas vaginalis is a medically important flagellated protozoan that infects the **urogenital tract of humans**. It is the causative agent of **trichomoniasis**, one of the most common protozoal infections transmitted through sexual contact. Unlike many other protozoa, Trichomonas vaginalis exists **only in the trophozoite form** and does not form cysts.

From a medical zoology perspective, this organism is important because it shows clear adaptation to life in the urogenital environment and demonstrates a direct mode of transmission. The parasite produces local inflammatory changes in the genital mucosa and plays a significant role in reproductive health.

Morphology

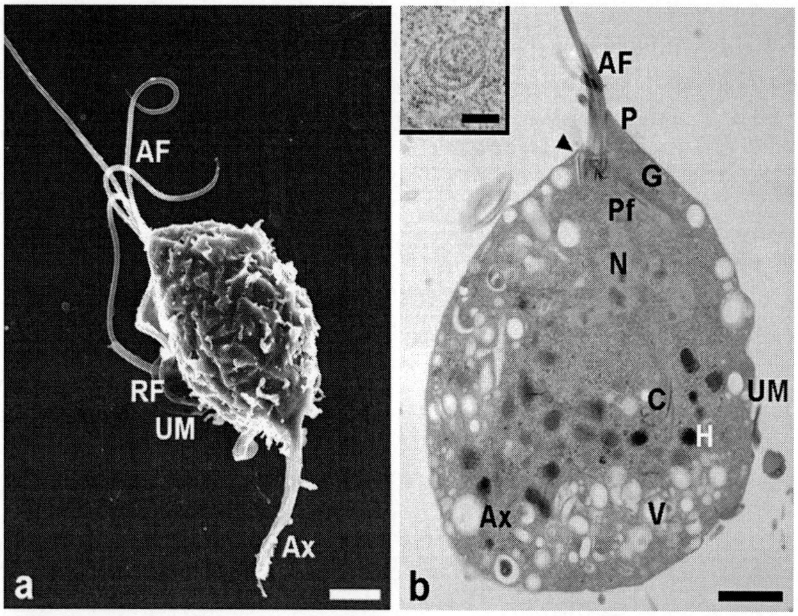

Trichomonas vaginalis exists only as a **trophozoite**, which is the active, motile, and infective form of the parasite. There is **no cyst stage**, which is an important distinguishing feature.

The trophozoite is **pear shaped or oval** and measures approximately **7 to 23 micrometers in length**. The anterior end is broad, while the posterior end tapers and may project outward as a rigid structure.

A **single nucleus** is present near the anterior end. The nucleus contains a central karyosome and lacks peripheral chromatin. The cytoplasm is finely granular.The organism possesses **five flagella**. Four flagella arise from the anterior end and are free, while the fifth flagellum runs backward along the body to form an **undulating membrane**. The undulating membrane extends about half the length of the body and aids in motility within genital secretions.A prominent **axostyle** is present. The axostyle is a rigid rod like internal structure that runs longitudinally through the body and often projects beyond the posterior end. It provides structural support and helps maintain body shape.

The trophozoite also contains **axonemes**, which form the internal microtubular framework of the flagella and contribute to motility. Hydrogenosomes are present instead of mitochondria, reflecting adaptation to anaerobic conditions.Because the trophozoite lacks a protective cyst wall, it does not survive for long outside the human body. This explains why transmission occurs mainly through **direct sexual contact** rather than through the environment.

Origin of Name and Discovery of Trichomonas vaginalis

The name Trichomonas vaginalis is derived from Greek and Latin terms that describe the structure and habitat of the organism.The word **Tricho** is derived from the Greek word meaning **hair**, which refers to the presence of multiple flagella that resemble hair like structures. The term **monas** means **single unit**, indicating that the organism is unicellular. Together, the genus name Trichomonas refers to a single celled organism bearing hair like flagella.The species name **vaginalis** is derived from Latin and indicates the **primary site of infection**, the vagina. This reflects the organism's localization in the urogenital tract of humans.

Trichomonas vaginalis was first described in the year **1836** by the French physician and parasitologist **Alfred François Donné**, who identified the organism in vaginal secretions using microscopy. His work provided one of the earliest microscopic descriptions of a human protozoal pathogen.Thus, the name Trichomonas vaginalis describes both the **structural characteristics** and **anatomical habitat** of the organism, while its discovery marks an important milestone in the early history of medical parasitology.

7. Flagellates of Medical Importance

Trichomonas vaginalis inhabits the **urogenital tract of humans**. In females, the parasite is commonly found in the **vagina, cervix, and urethra**. In males, it may be present in the **urethra, prostate gland, and seminal vesicles**. Humans are the **only known host**, and there is no animal reservoir.

The parasite survives best in the **warm, moist environment** of the genital tract. Because Trichomonas vaginalis exists only in the trophozoite form and does not form cysts, it has **poor survival outside the human body**. This biological characteristic explains its mode of transmission.

Transmission occurs primarily through **sexual contact**. During sexual intercourse, trophozoites are transferred directly from an infected individual to an uninfected partner through genital secretions. The infection is therefore classified as a **sexually transmitted protozoal infection**.

Nonsexual transmission is rare but may occasionally occur through **contaminated fomites** such as towels or undergarments, provided conditions remain moist. Such transmission is uncommon and epidemiologically insignificant compared to sexual transmission.

In males, infection is often asymptomatic, allowing them to act as **silent carriers** and transmit the parasite to female partners. In females, the organism multiplies actively in the vaginal environment, leading to symptomatic infection and increased risk of spread.

Thus, the habitat and mode of transmission of Trichomonas vaginalis are closely linked to its lack of cyst stage, dependence on direct human to human contact, and adaptation to the urogenital environment.

Habitat and Mode of Transmission

Trichomonas vaginalis inhabits the **urogenital tract of humans**. In females, the parasite is commonly found in the **vagina, cervix, and urethra**. In males, it may be present in the **urethra, prostate gland, and seminal vesicles**. Humans are the **only known host**, and there is no animal reservoir.

The parasite survives best in the **warm, moist environment** of the genital tract. Because Trichomonas vaginalis exists only in the trophozoite form and does not form cysts, it has **poor survival outside the human body**. This biological characteristic explains its mode of transmission.

Transmission occurs primarily through **sexual contact**. During sexual intercourse, trophozoites are transferred directly from an infected individual to an uninfected partner through genital secretions. The infection is therefore classified as a **sexually transmitted protozoal infection**.

Nonsexual transmission is rare but may occasionally occur through **contaminated fomites** such as towels or undergarments, provided conditions remain moist. Such transmission is uncommon and epidemiologically insignificant compared to sexual transmission.

In males, infection is often asymptomatic, allowing them to act as **silent carriers** and transmit the parasite to female partners. In females, the organism multiplies actively in the vaginal environment, leading to symptomatic infection and increased risk of spread.

Thus, the habitat and mode of transmission of Trichomonas vaginalis are closely linked to its lack of cyst stage, dependence on direct human to human contact, and adaptation to the urogenital environment.

Life Cycle of Trichomonas vaginalis

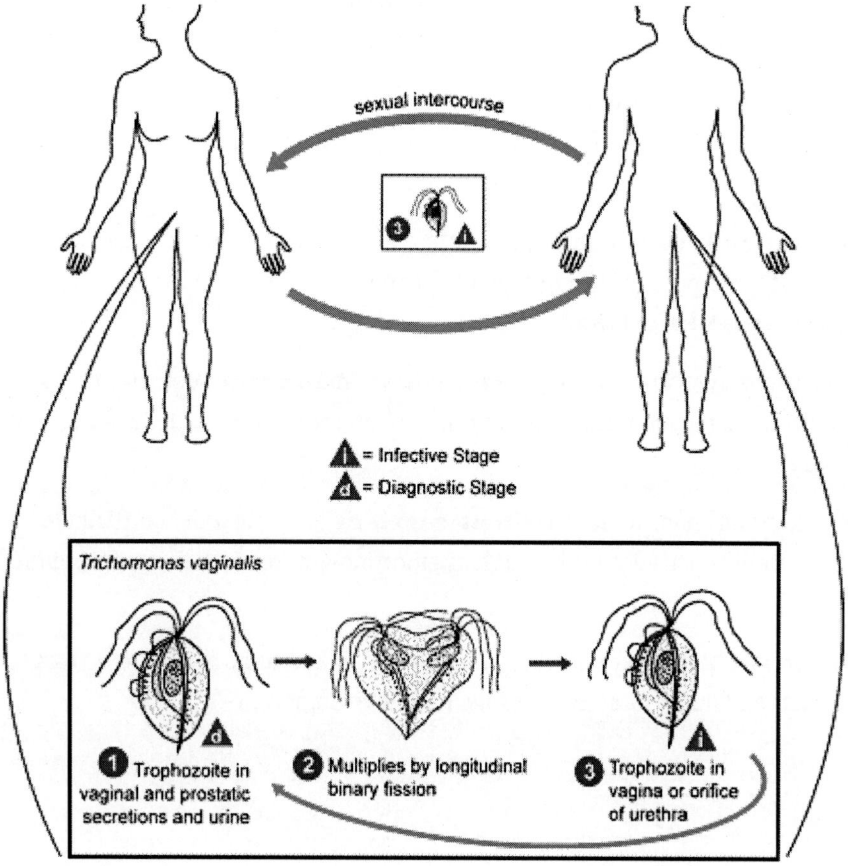

Trichomoniasis

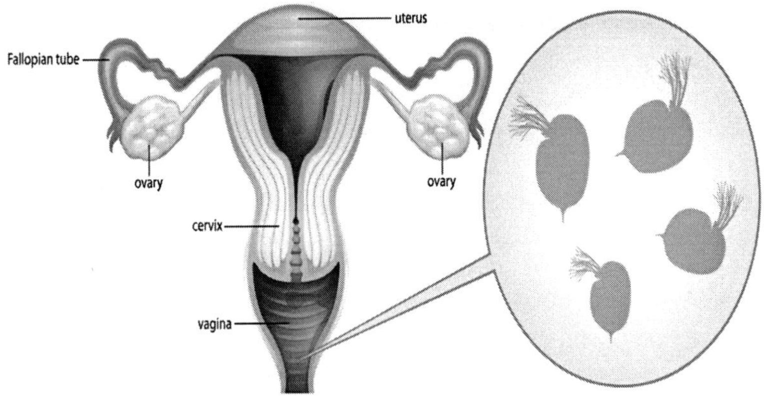

Trichomoniasis is a sexually transmitted infection caused by a parasite called Trichomonas vaginalis. It can cause symptoms such as itching, burning, and a foul-smelling discharge.

The life cycle of Trichomonas vaginalis is **simple, direct, and monoxenous**, meaning it is completed in a single host, the human being. There is **no intermediate host** and **no cyst stage**. The parasite exists only in the **trophozoite form**, which is both the infective and diagnostic stage.

Transmission occurs during **direct sexual contact**. During intercourse, trophozoites present in genital secretions of an infected individual are transferred directly to the urogenital tract of the partner. Because the organism lacks a cyst stage, it does not survive for long outside the human body, which explains why transmission depends on close and direct contact.

After transmission, the trophozoites establish themselves in the **urogenital tract**. In females, the parasite commonly inhabits the vagina, cervix, and urethra. In males, it may be found in the urethra, prostate gland, and seminal vesicles. The warm and moist environment of the genital tract provides favorable conditions for survival and multiplication.

The trophozoites multiply by **longitudinal binary fission**. There is no sexual reproduction. As multiplication continues, large numbers of trophozoites accumulate in genital secretions, leading to inflammation and clinical manifestations in susceptible individuals.

The parasite does not invade tissues or enter the bloodstream. It remains localized to the mucosal surfaces of the urogenital tract. Because trophozoites are fragile and quickly destroyed outside the host, they are transmitted only through direct contact, and environmental spread is negligible.

Thus, the life cycle of Trichomonas vaginalis involves direct transfer of trophozoites from one human host to another, multiplication in the urogenital tract, and continued transmission through sexual contact. Understanding this life cycle is essential for explaining the epidemiology, laboratory diagnosis, treatment, and prevention of trichomoniasis.

Pathogenicity and Disease Caused by Trichomonas vaginalis

Trichomonas vaginalis causes a disease known as **trichomoniasis**, which primarily affects the urogenital tract. The pathogenicity of the parasite is related to its **direct contact with mucosal surfaces**, active motility, and induction of local inflammatory responses.

After transmission, trophozoites adhere to the epithelial lining of the vagina, cervix, or urethra. The organism does not invade deeper tissues but remains on the mucosal surface. Its attachment and movement cause **mechanical irritation** of the epithelium. This irritation leads to damage of superficial epithelial cells and disruption of the normal protective barrier.

The parasite produces **cytotoxic substances and enzymes** that contribute to epithelial cell destruction and inflammation. These substances increase local tissue damage and promote inflammatory reactions. As a result, there is congestion, edema, and increased secretion from the affected mucosa.

Inflammation of the vaginal mucosa alters the normal vaginal environment. The usual acidic pH may become less acidic, favoring further multiplication of the parasite. The inflammatory process also attracts immune cells, which intensify local symptoms.

In males, the parasite often produces minimal tissue damage. The infection may remain asymptomatic or cause mild inflammation of the urethra or prostate. Because of this, males frequently act as carriers and play an important role in transmission.

Thus, the disease caused by Trichomonas vaginalis is mainly due to **local mucosal damage and inflammation**, rather than deep tissue invasion. Understanding pathogenicity explains the clinical features, laboratory findings, and rationale for treatment and prevention.

Clinical Features of Trichomoniasis

The clinical features of trichomoniasis vary according to **sex, immune status, and parasite load**. Infection may be symptomatic or asymptomatic, and this variation plays an important role in continued transmission of the disease.

In **females**, trichomoniasis commonly produces **symptomatic infection**. The most frequent complaint is **vaginal discharge**, which is often profuse, frothy, and may have an unpleasant odor. The discharge is usually yellowish or greenish in color. Patients may experience **itching, burning sensation, and irritation** in the genital area.

Inflammation of the vaginal mucosa leads to **vaginitis**, which may cause discomfort during walking or sitting. **Dysuria** and increased frequency of urination may occur due to involvement of the urethra. On clinical examination, the cervix may show punctate hemorrhages, producing a characteristic appearance commonly described as **strawberry cervix**.

In **males**, infection is frequently **asymptomatic**. When symptoms are present, they are usually mild and include **urethral irritation, burning sensation during urination, and mild discharge**. Occasionally, inflammation of the prostate or epididymis may occur. Because symptoms are minimal or absent, males often remain undiagnosed and act as **carriers**, transmitting infection to female partners.

Systemic symptoms such as fever are usually absent. The disease remains localized to the urogenital tract and does not involve internal organs or bloodstream.

Chronic infection may persist if untreated and can increase susceptibility to other sexually transmitted infections. In females, persistent inflammation may contribute to reproductive health complications.

Thus, the clinical features of trichomoniasis range from asymptomatic carriage to symptomatic urogenital infection, with more pronounced manifestations in females. Recognition of these features is important for diagnosis, treatment, and prevention of further transmission.

Pathology of Trichomoniasis

The pathology of trichomoniasis is confined mainly to the **urogenital mucosa** and is characterized by **local inflammatory changes** rather than deep tissue invasion. The parasite remains on the surface of the epithelium and produces disease through irritation and inflammatory reactions.

In females, Trichomonas vaginalis attaches to the **vaginal and cervical epithelium**. The attachment and active motility of trophozoites cause **desquamation of superficial epithelial cells**. This results in congestion, edema, and increased mucosal secretions. Small capillary hemorrhages may occur on the cervical surface, producing the classical appearance known as strawberry cervix.Inflammation leads to **thickening of the mucosa** and infiltration of inflammatory cells such as neutrophils and lymphocytes. The normal vaginal environment is disturbed, which favors further multiplication of the parasite and persistence of infection.

In males, pathological changes are usually **mild or minimal**. The organism may cause low grade inflammation of the urethra or prostate. Because tissue damage is limited, symptoms are often absent, allowing chronic carriage.There is **no ulceration or deep tissue destruction**, and the parasite does not enter the bloodstream. The pathological effects are mainly functional and inflammatory, explaining the localized nature of the disease.Thus, the pathology of trichomoniasis is characterized by superficial epithelial damage, inflammation, and increased secretions of the urogenital mucosa, which form the basis of the clinical manifestations.

Epidemiology and Susceptibility of Trichomoniasis

Trichomoniasis is a **common sexually transmitted protozoal infection** with worldwide distribution. It occurs in both developed and developing countries and is more prevalent in populations with limited access to sexual health education and medical facilities. The infection affects **sexually active individuals**, with higher prevalence in adults of reproductive age.Humans are the **only natural host** of Trichomonas vaginalis. There is no animal reservoir. Transmission occurs mainly through **sexual contact**, and the prevalence of infection closely follows sexual behavior patterns. The absence of a cyst stage limits environmental survival, making direct person to person transmission essential for continuation of the parasite.

The disease is **more frequently diagnosed in females** than in males. This is partly due to more prominent symptoms in females and easier laboratory detection. In males, infection is often asymptomatic, allowing them to act as **silent carriers** and contribute significantly to ongoing transmission.Susceptibility to trichomoniasis is influenced by several host factors. Individuals with **multiple sexual partners**, poor genital hygiene, or previous sexually transmitted infections are at increased risk. Alteration of the normal vaginal environment also increases susceptibility in females.Asymptomatic carriage plays a major role in the epidemiology of trichomoniasis. Infected individuals without symptoms may continue sexual activity and spread the infection unknowingly. Because of this, trichomoniasis remains highly prevalent in many communities.

Thus, the epidemiology and susceptibility of trichomoniasis are closely related to sexual behavior, lack of symptoms in carriers, and limited environmental survival of the parasite. Understanding these factors is essential for effective diagnosis, treatment, and prevention.

Laboratory Diagnosis of Trichomoniasis

Laboratory diagnosis of trichomoniasis is based on **demonstration of the trophozoite stage** of Trichomonas vaginalis in appropriate clinical specimens. Because the parasite does not form cysts and survives only for a short time outside the human body, **fresh specimen examination is essential** for accurate diagnosis.In **females**, the most commonly examined specimens are **vaginal discharge** and **cervical secretions**. In **males**, specimens include **urethral discharge**, **first void urine sediment**, or **prostatic secretions**. Proper collection and immediate examination increase the likelihood of detecting the parasite.

The simplest and most widely used diagnostic method is **direct wet mount examination**. A small amount of fresh specimen is mixed with normal saline and examined under the microscope. Motile trophozoites showing characteristic **jerky and twitching movements** are observed. Identification is based on the presence of pear shaped trophozoites with flagella and an undulating membrane.Stained smears may also be used for identification. Staining improves visualization of nuclear structure, flagella, and axostyle, although motility cannot be assessed in stained preparations.Repeated examination may be required because parasite numbers can vary. In males, diagnosis is often more difficult due to low parasite load and intermittent shedding, which explains frequent false negative results.Thus, laboratory diagnosis of trichomoniasis relies primarily on microscopic demonstration of motile trophozoites in fresh genital specimens. Prompt examination and correct specimen selection are crucial for reliable diagnosis.

Treatment of Trichomoniasis

For educational purpose only

Treatment of trichomoniasis is aimed at complete elimination of Trichomonas vaginalis, relief of symptoms, and prevention of reinfection. The following treatment regimens are mentioned **strictly for academic understanding** for MBBS and MD students. Clinical use must always follow physician judgment and institutional guidelines.

Drug name	Dose in adults	Dose in children	Duration
Metronidazole	2 g single oral dose or 400 mg two times per day	15 to 30 mg per kg body weight per day in divided doses	1 day or 7 days
Tinidazole	2 g single oral dose	Dose adjusted according to body weight	1 day

Important clinical points

Both sexual partners must be treated **simultaneously**, even if one partner is asymptomatic. This is essential to prevent reinfection. Sexual intercourse should be avoided until treatment is completed and symptoms have resolved.

Supportive care

Maintenance of genital hygiene and treatment of associated infections help in faster recovery. Symptomatic relief usually occurs within a few days after effective therapy.

Academic note

The drug names, doses, and duration are included **only for educational completeness**. This information is not intended for self medication and does not replace clinical protocols. Prescription and monitoring must always be done by a qualified medical practitioner.

7. Flagellates of Medical Importance

Leishmania donovani

Introduction

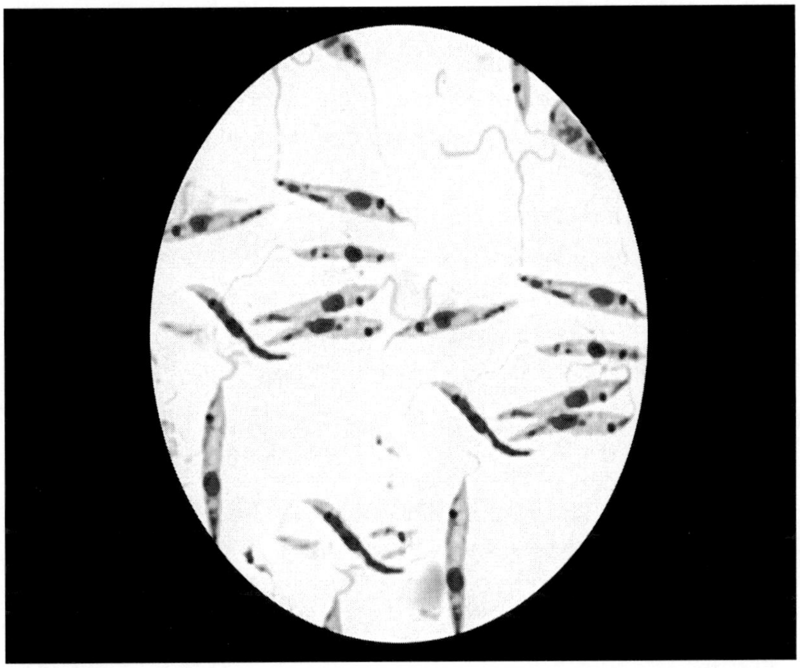

Leishmania donovani is a medically important **blood and tissue flagellate** responsible for **visceral leishmaniasis**, commonly known as kala azar. It is a serious systemic protozoal disease characterized by prolonged fever, enlargement of spleen and liver, anemia, and progressive weakness. The disease is endemic in several tropical and subtropical regions and represents a major public health problem.

From a medical zoology perspective, Leishmania donovani is important because it shows **dual morphology**, adapting to two different hosts. One form lives inside human cells, while the other form develops inside the insect vector. This dual adaptation explains the transmission pattern, pathogenicity, and chronic nature of the disease.

The parasite primarily infects cells of the **reticuloendothelial system**, especially macrophages present in the spleen, liver, bone marrow, and lymph nodes. Unlike intestinal flagellates, Leishmania donovani does not remain confined to a single organ system but produces widespread systemic involvement.

Transmission occurs through the bite of an infected **female sandfly**, which introduces the parasite into the human body during blood feeding. Because transmission depends on an arthropod vector, visceral leishmaniasis is classified as a **vector borne protozoal disease**.

The study of Leishmania donovani helps students understand the relationship between parasite morphology, intracellular survival, vector transmission, and systemic disease. This organism provides an excellent model for teaching concepts related to tissue flagellates, host parasite interaction, and public health significance in medical zoology.

Origin and Meaning of the Name and Discovery of Leishmania donovani

The name Leishmania donovani has historical and scientific significance and reflects the contributions of two pioneers in parasitology. The genus name **Leishmania** is derived from **William Boog Leishman**, a British pathologist who first observed the parasite in tissue smears from patients suffering from kala azar. His work provided early microscopic evidence of the organism within human cells.

The species name **donovani** is derived from **Charles Donovan**, an Irish physician who independently identified the same parasite in splenic aspirates of kala azar patients in India. He established the clear association between the organism and visceral leishmaniasis. The intracellular forms of the parasite observed in human tissues are commonly referred to as **Leishman Donovan bodies**, or LD bodies, in recognition of their contributions.Thus, the name Leishmania donovani honors both Leishman and Donovan for their roles in the discovery and characterization of the parasite. The nomenclature reflects the historical development of knowledge about visceral leishmaniasis and marks an important milestone in medical parasitology.

Morphology

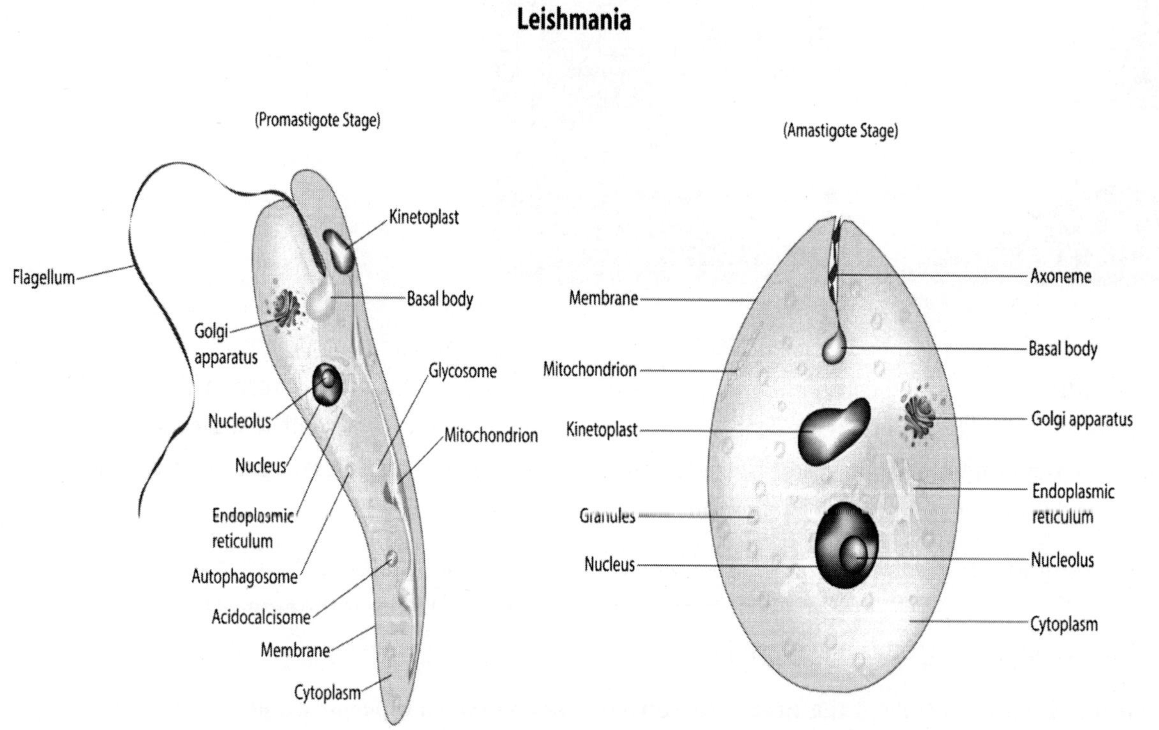

Leishmania donovani shows **dimorphism**, meaning it exists in two distinct morphological forms depending on the host in which it lives. One form is found in the human host and the other in the insect vector. This dual morphology is a key feature of the parasite and is essential for understanding its life cycle and pathogenicity.The form found in humans is known as the **amastigote form**, also called the **Leishman Donovan body**. It is a small, round to oval structure measuring approximately **two to four micrometers** in diameter. The amastigote is found **inside macrophages** of the reticuloendothelial system. It contains a single nucleus and a rod shaped **kinetoplast**, which lies close to the nucleus. Flagella are absent in this stage, which is an adaptation to intracellular life. The cytoplasm is clear and finely granular. The amastigote multiplies within macrophages by binary fission.The form found in the sandfly vector is known as the **promastigote form**. It is elongated and spindle shaped, measuring approximately **fifteen to twenty micrometers** in length. A single nucleus is present near the center of the body. In front of the nucleus lies a prominent kinetoplast. From the anterior end arises a **single free flagellum**, which is responsible for active motility. An undulating membrane is absent in this form. The promastigote is actively motile and multiplies in the gut of the sandfly.

The transformation between amastigote and promastigote forms represents an important adaptive mechanism. The amastigote form is specialized for survival within human macrophages, while the promastigote form is adapted for survival and movement within the insect vector.Thus, the morphology of Leishmania donovani clearly reflects its dual host life cycle and explains its ability to survive intracellularly in humans and extracellularly in the sandfly. Understanding these morphological forms is essential for diagnosis, life cycle interpretation, and disease correlation.

Habitat and Mode of Transmission

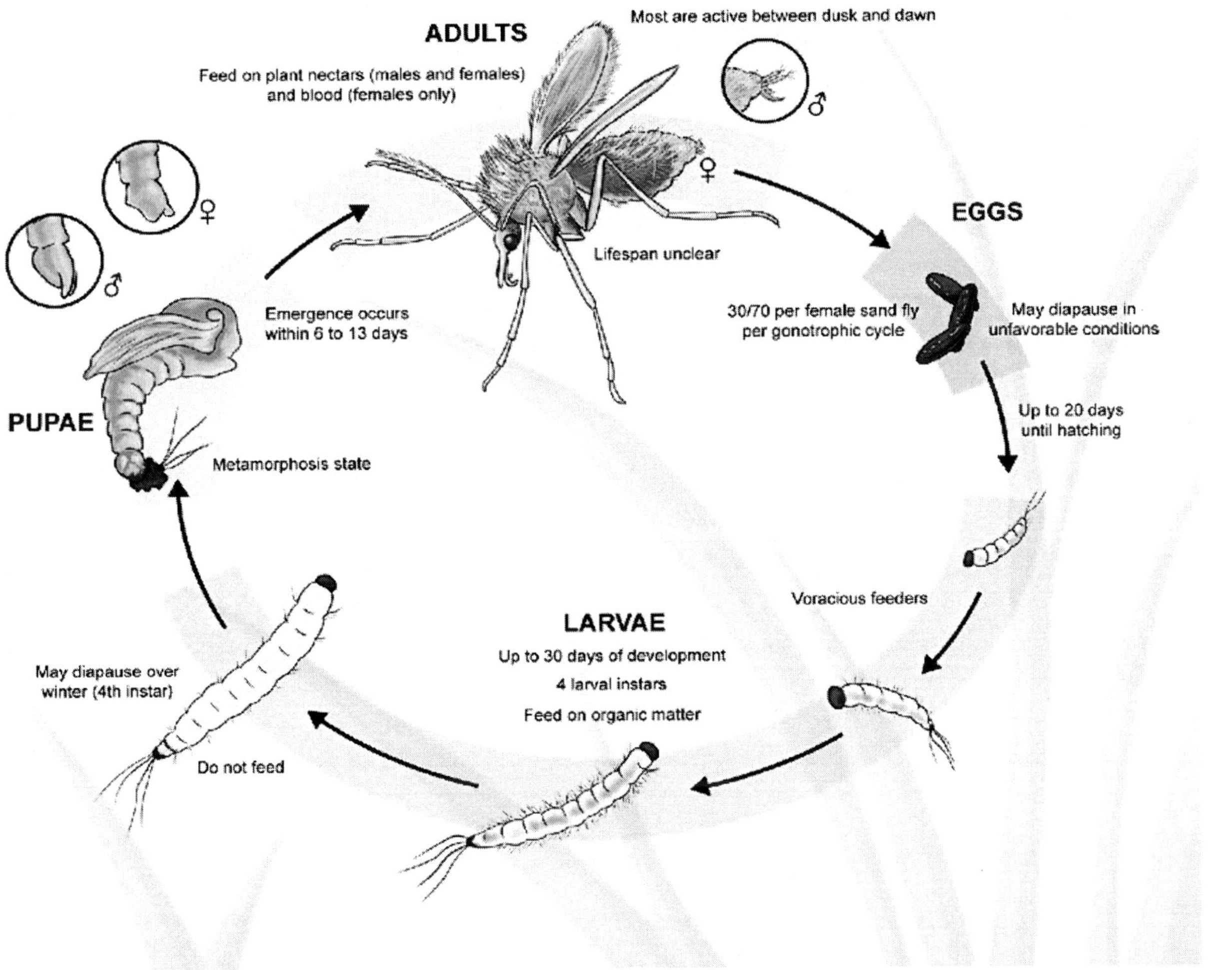

Leishmania donovani inhabits different environments in its two hosts, showing clear biological adaptation. In the **human host**, the parasite is found in the **amastigote form** and lives **inside macrophages** of the reticuloendothelial system. The principal sites of localization include the **spleen, liver, bone marrow, and**

lymph nodes. Within these organs, the parasite multiplies intracellularly and produces systemic disease.In the **insect vector**, the parasite exists in the **promastigote form**. It inhabits the **alimentary canal of the female sandfly**, particularly species of the genus Phlebotomus in the Old World. The sandfly provides a suitable environment for multiplication and development of the parasite.Transmission of Leishmania donovani occurs through the **bite of an infected female sandfly**. During blood feeding, the sandfly injects **promastigote forms** of the parasite into the human skin. These promastigotes are rapidly taken up by macrophages, where they transform into amastigotes and begin intracellular multiplication.

Humans act as the **definitive host**, while the sandfly serves as the **vector host**. In endemic areas, infected humans act as the main reservoir of infection, maintaining the parasite in the community.Transmission is closely associated with environmental and socioeconomic factors such as poor housing, overcrowding, and presence of sandfly breeding sites. Because transmission depends on a vector, visceral leishmaniasis is classified as a **vector borne protozoal disease**.Thus, the habitat and mode of transmission of Leishmania donovani explain its systemic nature, intracellular survival, and epidemiological pattern, forming the basis for understanding its life cycle, pathology, and control measures.

Life Cycle of Leishmania donovani

The life cycle of Leishmania donovani is **indirect and heteroxenous**, as it requires **two hosts** to complete development. These hosts are the **human being** and the **female sandfly**. The parasite shows **two morphological forms**, each adapted to a specific host.

In the **human host**, infection begins when an infected female sandfly bites the skin during blood feeding. At this time, the sandfly injects the **promastigote form** of the parasite into the skin. The promastigotes are actively motile and are quickly taken up by tissue macrophages.Inside the macrophages, the promastigotes transform into the **amastigote form**. This transformation is essential for survival within human cells. The amastigotes multiply by **binary fission** inside macrophages, causing the infected cells to enlarge and eventually rupture. Released amastigotes then infect new macrophages and spread through the **reticuloendothelial system**, involving the spleen, liver, bone marrow, and lymph nodes.

In the **sandfly vector**, the life cycle continues when a female sandfly takes a blood meal from an infected human. During feeding, the sandfly ingests macrophages containing amastigotes. Inside the sandfly gut, the amastigotes are released from host cells and transform into **promastigotes**.The promastigotes multiply actively in the alimentary canal of the sandfly and migrate toward the anterior part of the gut. They become elongated and highly motile, preparing for transmission. When the sandfly bites another human host, these promastigotes are inoculated into the skin, completing the cycle.Thus, the life cycle of Leishmania donovani alternates between **amastigote form in humans** and **promastigote form in the sandfly**. Understanding this life cycle is essential for explaining the intracellular nature of the disease, its chronic course, laboratory diagnosis, and the role of vector control in prevention.

Pathogenicity and Disease Caused by Leishmania donovani

Leishmania donovani causes **visceral leishmaniasis**, commonly known as **kala azar**. The pathogenicity of this parasite is closely related to its ability to **survive and multiply inside macrophages** of the reticuloendothelial system. This intracellular localization allows the parasite to evade host defense mechanisms and produce a chronic systemic disease.

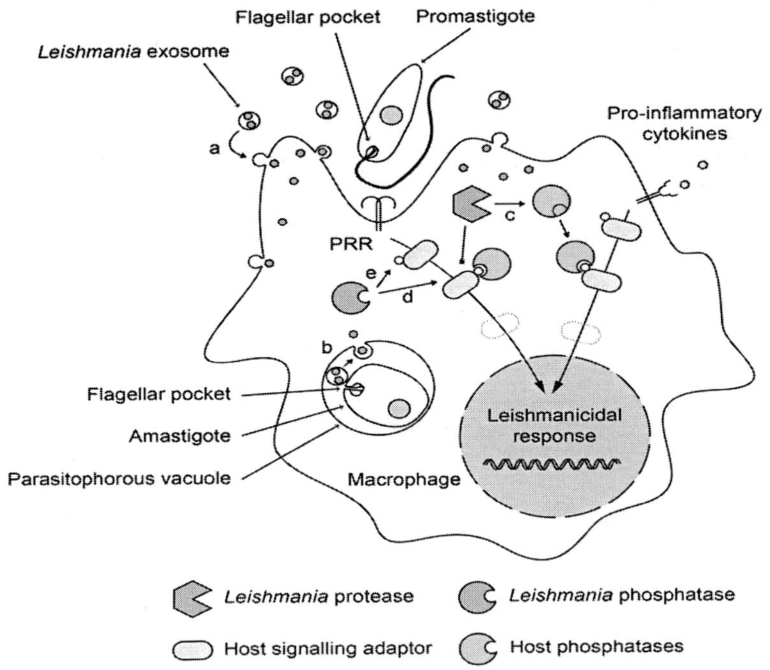

After transmission by the bite of an infected sandfly, promastigotes enter the human body and are phagocytosed by macrophages. Inside these cells, the parasites transform into amastigotes and multiply by binary fission. The infected macrophages enlarge and eventually rupture, releasing amastigotes that infect new macrophages. This continuous cycle leads to progressive involvement of organs rich in macrophages.

The **spleen** is the most severely affected organ. Massive multiplication of parasites results in marked splenomegaly due to hyperplasia of the reticuloendothelial tissue. The **liver** is also involved, leading to hepatomegaly caused by infiltration of infected macrophages in hepatic sinusoids. Involvement of the **bone marrow** interferes with normal blood cell production.

As the disease progresses, there is **suppression of bone marrow activity**, resulting in anemia, leukopenia, and thrombocytopenia. This leads to weakness, increased susceptibility to infections, and bleeding tendencies. Persistent infection also causes prolonged fever and severe weight loss due to chronic inflammation and immune dysfunction.

The immune response in visceral leishmaniasis is impaired. Although antibodies are produced, they are not protective because the parasite resides inside cells. Cell mediated immunity is reduced, allowing continued survival and multiplication of the parasite. This immune suppression explains the chronic and progressive nature of the disease.

Thus, Leishmania donovani produces disease by intracellular multiplication within macrophages, widespread involvement of the reticuloendothelial system, and suppression of normal immune and hematopoietic functions. Understanding pathogenicity is essential for correlating clinical features, laboratory findings, and treatment strategies.

Clinical Features of Visceral Leishmaniasis

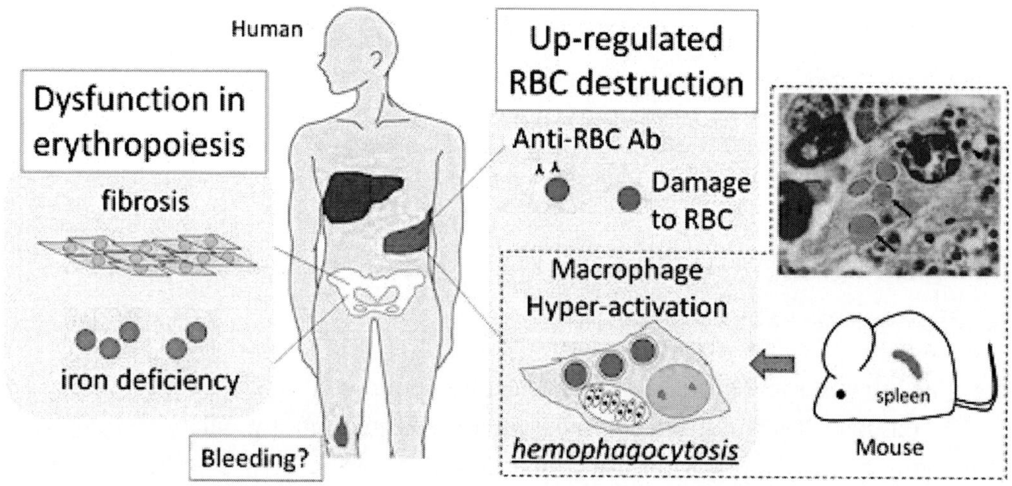

The clinical features of visceral leishmaniasis develop gradually and reflect **systemic involvement of the reticuloendothelial system**. The disease is chronic in nature and, if untreated, may become fatal.

The most common presenting feature is **prolonged fever**. The fever is usually irregular and persists for weeks or months. It is often accompanied by **chills, weakness, and loss of appetite**. As the disease progresses, the patient develops marked **weight loss and wasting**.**Splenomegaly** is the most prominent physical finding and may become massive. The spleen is firm and non tender. **Hepatomegaly** is also commonly present, though it is usually less marked than splenic enlargement. Enlargement of lymph nodes may be seen in some cases.Due to involvement of the bone marrow, patients develop **anemia**, which leads to pallor, fatigue, and breathlessness on exertion. Reduction in white blood cells increases susceptibility to secondary infections, while low platelet counts may cause bleeding tendencies such as gum bleeding or nose bleeding.

Skin changes may occur in advanced cases. The skin may become **darkened and dry**, which is the reason the disease is popularly known as kala azar, meaning black fever. Hair loss and brittle nails may also be observed due to chronic illness and nutritional deficiency.

In children, the disease may present with **growth retardation and failure to thrive**. Recurrent infections and poor nutritional status further worsen the condition.Thus, the clinical features of visceral leishmaniasis include prolonged fever, massive splenomegaly, hepatomegaly, anemia, weight loss, and immune suppression. These features correlate closely with the pathological changes produced by intracellular multiplication of the parasite.

Pathology of Visceral Leishmaniasis

The pathology of visceral leishmaniasis is characterized by **widespread involvement of the reticuloendothelial system** and progressive dysfunction of multiple organs. The disease process is mainly due to **intracellular multiplication of the parasite within macrophages**, leading to chronic inflammation and organ enlargement.The **spleen** is the most severely affected organ. Extensive multiplication of amastigotes within splenic macrophages causes marked hyperplasia of reticuloendothelial tissue. This results in massive enlargement of the spleen. Normal splenic architecture becomes distorted, and excessive sequestration of blood cells occurs, contributing to anemia, leukopenia, and thrombocytopenia.

The **liver** shows infiltration of infected macrophages within the hepatic sinusoids. This leads to enlargement of the liver due to reticuloendothelial hyperplasia. Liver cells themselves are usually preserved in early stages, but prolonged infection may result in functional impairment.

The **bone marrow** is heavily involved in advanced disease. Macrophages containing Leishman Donovan bodies replace normal hematopoietic tissue. This suppresses normal blood cell production and is responsible for anemia, reduced white blood cell count, and low platelet levels. Bone marrow involvement plays a major role in immune suppression and susceptibility to secondary infections.

The **lymph nodes** may show enlargement due to infiltration of parasitized macrophages. In some endemic regions, lymph node involvement is more prominent and contributes to the spread of infection.

The **immune system** is profoundly affected. Although antibodies are produced, they do not eliminate the parasite because it resides inside cells. Cell mediated immunity is suppressed, allowing continuous survival and multiplication of the organism. This immune dysfunction explains the chronic course of the disease and poor response to secondary infections.

Thus, the pathology of visceral leishmaniasis is dominated by reticuloendothelial hyperplasia, organ enlargement, bone marrow suppression, and immune dysfunction. These pathological changes form the biological basis of the clinical features and complications of the disease.

Epidemiology and Susceptibility of Visceral Leishmaniasis

Countries where visceral leishmaniasis is endemic, 2023

Our World in Data

Leishmaniasis is a disease caused by parasites. In the visceral form, the parasites affect the liver, spleen, and bone marrow, causing symptoms such as fever, weight loss, anemia, and swelling of these organs.

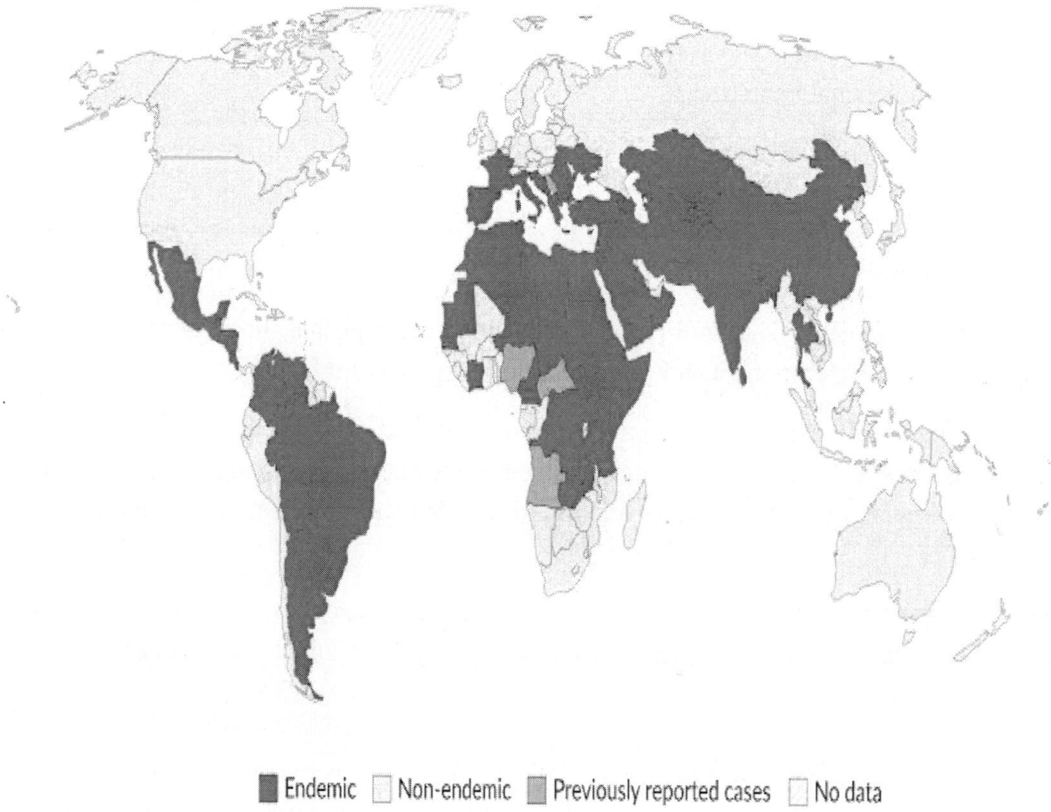

Data source: World Health Organization - Global Health Observatory (2025) OurWorldinData.org/neglected-tropical-diseases |

Note: A disease outbreak is endemic in a country if it is consistently present in the country. "Previously reported cases" means that at least one locally transmitted case has been reported, but the whole transmission cycle has not been demonstrated in the country.

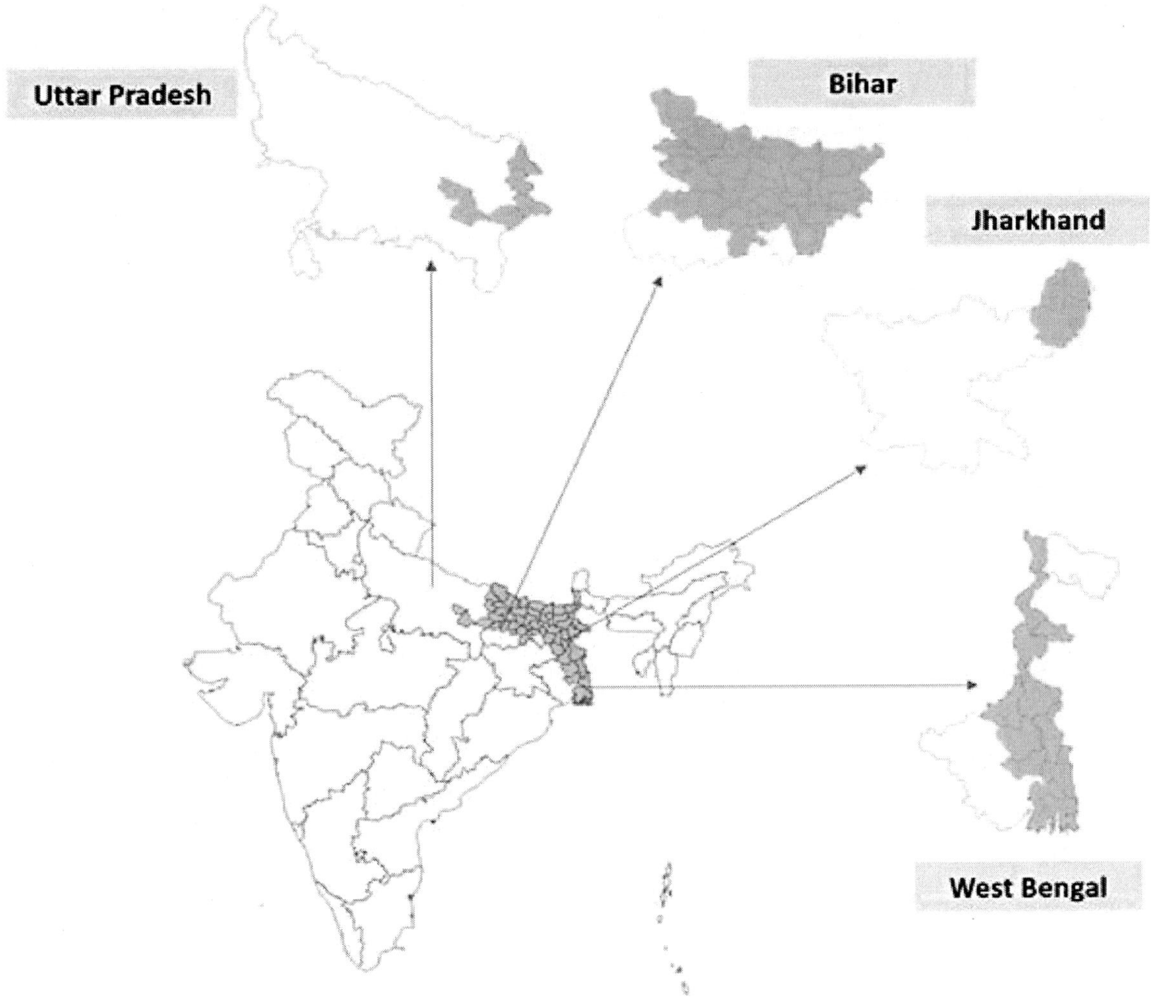

Visceral leishmaniasis is a **geographically restricted disease** with high prevalence in specific tropical and subtropical regions. It is endemic in parts of **India, Bangladesh, Nepal, Sudan, South Sudan, Ethiopia, and Brazil**. In India, the disease is mainly concentrated in eastern regions, particularly Bihar, Jharkhand, West Bengal, and Uttar Pradesh.The occurrence of the disease is closely related to the **distribution of the sandfly vector** and environmental conditions that favor its breeding. Poor housing, presence of cracks in walls, damp surroundings, accumulation of organic waste, and proximity to vegetation create suitable habitats for sandflies. Transmission is more common in rural and peri urban areas.

Humans act as the **main reservoir of infection** in endemic regions. Infected individuals, especially those with active disease or untreated cases, serve as sources of infection for sandflies, thereby maintaining transmission within the community.Susceptibility to visceral leishmaniasis depends on several host factors. **Malnutrition** significantly increases susceptibility, particularly in children. Individuals with **reduced cell mediated immunity** are more prone to severe disease. Poverty, overcrowding, and limited access to healthcare also increase risk.The disease affects **all age groups**, but children and young adults are commonly affected in endemic areas. Both males and females can be infected, though higher incidence in males is often reported due to increased outdoor exposure during sandfly feeding hours.Asymptomatic infections are common in endemic regions. Such individuals may not show clinical signs but can still contribute to transmission. Progression from asymptomatic infection to clinical disease depends on immune status and nutritional condition of the host.Thus, the epidemiology and susceptibility of visceral leishmaniasis are influenced by vector distribution, environmental conditions, socioeconomic factors, nutritional status, and host immunity. Understanding these factors is essential for planning diagnosis, control programs, and preventive strategies.

Laboratory Diagnosis of Visceral Leishmaniasis

Laboratory diagnosis of visceral leishmaniasis is based on **demonstration of the parasite in clinical specimens** obtained from affected organs. Because the parasite is intracellular and localized mainly in the reticuloendothelial system, appropriate specimen selection is essential for accurate diagnosis.

The **most definitive method** is the demonstration of **amastigote forms**, also known as **Leishman Donovan bodies**, within macrophages. These bodies are small, round to oval structures containing a nucleus and a kinetoplast.

Bone marrow aspiration is the most commonly used diagnostic procedure. Bone marrow smears are stained and examined microscopically to detect intracellular amastigotes. This method is widely preferred because it provides good diagnostic yield with relatively lower risk compared to other invasive procedures.

Splenic aspiration has the highest diagnostic sensitivity, as the spleen contains a large number of parasites. However, this procedure carries a risk of bleeding and is performed only by experienced personnel in specialized centers.

Lymph node aspiration may be useful in cases where lymphadenopathy is prominent. The aspirate is examined for the presence of amastigotes within macrophages.

In addition to direct microscopy, **culture methods** may be used. Aspirated material can be cultured in suitable media to demonstrate transformation of amastigotes into promastigotes. Although culture increases sensitivity, it is time consuming and requires specialized laboratory facilities.

Laboratory diagnosis must always be correlated with **clinical features and epidemiological history**. Repeated examinations may be necessary in early or low intensity infections.

Thus, laboratory diagnosis of visceral leishmaniasis relies mainly on microscopic demonstration of Leishman Donovan bodies in tissue aspirates, supported by culture techniques where available. Accurate diagnosis is essential for timely treatment and control of the disease.

7. Flagellates of Medical Importance

Leishmania donovani

Treatment of Visceral Leishmaniasis

For educational purpose only

Treatment of visceral leishmaniasis aims to eliminate the parasite, restore normal organ function, and prevent complications. The drugs mentioned below are included **strictly for academic understanding** . Clinical use must follow national guidelines and specialist supervision.

Drug name	Dose in adults	Dose in children	Duration
Sodium stibogluconate	20 mg per kg body weight per day by injection	20 mg per kg body weight per day	28 to 30 days
Amphotericin B	0.75 to 1 mg per kg body weight on alternate days	Dose adjusted according to body weight	15 to 20 doses
Liposomal amphotericin B	10 mg per kg body weight single dose or divided doses	Dose adjusted according to body weight	As per protocol
Miltefosine	50 mg two times per day	Dose adjusted according to body weight	28 days

Supportive management

Supportive care includes correction of anemia, nutritional rehabilitation, and management of secondary infections. Adequate rest and monitoring of organ function are important during therapy.

Academic note

The drug names, doses, and duration are provided **only for educational purpose** to explain principles of management. This content does not promote self medication and does not replace clinical judgment or institutional treatment protocols.

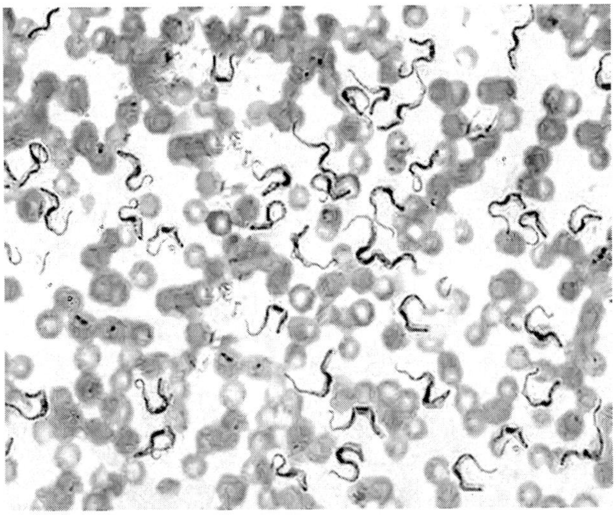

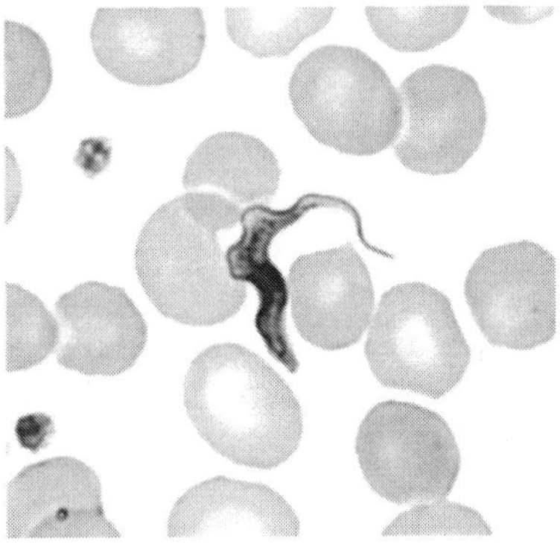

Trypanosoma species

Introduction

AFRICAN SLEEPING SICKNESS

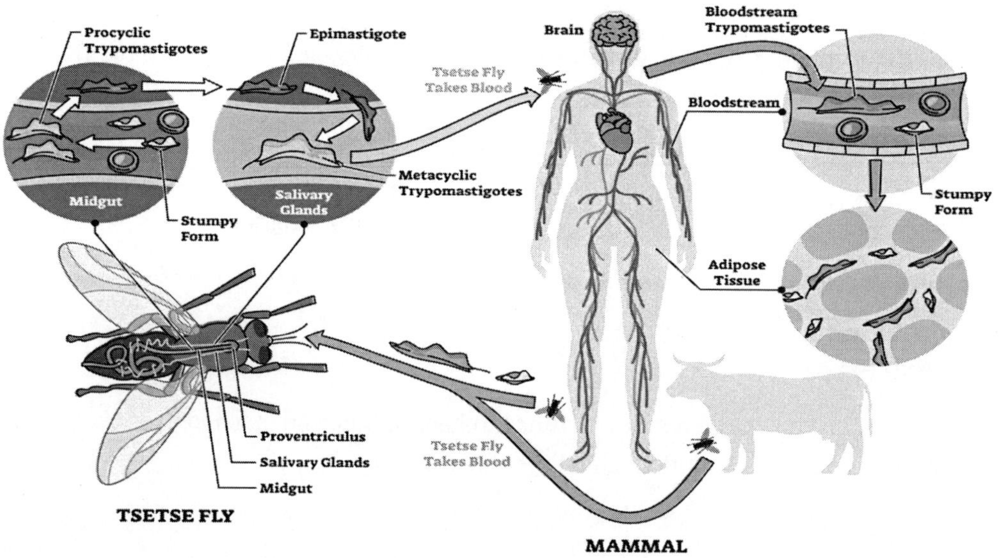

Trypanosoma species are **blood and tissue flagellates** of major medical importance. They are responsible for serious systemic diseases in humans, most notably **African trypanosomiasis**, commonly known as **sleeping sickness**. These parasites circulate in the blood and lymphatic system and may later invade the central nervous system, producing progressive and often fatal illness if untreated.

From a medical zoology perspective, Trypanosoma species are important because they show **marked morphological adaptation**, active motility, and a complex relationship with their insect vectors. Unlike intestinal or urogenital flagellates, these organisms live freely in body fluids and demonstrate continuous movement, which helps them evade host immune responses.

Trypanosoma species are transmitted through the bite of **blood sucking insect vectors**. Transmission depends on biological development of the parasite inside the vector, making these infections classical examples of **vector transmitted protozoal diseases**. Humans act as the main host, while insects serve as vector hosts that facilitate spread of infection.

The parasite shows different developmental forms in the human host and the insect vector. In humans, the organism is found mainly in the **trypomastigote form**, which circulates in blood, lymph, and cerebrospinal fluid. This form is responsible for clinical manifestations of disease.

The study of Trypanosoma species helps students understand concepts such as blood flagellates, immune evasion, vector dependence, and nervous system involvement. These organisms provide an important link between parasitology, public health, and epidemiology within medical zoology.

Origin and Meaning of the Name and Discovery of Trypanosoma species

The name Trypanosoma is derived from Greek words that describe the shape and movement of the organism. The word **trypanon** means auger or borer, and **soma** means body. Together, the term Trypanosoma refers to a corkscrew shaped organism that moves actively in blood by twisting and boring movements. This name accurately reflects the characteristic appearance and motility of the parasite seen under the microscope.

The discovery of Trypanosoma species is closely linked with the study of African sleeping sickness. In the year 1901, **William Boog Leishman** and **Charles Donovan** contributed to early protozoal discoveries, but the specific identification of human African trypanosomes was later established by **David Bruce**. Bruce demonstrated the role of the tsetse fly in transmission and established the connection between the parasite and sleeping sickness.

Two major species infect humans in Africa.

1. **Trypanosoma gambiense** causes the chronic form of sleeping sickness in West and Central Africa.
2. **Trypanosoma rhodesiense** causes the acute form of the disease in East and Southern Africa.

The historical discoveries of Trypanosoma species played a crucial role in understanding vector transmitted diseases and established the foundation of modern medical parasitology. The naming and discovery of these organisms highlight the relationship between parasite morphology, mode of transmission, and disease pattern.

Morphology of Trypanosoma species

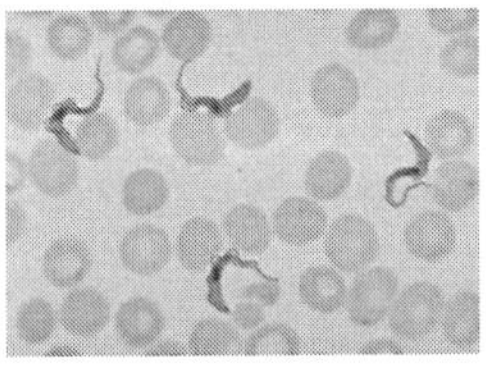

Trypanosoma species show a **well defined and characteristic morphology** that allows easy identification in blood and tissue smears. In the human host, the parasite is found mainly in the **trypomastigote form**, which is the diagnostic and pathogenic stage.

The trypomastigote is an **elongated spindle shaped organism** with tapering ends. Its length usually ranges from **fifteen to thirty micrometers**, while the width is approximately **one to three micrometers**. The body is flexible and shows active movement in blood and lymph.

A **single central nucleus** is present, which is oval in shape and lies near the middle of the body. The nucleus contains a central karyosome and is clearly visible in stained blood smears.

One of the most important diagnostic structures is the **kinetoplast**. The kinetoplast is a small, dense, rod shaped or dot like structure located near the posterior end of the organism. It contains mitochondrial DNA and is closely associated with the basal body of the flagellum. Presence of the kinetoplast helps differentiate Trypanosoma from other blood parasites.

A **single flagellum** arises from the basal body near the kinetoplast. The flagellum runs along the length of the body and is attached to the cell membrane, forming a prominent **undulating membrane**. The undulating membrane is well developed and plays an important role in motility within viscous body fluids such as blood and lymph.

The free end of the flagellum extends beyond the anterior end of the body. Coordinated movement of the flagellum and undulating membrane produces the characteristic **wriggling and twisting motion** of the parasite.

The cytoplasm is finely granular and contains organelles necessary for survival in the host environment. The parasite lacks a cyst stage and remains motile throughout its life in the human host.

Thus, the morphology of Trypanosoma species is characterized by an elongated body, single nucleus, posterior kinetoplast, single flagellum, and well developed undulating membrane. These features are essential for identification, diagnosis, and understanding of its pathogenic behavior.

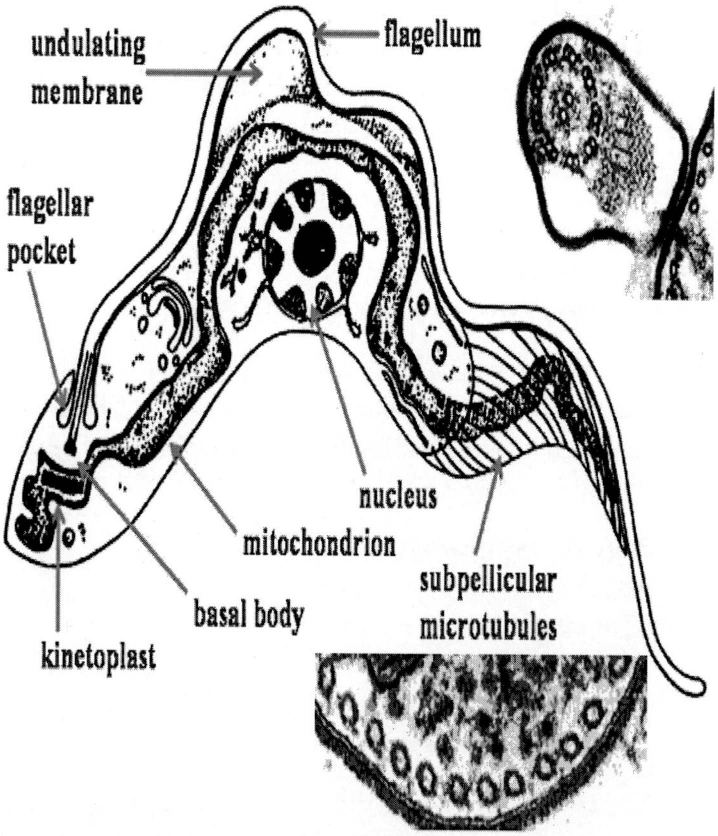

Habitat and Mode of Transmission of Trypanosoma species

Fig : Tsetse fly

Trypanosoma species inhabit **blood, lymphatic system, and cerebrospinal fluid** of the human host. During the early stage of infection, the parasites are mainly found circulating freely in the **blood and lymph**. As the disease progresses, the organisms invade the **central nervous system**, leading to serious neurological manifestations.In the human body, Trypanosoma exists in the **trypomastigote form**, which is actively motile and multiplies by longitudinal binary fission. The parasite does not invade cells but remains extracellular in body fluids, which is a distinguishing feature of Trypanosoma infections.

Transmission of Trypanosoma species occurs through the bite of an infected **tsetse fly of the genus Glossina**. The fly acts as a **biological vector**, meaning the parasite undergoes development inside the insect before becoming infective to humans.When a tsetse fly bites an infected person, it ingests blood containing trypomastigotes. Inside the fly, the parasite undergoes developmental changes and multiplies. After completing its development, the infective forms migrate to the salivary glands of the fly.

During a subsequent blood meal, the infected tsetse fly injects the parasite into a new human host along with saliva. The parasites then enter the bloodstream, multiply, and spread through the lymphatic system and later the nervous system.Humans act as the **main host**, while the tsetse fly serves as the **vector host**. Transmission is closely related to the geographical distribution of the tsetse fly, which explains why African trypanosomiasis is restricted to specific regions of Africa.Thus, the habitat and mode of transmission of Trypanosoma species explain the systemic nature of the disease, its neurological involvement, and its dependence on insect vectors for survival and spread.

Life Cycle of Trypanosoma species

The life cycle of Trypanosoma species is **indirect and heteroxenous**, as it is completed in **two hosts**, the human being and the **tsetse fly of the genus Glossina**. The parasite shows different developmental forms in the human host and in the insect vector, each adapted to its environment.In the human host, infection begins when an infected tsetse fly bites during blood feeding. At the time of the bite, the fly injects infective trypomastigote forms present in its salivary glands into the human bloodstream. These parasites enter the blood and lymphatic system, where they multiply by longitudinal binary fission.

The trypomastigotes circulate freely in the **blood and lymph** during the early stage of infection. As the disease progresses, the parasites invade the **cerebrospinal fluid**, leading to involvement of the central nervous system. In humans, the parasite remains extracellular and does not form a cyst stage.The **insect vector stage** begins when a tsetse fly feeds on the blood of an infected human and ingests trypomastigotes. Inside the midgut of the fly, the parasites transform into developmental forms and multiply. They then migrate to the salivary glands of the fly, where they undergo further transformation into infective trypomastigotes.

These infective forms accumulate in the salivary glands and are ready to be transmitted during the next blood meal. When the infected tsetse fly bites another human, the parasites are inoculated into the bloodstream, thus continuing the cycle.Thus, the life cycle of Trypanosoma species involves **alternation between the human host and the tsetse fly vector**, with blood circulation and nervous system involvement in humans and developmental transformation inside the insect. Understanding this life cycle is essential for explaining disease progression, laboratory diagnosis, and the importance of vector control in prevention.

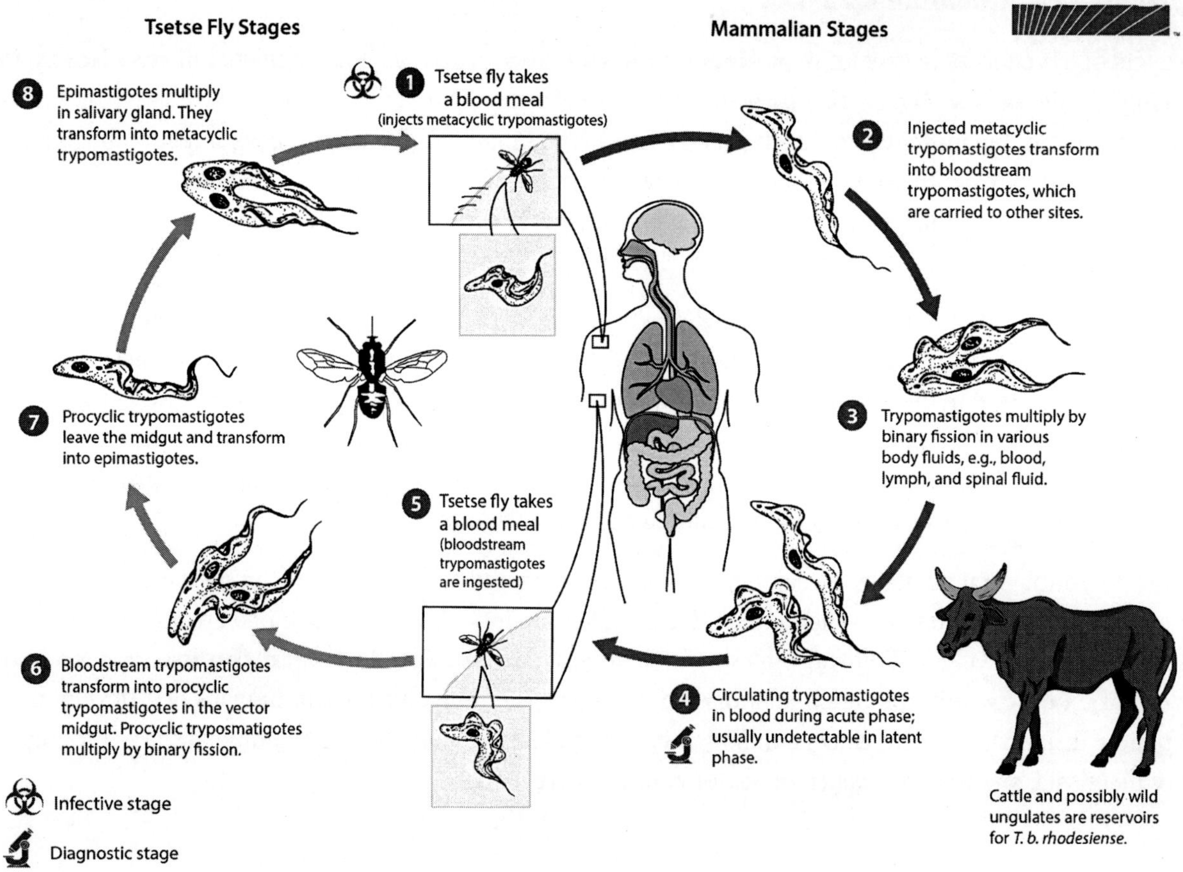
Tsetse Fly Stages
Mammalian Stages
1 Tsetse fly takes a blood meal (injects metacyclic trypomastigotes)
2 Injected metacyclic trypomastigotes transform into bloodstream trypomastigotes, which are carried to other sites.
3 Trypomastigotes multiply by binary fission in various body fluids, e.g., blood, lymph, and spinal fluid.
4 Circulating trypomastigotes in blood during acute phase; usually undetectable in latent phase.
5 Tsetse fly takes a blood meal (bloodstream trypomastigotes are ingested)
6 Bloodstream trypomastigotes transform into procyclic trypomastigotes in the vector midgut. Procyclic tryposmatigotes multiply by binary fission.
7 Procyclic trypomastigotes leave the midgut and transform into epimastigotes.
8 Epimastigotes multiply in salivary gland. They transform into metacyclic trypomastigotes.
Infective stage
Diagnostic stage
Cattle and possibly wild ungulates are reservoirs for *T. b. rhodesiense*.

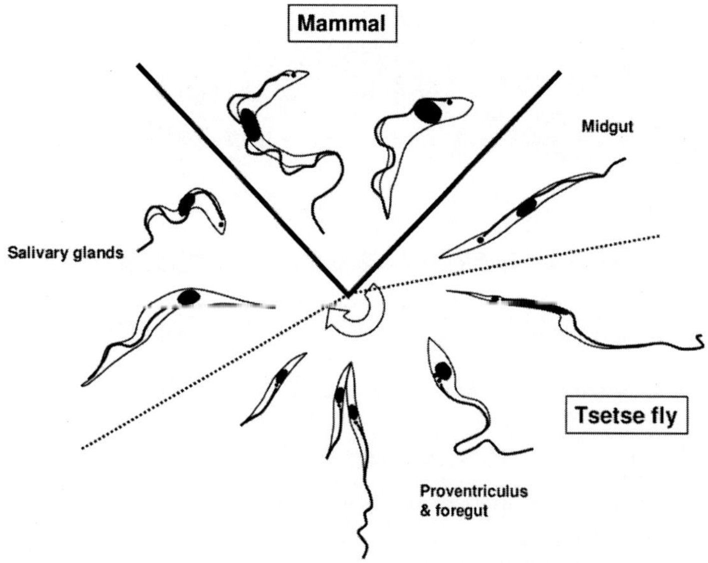
Mammal
Midgut
Salivary glands
Tsetse fly
Proventriculus & foregut

Pathogenicity and Disease Caused by Trypanosoma species

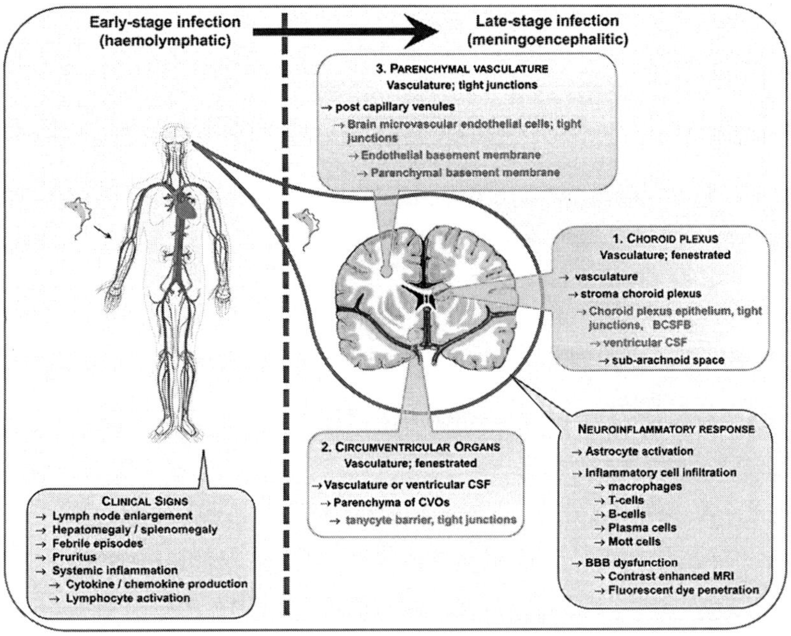

A

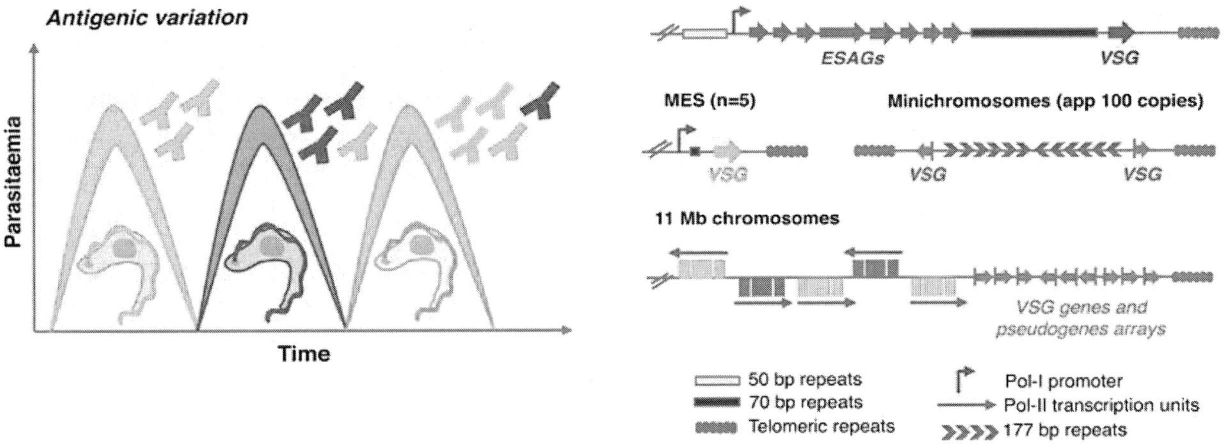

Trypanosoma species cause **African trypanosomiasis**, commonly known as **sleeping sickness**. The disease is a progressive systemic infection that primarily involves the **blood, lymphatic system, and central nervous system**. The pathogenicity of the parasite is related to its **extracellular survival**, rapid multiplication, and ability to evade the host immune response.

After transmission by the bite of an infected tsetse fly, the parasites enter the bloodstream and multiply freely as trypomastigotes. During the early stage of infection, known as the **hemolymphatic stage**, the parasites circulate in blood and lymph. Their presence leads to generalized inflammatory responses, lymph node enlargement, and immune activation.

One of the most important mechanisms of pathogenicity is **antigenic variation**. Trypanosoma species repeatedly change the surface glycoproteins on their body. This allows the parasite to escape immune destruction and causes repeated waves of parasitemia. As a result, the disease becomes chronic and difficult to eliminate naturally.

As the infection progresses, the parasites cross the blood brain barrier and invade the **central nervous system**. This stage is known as the **neurological stage**. Involvement of the brain leads to inflammation of neural tissues and disruption of normal neurological function.

The severity and course of disease depend on the species involved.
1. Trypanosoma gambiense causes a **chronic form** of the disease with slow progression.
2. Trypanosoma rhodesiense causes a **more acute and rapidly progressive form**.

The pathological effects are not due to toxin production but result from **persistent parasitemia, immune mediated damage, and inflammation of affected tissues**. If untreated, the disease eventually leads to severe neurological impairment, coma, and death. Thus, Trypanosoma species produce disease through continuous multiplication in blood and lymph, immune evasion by antigenic variation, and late invasion of the central nervous system. Understanding pathogenicity explains the clinical stages, diagnostic approach, and urgency of treatment.

Clinical Features of African Trypanosomiasis

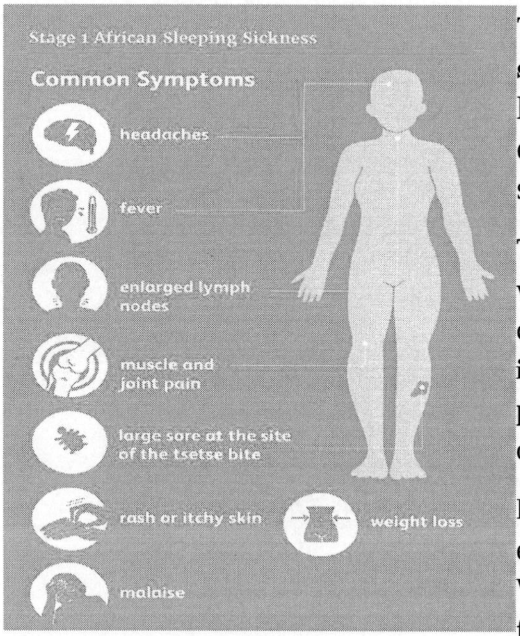

The clinical features of African trypanosomiasis develop in **stages** and reflect progressive involvement of the blood, lymphatic system, and central nervous system. The course of the disease varies according to the species involved and the immune status of the host.

The **early stage**, also known as the hemolymphatic stage, begins weeks to months after infection. During this stage, the parasites circulate in the blood and lymph. Patients commonly present with **intermittent fever**, headache, weakness, and generalized body pain. The fever often shows a relapsing pattern due to periodic waves of parasitemia.

Lymphadenopathy is a characteristic feature, especially enlargement of posterior cervical lymph nodes. This is known as **Winterbottom sign** and is particularly prominent in the chronic form of the disease. Splenomegaly and hepatomegaly may also be present due to reticuloendothelial system involvement.As the disease progresses, the parasites invade the **central nervous system**, leading to the neurological stage. This stage is marked by **sleep disturbances**, which give the disease its common name, sleeping sickness. Patients develop excessive daytime sleepiness and insomnia at night, indicating disruption of normal sleep wake cycles.

Neurological manifestations include **mental confusion, personality changes, irritability, poor concentration, and memory impairment**. Motor disturbances such as tremors, poor coordination, and speech difficulties may also occur. In advanced cases, seizures and progressive weakness are observed.If untreated, the disease progresses to severe neurological damage. Patients may develop **coma**, followed by death. The chronic form progresses slowly over months or years, while the acute form progresses rapidly and may become fatal within a short period.

Thus, the clinical features of African trypanosomiasis range from early systemic symptoms to severe neurological involvement. Recognition of these stages is essential for timely diagnosis, appropriate treatment, and prevention of irreversible complications.

topic

Pathology of African Trypanosomiasis

The pathology of African trypanosomiasis reflects **progressive involvement of blood, lymphatic system, and central nervous system**. The disease is characterized by inflammatory changes produced by persistent presence of parasites in body fluids and later in nervous tissue.In the **early hemolymphatic stage**, the parasites multiply freely in the blood and lymph. This leads to **chronic inflammation** with enlargement of lymph nodes, spleen, and liver. Lymph nodes show hyperplasia due to continuous immune stimulation. The posterior cervical lymph nodes are particularly affected.

Persistent parasitemia results in **immune mediated tissue damage**. Although antibodies are produced, the parasite evades immune clearance by antigenic variation. This continuous immune activation causes fever, anemia, and general tissue stress. Blood vessels may show increased permeability, contributing to edema and inflammation.In the **central nervous system stage**, the parasites cross the blood brain barrier and enter the cerebrospinal fluid and brain tissue. This produces **meningoencephalitis**, characterized by infiltration of inflammatory cells around blood vessels and within neural tissue. Neuronal function becomes progressively impaired.Pathological changes in the brain include inflammation of meninges, degeneration of nerve cells, and disruption of normal neural pathways. These changes are responsible for sleep disturbances, behavioral abnormalities, and neurological deficits seen in advanced disease.There is no localized tissue necrosis or abscess formation. The damage is mainly functional and inflammatory, resulting from prolonged infection and immune response rather than direct destruction by the parasite.

Thus, the pathology of African trypanosomiasis involves systemic inflammation in early stages and inflammatory damage to nervous tissue in later stages. These pathological changes form the structural basis of the clinical features and underline the seriousness of untreated disease.

Epidemiology and Susceptibility of African Trypanosomiasis

African trypanosomiasis is a **geographically restricted disease** confined to regions of **sub Saharan Africa**, corresponding to the distribution of the **tsetse fly vector**. The disease occurs in rural and forested areas where the vector breeds and feeds on humans and animals.Two epidemiological forms are recognized based on species distribution and disease pattern. Infection caused by Trypanosoma gambiense occurs mainly in **West and Central Africa** and is characterized by a **chronic course**. Infection caused by Trypanosoma rhodesiense occurs in **East and Southern Africa** and shows a **more acute and severe course**.

Humans act as the **primary reservoir** in the West African form, which facilitates person to person transmission through the vector. In the East African form, **wild and domestic animals** serve as important reservoirs, making control more difficult.Susceptibility to infection depends on **exposure to the tsetse fly**, occupational activities, and environmental factors. People involved in farming, fishing, hunting, or forest related work are at higher risk due to frequent contact with vector habitats. Poverty, poor housing, and lack of protective measures increase susceptibility.Both males and females are susceptible, but adult males are more commonly affected due to outdoor occupational exposure. Children may also be infected, particularly in endemic villages. Immunity following infection is incomplete, and reinfection can occur.Asymptomatic infections may exist in endemic areas, especially in the chronic form. Such individuals act as reservoirs and contribute to sustained transmission. Seasonal variation in disease incidence is related to changes in vector density and human activity patterns.

Thus, the epidemiology and susceptibility of African trypanosomiasis are closely linked to vector distribution, human behavior, reservoir hosts, and environmental conditions. Understanding these factors is essential for disease surveillance, diagnosis, and implementation of effective control programs.

Laboratory Diagnosis of African Trypanosomiasis

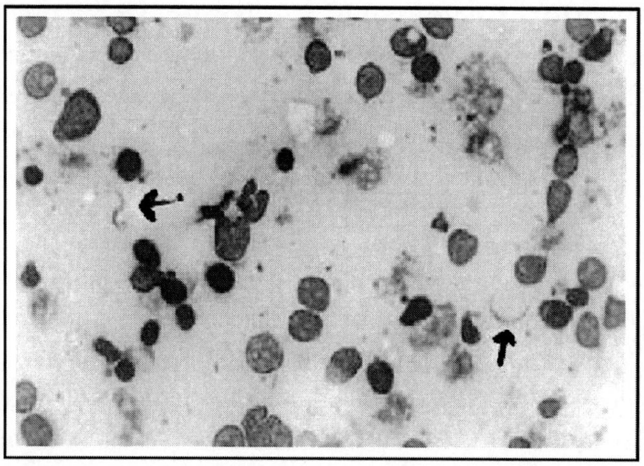

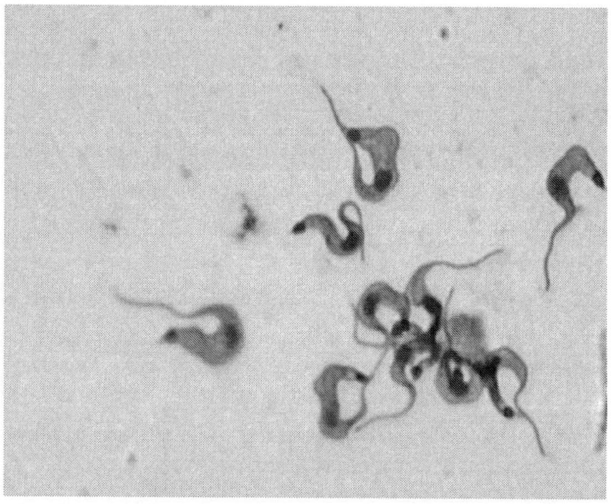

Laboratory diagnosis of African trypanosomiasis is based on **demonstration of the parasite in clinical specimens**, supported by clinical features and epidemiological history. Since the parasite is present in different body fluids at different stages of the disease, the choice of specimen depends on the stage of infection.

In the **early hemolymphatic stage**, Trypanosoma parasites are found circulating in the **blood and lymphatic system**. **Peripheral blood examination** is an important diagnostic method. Thin and thick blood smears stained with appropriate stains are examined microscopically to detect motile trypomastigote forms. The parasites are seen as elongated organisms with a nucleus, kinetoplast, flagellum, and undulating membrane.

Lymph node aspiration, particularly from enlarged posterior cervical lymph nodes, is a useful diagnostic method. The aspirate is examined microscopically for the presence of motile trypanosomes. This method is especially helpful in the chronic form of the disease.

As the disease progresses to the **central nervous system stage**, parasites may be detected in the **cerebrospinal fluid**. Examination of cerebrospinal fluid is essential to confirm nervous system involvement and to assess disease stage. Detection of parasites in cerebrospinal fluid indicates advanced infection.

Repeated examination may be required because parasitemia can be intermittent due to antigenic variation. Diagnosis should always be correlated with clinical findings such as fever, lymphadenopathy, and neurological symptoms.

Thus, laboratory diagnosis of African trypanosomiasis involves microscopic demonstration of Trypanosoma in blood, lymph node aspirates, or cerebrospinal fluid, depending on the stage of disease. Accurate diagnosis is essential for staging, treatment planning, and prevention of irreversible neurological damage.

Treatment of African Trypanosomiasis

For educational purpose only

Treatment of African trypanosomiasis depends on the stage of disease and the species involved. The objective of treatment is elimination of the parasite and prevention of progression to involvement of the nervous system. The following information is provided for **academic understanding and conceptual correlation only** and is **not intended for clinical use or independent prescribing**.

Stage of disease	Drug name	Dose in adults	Duration
Early stage without nervous system involvement	Pentamidine	4 mg per kg body weight by injection once daily	7 days
Early stage in acute form	Suramin	20 mg per kg body weight by injection at weekly intervals	5 doses
Late stage with nervous system involvement	Melarsoprol	2 to 3 mg per kg body weight per day by injection	10 days
Late stage alternative regimen	Eflornithine	100 mg per kg body weight every 6 hours by injection	14 days

Supportive management

Supportive care includes management of anemia, nutritional support, and monitoring of neurological status. Hospitalization is usually required in advanced cases due to drug toxicity and need for close observation.

8. Malaria Parasite

Introduction

Malaria is one of the most important **protozoal diseases of humans** and continues to be a major public health problem in many parts of the world. The disease is caused by **malarial parasites of the genus Plasmodium**, which infect red blood cells and produce periodic fever, anemia, and systemic complications.

From a medical zoology perspective, malaria is significant because it demonstrates a **complex life cycle involving two hosts**, human beings and the female Anopheles mosquito. The parasite shows different morphological forms in each host, reflecting a high degree of biological adaptation. Understanding these forms is essential for learning morphology, life cycle, transmission, and diagnosis.Malaria parasites are **intracellular blood protozoa**. In the human host, they multiply inside red blood cells and liver cells, while in the mosquito they undergo sexual development. This dual host requirement makes malaria a classic example of a **vector borne protozoal disease**.

Clinically, malaria is characterized by **intermittent fever with chills and rigors**, anemia, splenomegaly, and weakness. Severe forms of malaria may involve the brain, kidneys, and other vital organs. From a zoological and parasitological viewpoint, these clinical features are directly related to the parasite's life cycle and destruction of red blood cells.

Origin and Meaning of the Name and Discovery

The term **malaria** is derived from the Italian words mal aria, meaning **bad air**. This name originated from the ancient belief that the disease was caused by foul air arising from marshy areas. Although this concept was incorrect, it reflected the long association between malaria and stagnant water where mosquitoes breed.

The causative organism of malaria belongs to the genus **Plasmodium**. The name Plasmodium refers to the amorphous, living protoplasmic nature of the parasite observed under the microscope during its early descriptions.

The discovery of the malaria parasite is a landmark in medical science. In 1880, the French army surgeon **Alphonse Laveran** first observed the parasite in the red blood cells of malaria patients while working in Algeria. He demonstrated that malaria is caused by a protozoan parasite and not by bad air or miasma. For this discovery, he was later awarded the Nobel Prize.

The role of the mosquito in transmission was established later. In 1897, the British physician **Ronald Ross** demonstrated that malaria is transmitted by the bite of female **Anopheles** mosquitoes. His work proved that the parasite undergoes development inside the mosquito and is transmitted to humans during blood feeding. This discovery laid the foundation for malaria control through vector control measures.

Thus, the naming and discovery of the malaria parasite represent major milestones in parasitology. They transformed malaria from a mysterious fever associated with environment into a scientifically understood **vector borne protozoal disease**. This historical background helps students appreciate the development of concepts related to parasite life cycle, transmission, and prevention.

Classification of Malaria Parasites

Malaria parasites belong to the genus **Plasmodium**, which includes several species capable of infecting humans. Classification of malaria parasites is based on **morphological features, life cycle characteristics, type of fever produced**, and **severity of disease**. This classification is important for understanding clinical presentation, diagnosis, and epidemiology.From a medical zoology point of view, malaria parasites infect **red blood cells** and show distinct developmental stages within them. Different species produce characteristic changes in red blood cells, which help in microscopic identification.

The malaria parasites of human importance are classified as follows.

1. Plasmodium vivax
This species causes benign tertian malaria. It produces fever at intervals of forty eight hours. The parasite enlarges infected red blood cells and is widely distributed in tropical and temperate regions.

2. Plasmodium falciparum
This species causes malignant tertian malaria and is the most dangerous form. Fever pattern may be irregular. It infects red blood cells of all ages and is responsible for severe complications such as cerebral malaria.

3. Plasmodium malariae
This species causes quartan malaria with fever occurring at intervals of seventy two hours. It infects older red blood cells and usually produces a chronic but milder infection.

4. Plasmodium ovale
This species causes a mild tertian malaria. It is less common and mainly found in certain regions of Africa and nearby areas. It produces oval shaped red blood cells with characteristic morphological changes.

These species differ in their **morphology, pathogenicity, fever pattern, and geographical distribution**, but all require **two hosts**, human beings and the female Anopheles mosquito, to complete their life cycle.Thus, classification of malaria parasites provides a structured framework for studying their morphology, life cycle, disease pattern, laboratory diagnosis, and control measures.

General Characteristics of Malaria Parasites

Malaria parasites are **unicellular protozoa** belonging to the genus Plasmodium. They are **obligate intracellular parasites**, meaning they can survive and multiply only inside host cells. In the human host, malaria parasites primarily infect **liver cells and red blood cells**, while in the mosquito they undergo sexual development.Malaria parasites exhibit a **complex life cycle** involving two hosts. Human beings act as the **intermediate host**, where asexual multiplication occurs, and the female Anopheles mosquito serves as the **definitive host**, where sexual reproduction takes place. This dual host requirement is a defining characteristic of malaria parasites.

In human blood, malaria parasites show **distinct developmental stages** inside red blood cells. These stages include ring forms, trophozoites, schizonts, and gametocytes. Each stage has characteristic morphological features that are useful for microscopic identification and species differentiation.Malaria parasites multiply by **asexual reproduction** in humans through a process known as schizogony. This leads to destruction of red blood cells and release of merozoites, which is responsible for fever, anemia, and other clinical manifestations. In the mosquito, the parasites undergo sexual reproduction, leading to formation of infective stages.The parasites show **host cell specificity**. Some species infect young red blood cells, while others infect older cells or red blood cells of all ages. This preference influences parasite load, severity of disease, and clinical outcome.Malaria parasites do not form cysts and are not transmitted directly from person to person. Transmission occurs only through the **bite of an infected female Anopheles mosquito**, which injects infective forms into the human host during blood feeding.Thus, malaria parasites are intracellular blood protozoa with a complex life cycle, specific host cell preference, and vector dependent transmission. These general characteristics form the foundation for understanding morphology, life cycle, pathogenicity, diagnosis, and control of malaria.

Morphology of Malaria Parasite

The malaria parasite belonging to the genus **Plasmodium** shows **distinct morphological forms** during its development in the human host. These forms are seen inside red blood cells and are of great importance for **microscopic diagnosis and species identification**.

In human blood, the malaria parasite passes through the following morphological stages.

The **ring stage** is the earliest form seen in red blood cells. It appears as a delicate ring shaped structure with a thin rim of cytoplasm surrounding a central vacuole. A small chromatin dot representing the nucleus is seen on the ring. This stage is commonly observed in peripheral blood smears and is especially prominent in Plasmodium falciparum infection.

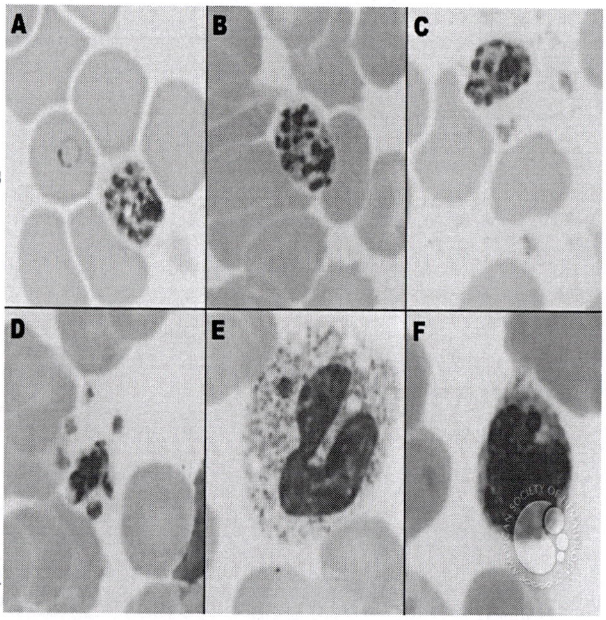

Figure . Morphological stages of malaria parasite in human red blood cells

A Ring stage of Plasmodium inside red blood cell
B Early trophozoite stage showing increased cytoplasm
C Late trophozoite stage with pigment deposition
D Developing schizont with nuclear division
E Mature schizont showing multiple merozoites
F Gametocyte stage of Plasmodium

The **trophozoite stage** is the growing and feeding form of the parasite. It is larger than the ring stage and shows increased cytoplasmic mass. The parasite feeds on hemoglobin of the red blood cell and produces pigment granules known as hemozoin. The appearance of the trophozoite varies among species and helps in differentiation.

The **schizont stage** represents the stage of asexual multiplication. The nucleus divides repeatedly to form multiple nuclei, followed by segmentation of cytoplasm. Each segment develops into a **merozoite**. A mature schizont contains several merozoites arranged in a characteristic pattern. Rupture of the red blood cell releases merozoites into the bloodstream, leading to fever.

The **gametocyte stage** is the sexual form of the parasite. Gametocytes do not cause symptoms directly but are essential for transmission to the mosquito. Male and female gametocytes can be distinguished microscopically. In Plasmodium falciparum, gametocytes are crescent shaped, while in other species they are rounded or oval.

The red blood cell containing the parasite may show **structural changes** depending on the species. Enlargement of red blood cells, distortion of shape, and appearance of stippling may be observed. These changes are useful diagnostic features in species identification.

Thus, the morphology of the malaria parasite includes ring forms, trophozoites, schizonts, and gametocytes, each with distinct structural features. Understanding these stages is essential for correct laboratory diagnosis and correlation with clinical manifestations.

Life Cycle of Malaria Parasite

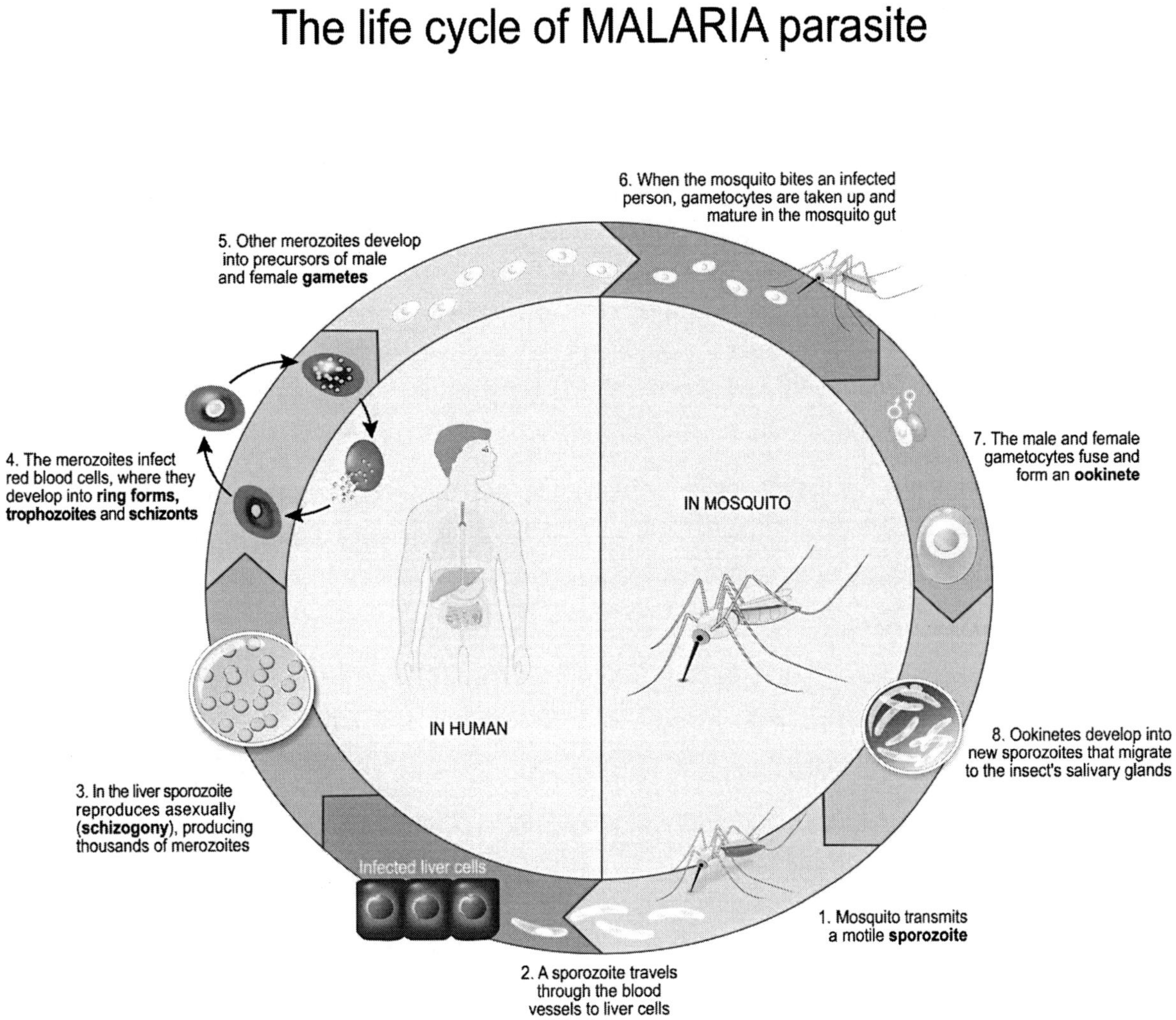

MALARIA

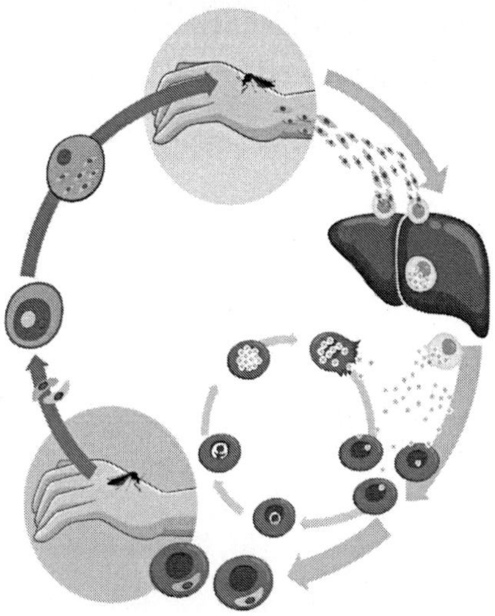

The life cycle of the malaria parasite is **complex and indirect**, involving **two hosts**, human beings and the female Anopheles mosquito. The parasite shows different developmental stages in each host. Understanding this life cycle is essential to explain transmission, clinical features, laboratory diagnosis, and control of malaria.**Life cycle in human host**

Human beings act as the **intermediate host**, in which **asexual reproduction** of the parasite takes place. Infection begins when an infected female Anopheles mosquito bites a human and injects **sporozoites** into the bloodstream along with its saliva.

The sporozoites quickly leave the bloodstream and enter **liver cells**. Inside liver cells, the parasite undergoes **pre erythrocytic schizogony**. The nucleus divides repeatedly to form a large number of **merozoites**. After maturation, the liver cells rupture and release merozoites into the bloodstream.The released merozoites invade **red blood cells** and initiate the **erythrocytic cycle**. Inside red blood cells, the parasite passes through ring stage, trophozoite stage, and schizont stage. The schizont ruptures the red blood cell and releases new merozoites, which infect fresh red blood cells. This repeated rupture of red blood cells is responsible for **periodic fever, chills, and anemia**.

Some merozoites do not continue the asexual cycle. Instead, they differentiate into **gametocytes**, which are the sexual forms of the parasite. Gametocytes circulate in the blood but do not cause symptoms. They are essential for transmission to the mosquito.

Life cycle in mosquito host

The female Anopheles mosquito acts as the **definitive host**, in which **sexual reproduction** of the parasite occurs. When a mosquito bites an infected human, it ingests blood containing gametocytes.

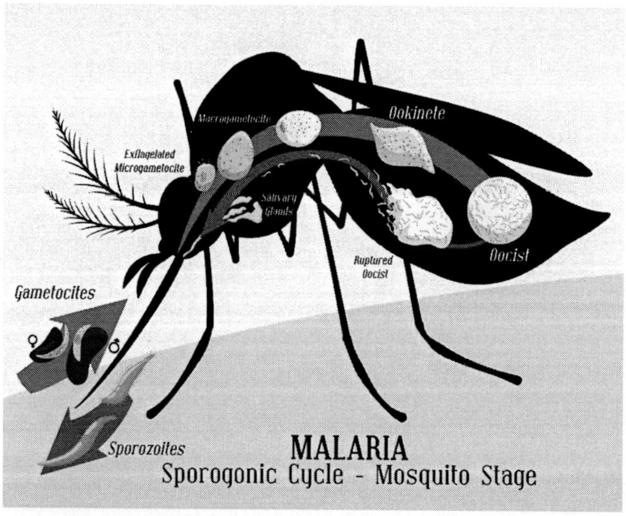

Inside the mosquito stomach, the male and female gametocytes mature into **gametes**. Fertilization occurs to form a **zygote**, which elongates to become a motile **ookinete**. The ookinete penetrates the stomach wall and develops into an **oocyst**.

Within the oocyst, repeated nuclear division occurs to produce numerous **sporozoites**. When the oocyst ruptures, sporozoites are released and migrate to the **salivary glands** of the mosquito. The mosquito is now infective.During the next blood meal, these sporozoites are injected into a new human host, thus completing the life cycle.Thus, the life cycle of the malaria parasite alternates between **asexual multiplication in humans** and **sexual reproduction in mosquitoes**. This dual host life cycle explains the periodic nature of fever, the importance of vector control, and the rationale behind preventive strategies.

Pathogenicity and Disease Caused by Malaria Parasite

Pathogenic process	Mechanism involved	Resulting disease effect
Invasion of red blood cells	Merozoites enter and multiply inside red blood cells	Initiation of blood stage infection
Rupture of red blood cells	Schizont maturation followed by cell rupture	Release of merozoites and toxic substances
Release of parasitic toxins	Liberation of malarial pigment and metabolic products	Fever chills rigors and sweating
Repeated red blood cell destruction	Continuous erythrocytic cycle	Anemia weakness and pallor
Accumulation of malarial pigment	Deposition of hemozoin in macrophages	Enlargement of spleen and liver
Increased splenic activity	Removal of infected and destroyed red blood cells	Splenomegaly and hypersplenism
Capillary blockage in severe malaria	Adhesion of infected red blood cells to vessel walls	Reduced blood flow and tissue hypoxia
Brain involvement in severe cases	Obstruction of cerebral capillaries	Cerebral malaria with convulsions and coma
Bone marrow suppression	Chronic infection and immune response	Reduced blood cell production
Metabolic disturbances	Hemolysis and organ dysfunction	Jaundice kidney involvement and complications

The pathogenic effects of malaria are mainly due to **cyclical destruction of red blood cells** and **host immune response**. Severity depends on parasite species parasite load and host immunity.

Malaria is caused by the **asexual multiplication of Plasmodium parasites inside human red blood cells**. The pathogenicity of malaria is directly related to destruction of red blood cells, release of toxic metabolic products, and host immune response to the parasite.After completion of the liver stage, large numbers of merozoites enter the bloodstream and invade red blood cells. Inside red blood cells, the parasites multiply and finally cause **rupture of the infected cells**. This rupture releases merozoites, malarial pigment, and toxic substances into the circulation. These events stimulate the immune system and produce the characteristic **malarial fever**.

The periodic rupture of red blood cells results in **fever with chills and rigors**, followed by sweating. Repeated cycles of red blood cell destruction lead to **anemia**, which causes weakness, pallor, and fatigue. Increased destruction of red blood cells also results in enlargement of the **spleen**, as it plays a major role in removal of infected cells.Malaria parasites digest hemoglobin and produce an insoluble pigment known as **hemozoin**. Accumulation of this pigment in macrophages contributes to inflammation and further tissue damage. The liver and spleen become enlarged due to increased activity of the reticuloendothelial system.

In severe malaria, especially caused by Plasmodium falciparum, infected red blood cells become sticky and adhere to capillary walls. This leads to **blockage of small blood vessels**, particularly in the brain. As a result, **cerebral malaria** may develop, producing altered consciousness, convulsions, and coma.Malaria may also cause complications such as kidney damage, jaundice, hypoglycemia, and respiratory distress. These complications are due to widespread tissue hypoxia, hemolysis, and metabolic disturbances.Thus, malaria produces disease through destruction of red blood cells, immune mediated reactions, vascular obstruction, and organ dysfunction. The severity of disease depends on parasite species, parasite load, and host immunity.

Clinical Features of Malaria

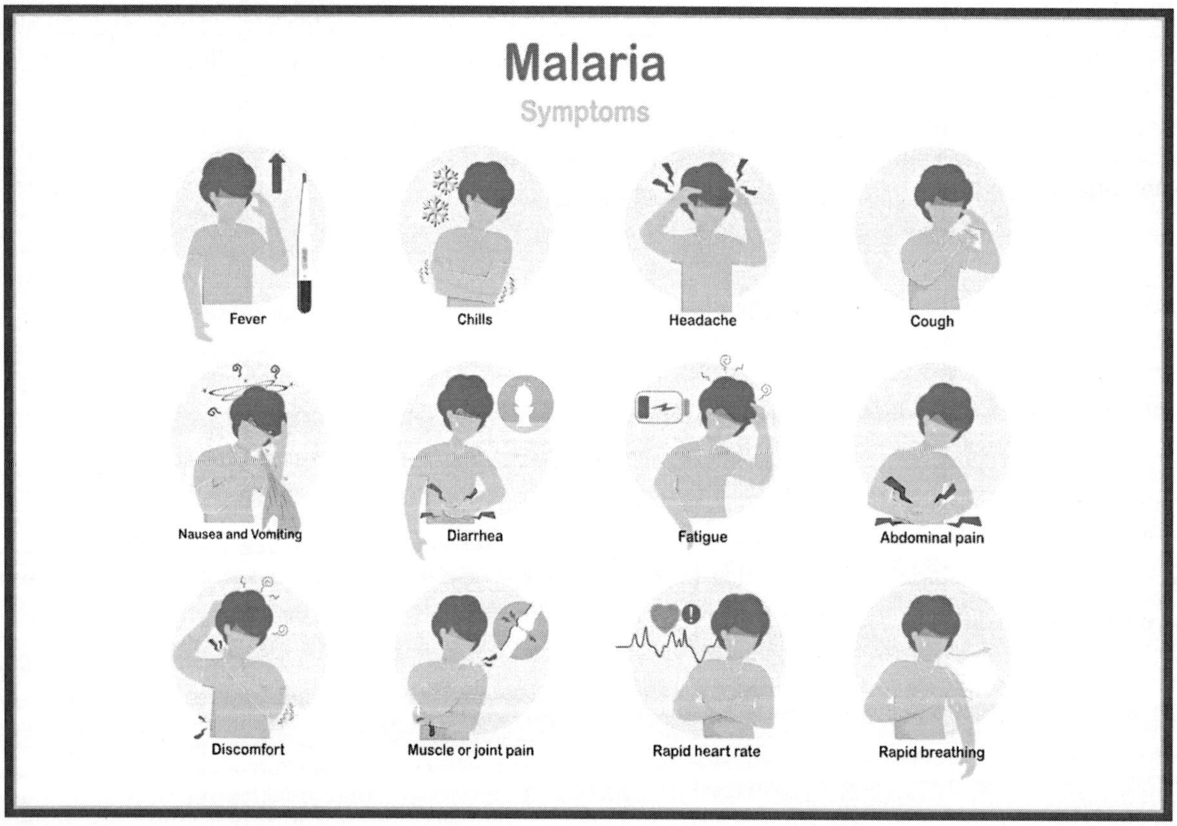

Malaria presents with a **characteristic pattern of fever and systemic symptoms** that result from cyclic destruction of red blood cells and release of parasitic products into the circulation. The severity of clinical features depends on the species of parasite, parasite load, and immune status of the host.

Clinical stage or system involved	Clinical features observed	Biological basis
Onset of illness	Fever with chills followed by sweating	Rupture of infected red blood cells
Febrile paroxysm	Cold stage hot stage and sweating stage	Release of merozoites and toxic substances
Blood system	Anemia weakness pallor	Repeated destruction of red blood cells
Spleen	Splenomegaly	Increased removal of infected cells
Liver	Hepatomegaly mild jaundice	Hemolysis and pigment deposition
General symptoms	Headache body ache fatigue	Systemic inflammatory response
Chronic infection	Weight loss reduced stamina	Persistent parasitemia
Severe malaria	Altered consciousness convulsions coma	Cerebral involvement mainly in Plasmodium falciparum
Renal involvement	Reduced urine output	Hemolysis and microvascular obstruction

The classical fever pattern of malaria reflects the **synchronous rupture of red blood cells**. Complications occur when parasitized cells obstruct small blood vessels or when parasite load becomes very high.

Pathology of Malaria

The pathology of malaria is mainly related to **repeated destruction of red blood cells**, accumulation of parasitic pigment, and involvement of the reticuloendothelial system. These pathological changes explain the major clinical manifestations and complications of the disease.

The **blood** is the primary site of pathological change. As the malaria parasite multiplies inside red blood cells, the cells rupture and are destroyed. Continuous destruction of red blood cells leads to **anemia**, which is a consistent pathological finding in malaria. The degree of anemia depends on parasite density and duration of infection.

The **spleen** shows marked pathological changes. It becomes enlarged due to increased activity in removing infected and damaged red blood cells. Hyperplasia of reticuloendothelial cells occurs, and malarial pigment accumulates within splenic macrophages. Prolonged infection may lead to hypersplenism.

The **liver** is also involved. Kupffer cells become enlarged and contain malarial pigment known as hemozoin. Mild hepatomegaly is common. Liver cells are usually preserved, but prolonged hemolysis may lead to jaundice due to increased bilirubin load.In severe malaria, particularly caused by **Plasmodium falciparum**, pathological changes occur in the **brain**. Infected red blood cells adhere to capillary walls, leading to obstruction of blood flow. Cerebral capillaries show congestion and inflammation, resulting in **cerebral malaria**, which may cause convulsions and coma.The **bone marrow** may show reduced effectiveness due to chronic infection and inflammatory response. This contributes further to anemia and reduced blood cell production.

Thus, the pathology of malaria involves destruction of red blood cells, enlargement of spleen and liver, accumulation of malarial pigment, and vascular obstruction in severe cases. These pathological changes form the structural basis of anemia, fever, splenomegaly, and life threatening complications of malaria.

Epidemiology and Susceptibility of Malaria

Malaria is a **widely distributed protozoal disease** that occurs mainly in **tropical and subtropical regions** of the world. It remains a major public health problem in many developing countries, particularly in regions where climatic conditions favor mosquito breeding.The disease is endemic in large parts of **Africa, South East Asia, South America, and the Indian subcontinent**. In India, malaria is commonly reported from rural and forested areas where **Anopheles mosquitoes** are abundant. Transmission intensity varies according to rainfall, temperature, humidity, and availability of stagnant water.

The epidemiology of malaria is closely linked to the **distribution of the female Anopheles mosquito**, which acts as the vector. Warm climate, stagnant water, poor drainage, and inadequate sanitation provide ideal breeding conditions for mosquitoes. Seasonal variation is commonly observed, with increased transmission during and after the rainy season.Humans serve as the **main reservoir of infection**. Infected individuals carrying gametocytes in their blood act as sources of infection for mosquitoes. Asymptomatic carriers play an important role in maintaining transmission in endemic areas.Susceptibility to malaria depends on several host factors. **Children, pregnant women, and non immune individuals** are more susceptible to severe disease. People living in endemic areas may develop partial immunity after repeated exposure, which reduces severity but does not prevent infection completely.

Malnutrition, anemia, and lowered immunity increase susceptibility and worsen disease outcome. Socioeconomic factors such as poverty, overcrowding, poor housing, and limited access to healthcare also contribute to higher transmission rates.Different species of Plasmodium show varying epidemiological patterns.

- Plasmodium falciparum is predominant in Africa and is associated with high mortality.
- Plasmodium vivax has a wider geographical distribution and causes recurrent infections.

Thus, the epidemiology and susceptibility of malaria are influenced by environmental conditions, vector distribution, host immunity, and socioeconomic factors. Understanding these aspects is essential for effective prevention and control strategies.

Laboratory Diagnosis of Malaria

Laboratory diagnosis of malaria is based on **demonstration of the parasite in blood**, supported by clinical features and epidemiological history. Accurate diagnosis is essential for confirmation of disease, identification of species, and assessment of severity.

The **peripheral blood examination** is the gold standard method for diagnosis. Blood smears are prepared and examined under the microscope to detect different stages of the malaria parasite inside red blood cells. Both thick and thin blood smears are used. Thick smear is more sensitive for detecting parasites, while thin smear is useful for **species identification** and study of morphology.

In a positive blood smear, various stages such as **ring forms, trophozoites, schizonts, and gametocytes** may be observed. The appearance of these stages and the changes in red blood cells help in differentiating between species of Plasmodium. Crescent shaped gametocytes are characteristic of Plasmodium falciparum, while enlarged red blood cells are seen in Plasmodium vivax infection.

Repeated blood examination may be necessary because parasitemia can be low or intermittent, especially in early infection. Blood samples should ideally be collected during or just before a febrile episode for better yield.

Rapid diagnostic tests are also used for detection of malarial antigens in blood. These tests provide quick results and are useful in field conditions and emergency settings. However, they do not replace microscopic examination, as they cannot reliably assess parasite density or identify all species.

Other laboratory findings such as anemia, low platelet count, and raised bilirubin support the diagnosis but are **not specific** for malaria.Thus, laboratory diagnosis of malaria relies primarily on microscopic demonstration of the parasite in peripheral blood, supported by rapid tests and clinical correlation. Mastery of blood smear examination remains essential for accurate diagnosis and teaching in medical parasitology.

Treatment of Malaria Parasite

For educational purpose only

Treatment of malaria depends on the **species of Plasmodium**, severity of disease, and presence of complications. The objective of treatment is elimination of blood stage parasites, prevention of complications, and interruption of transmission. The following information is provided **for academic understanding and conceptual correlation only** and is **not intended for clinical use**.

Type of malaria	Drug used	Adult dose	Duration
Uncomplicated malaria due to Plasmodium vivax	Chloroquine	600 mg followed by 300 mg	Total 3 days
Radical cure of Plasmodium vivax infection	Primaquine	15 mg once daily	14 days
Uncomplicated malaria due to Plasmodium falciparum	Artemisinin based combination therapy	As per standard combination	3 days
Severe malaria	Artesunate injection	As per body weight	As per protocol
Mixed infection	Artemisinin based combination therapy with primaquine	As per regimen	As prescribed

Supportive care

Supportive management includes control of fever, correction of anemia, maintenance of hydration, and monitoring for complications such as cerebral involvement or renal dysfunction.

Malaria in humans is caused by different species of the genus Plasmodium. Although these species share a common life cycle and mode of transmission, they differ significantly in their **morphology clinical presentation fever pattern severity and complications**. A comparative study of Plasmodium species is therefore essential for accurate diagnosis proper understanding of disease behavior and effective management.From a medical zoology and medical education perspective, comparative study helps students identify species based on **peripheral blood smear findings**, changes in red blood cells, type of fever produced, and clinical outcome. This approach is especially useful for practical examinations spotters and long answer questions.

The major human malaria parasites included in this comparative study are
Plasmodium vivax
Plasmodium falciparum
Plasmodium malariae
Plasmodium ovale

Each species shows distinct characteristics related to red blood cell preference morphology of developmental stages severity of infection and tendency for relapse. These differences are summarized in a systematic manner in the following comparative table to facilitate easy learning and quick revision.

Feature	Plasmodium vivax	Plasmodium falciparum	Plasmodium malariae	Plasmodium ovale
Red blood cell preference	Young red blood cells	Red blood cells of all ages	Older red blood cells	Young red blood cells
Size of infected red blood cell	Enlarged	Normal	Normal or slightly smaller	Enlarged and oval
Ring forms	Single ring common	Multiple rings common	Single ring	Single ring
Trophozoite appearance	Amoeboid	Compact	Band shaped	Compact
Schizont merozoites	12 to 24	8 to 32 (rarely in blood)	6 to 12 in rosette pattern	8 to 12
Gametocyte shape	Rounded	Crescent shaped	Rounded	Rounded
Fever periodicity	48 hours	Irregular	72 hours	48 hours
Severity of disease	Usually mild	Severe and life threatening	Chronic and mild	Mild
Relapse tendency	Present due to dormant liver stages	Absent	Absent	Present

9.Mosquitoes of Medical Importance

Introduction

Mosquitoes are among the most important **arthropods of medical importance** because they act as vectors for several human diseases. They transmit protozoal helminthic and viral infections and are responsible for a significant burden of morbidity and mortality worldwide.From a medical zoology perspective, mosquitoes are important not only because of the diseases they transmit but also because of their **biology behavior and breeding habits**, which directly influence disease transmission. Understanding mosquito structure and life cycle is essential for effective prevention and control strategies.

Only the **female mosquito** is responsible for disease transmission, as it requires blood for egg development. During blood feeding, the mosquito introduces infective agents into the human host. The male mosquito feeds on plant juices and does not participate in disease transmission.Mosquito borne diseases include malaria filariasis dengue chikungunya yellow fever and Japanese encephalitis. Each disease is associated with specific mosquito genera, and identification of these vectors is a core objective of medical zoology teaching.

General Characteristics of Mosquitoes

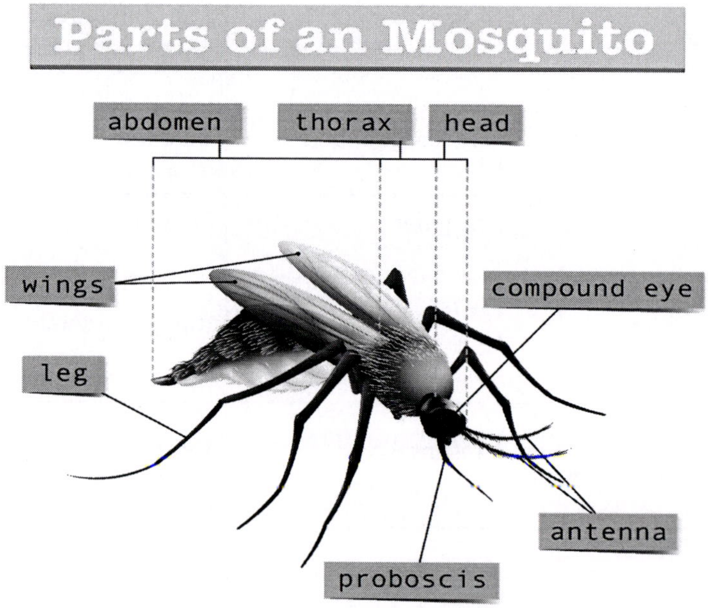

Mosquitoes are **small slender insects** belonging to the order Diptera. They are characterized by a delicate body, long legs, and a pair of narrow wings. From a medical zoology point of view, mosquitoes are important because of their **habit of blood feeding in females**, which enables transmission of disease causing organisms.

The body of a mosquito is divided into **head thorax and abdomen**. The head bears a pair of large compound eyes and a pair of antennae. The antennae are **plumose in males** and **less hairy in females**, a feature that helps in sex differentiation. Mouthparts are modified to form a **piercing and sucking proboscis**, which is well developed in females for blood feeding.

The thorax is well developed and bears **one pair of wings and three pairs of long legs**. Wings are narrow and covered with fine scales. The pattern of wing scales and the position of the body at rest are useful features for identification of mosquito genera.

The abdomen is long and segmented. It is capable of considerable expansion after blood feeding in females. The abdomen contains digestive and reproductive organs.Only the **female mosquito feeds on blood**, which is required for development of eggs. The male mosquito feeds on plant juices and does not transmit diseases. Female mosquitoes are attracted to humans by body heat carbon dioxide and odor.

Mosquitoes undergo **complete metamorphosis**, passing through egg larva pupa and adult stages. Their breeding is closely associated with **water**, as the immature stages are aquatic.Thus, mosquitoes possess specific structural and biological features that make them efficient disease vectors. Understanding these general characteristics forms the foundation for studying different mosquito genera diseases transmitted and control measures.

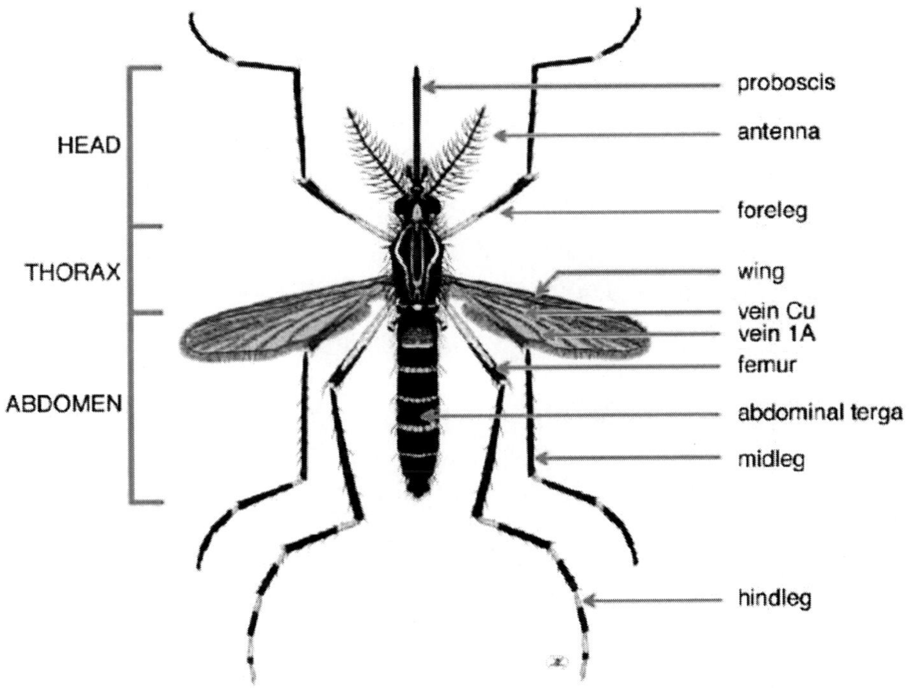

Life Cycle of Mosquito

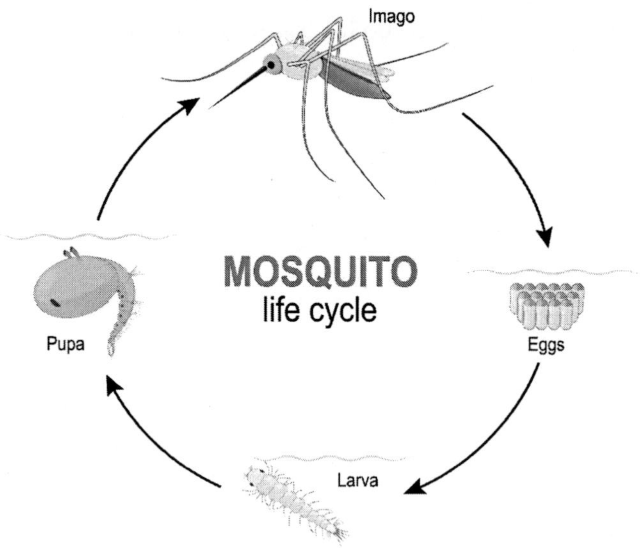

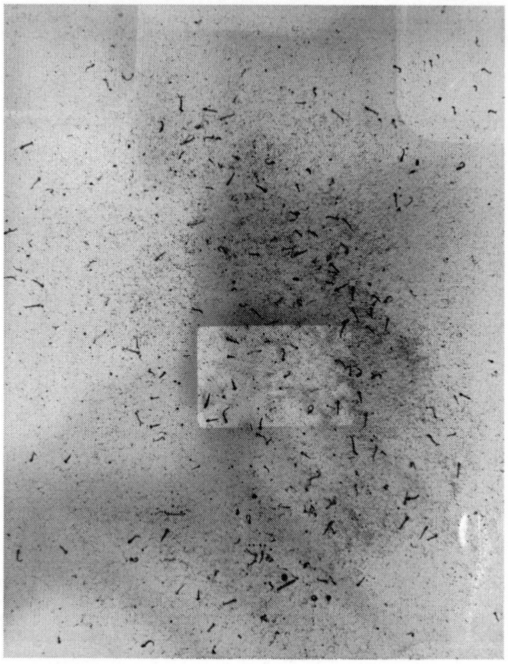

Mosquitoes undergo **complete metamorphosis**, meaning their life cycle consists of **four distinct stages**: egg larva pupa and adult. The first three stages are aquatic, while the adult stage is aerial. Knowledge of the mosquito life cycle is essential for understanding breeding habits and planning effective control measures.

Egg

Female mosquitoes lay eggs in or near water. The nature of egg laying varies among different genera. Eggs may be laid singly or in clusters and are adapted to survive in aquatic environments. The eggs hatch into larvae under favorable conditions of temperature and moisture.

Larva

The larva is an **active feeding stage** and is commonly called a wriggler because of its jerky movements in water. Larvae live in water and come to the surface for breathing. They feed on organic matter microorganisms and algae present in water.

The larval body is elongated and consists of head thorax and abdomen. The structure used for respiration differs among mosquito genera and is an important identifying feature. Larvae undergo several molts before transforming into pupae.

Pupa

The pupa is a **non feeding stage** and is commonly called a tumbler due to its tumbling movements in water. Although non feeding, it is an active stage. The pupa breathes through a pair of respiratory trumpets and floats near the water surface.

During the pupal stage, internal reorganization takes place, leading to development of adult structures. After completion of this stage, the adult mosquito emerges from the pupal case.

Adult

The adult mosquito emerges at the water surface and rests until its wings are fully expanded and hardened. The adult is capable of flight and reproduction. Mating occurs soon after emergence.

Female mosquitoes seek blood meals for egg development, while males feed on plant juices. Adult mosquitoes are responsible for disease transmission.

The life cycle of mosquitoes includes aquatic immature stages and a terrestrial adult stage. Understanding this life cycle is fundamental for identifying breeding sites and implementing mosquito control strategies.

Aedes mosquitoes transmit **dengue chikungunya yellow fever and Zika virus infection**. The adult mosquito has characteristic white markings on legs and body. Eggs are laid singly on damp surfaces just above the water line.

Aedes mosquitoes commonly breed in artificial water collections such as containers tyres and flower pots. They are aggressive day time biters.

Classification of Mosquitoes of Medical Importance

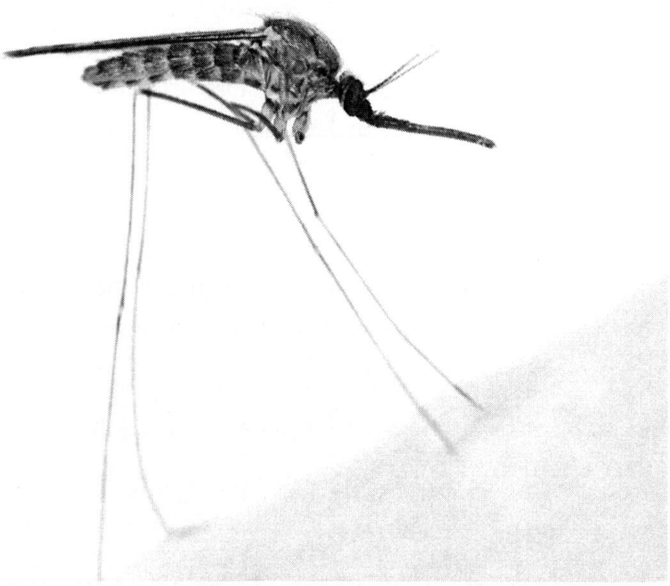

Mosquitoes of medical importance are classified on the basis of **morphological characters resting posture breeding habits and diseases transmitted**. From a medical zoology point of view, three genera are of major importance in human disease transmission.

The classification is mainly limited to
Anopheles
Culex
Aedes

These genera differ clearly in adult morphology larval structure egg laying pattern and public health importance. Correct identification is essential for diagnosis epidemiology and control measures.

- Genus **Anopheles**

Anopheles mosquitoes are the **vectors of malaria**. The adult mosquito rests at an angle with the surface. Eggs are laid singly on water and each egg has lateral air floats. The larva lies parallel to the water surface and lacks a respiratory siphon.Anopheles mosquitoes prefer clean water for breeding. Only the female transmits malaria by introducing malaria parasites during blood feeding.

- Genus **Culex**

Culex mosquitoes are vectors of **filariasis and certain viral diseases**. The adult rests parallel to the surface. Eggs are laid in clusters forming rafts on water. The larva hangs obliquely from the surface and possesses a long respiratory siphon.Culex mosquitoes commonly breed in stagnant polluted water such as drains and sewage collections.

- Genus **Aedes**

edes mosquitoes transmit **dengue chikungunya yellow fever and Zika virus infection**. The adult mosquito has characteristic white markings on legs and body. Eggs are laid singly on damp surfaces just above the water line.Aedes mosquitoes commonly breed in artificial water collections such as containers tyres and flower pots. They are aggressive day time biters.

Comparative Features of **Anopheles**, **Culex**, and **Aedes**

The following comparative table is designed for **clear identification and examination use**. It highlights adult larval egg characteristics and disease transmission in a simple and systematic manner.

Feature	Anopheles	Culex	Aedes
Adult resting position	Body at an angle to the surface	Body parallel to the surface	Body parallel to the surface
Adult markings	No prominent body markings	No prominent body markings	Distinct white markings on legs and body
Time of biting	Night biter	Night biter	Day biter
Egg laying pattern	Eggs laid singly	Eggs laid in clusters forming rafts	Eggs laid singly
Egg features	Each egg has lateral air floats	No air floats	No air floats
Breeding water	Clean water	Polluted stagnant water	Clean water in artificial containers
Larval position in water	Larva lies parallel to water surface	Larva hangs obliquely	Larva hangs obliquely
Respiratory siphon in larva	Absent	Present and long	Present and short
Important diseases transmitted	Malaria	Filariasis Japanese encephalitis	Dengue chikungunya yellow fever Zika
Public health importance	Very high	High	Very high

Diseases Transmitted by Mosquitoes

Malaria Transmission and Life Cycle

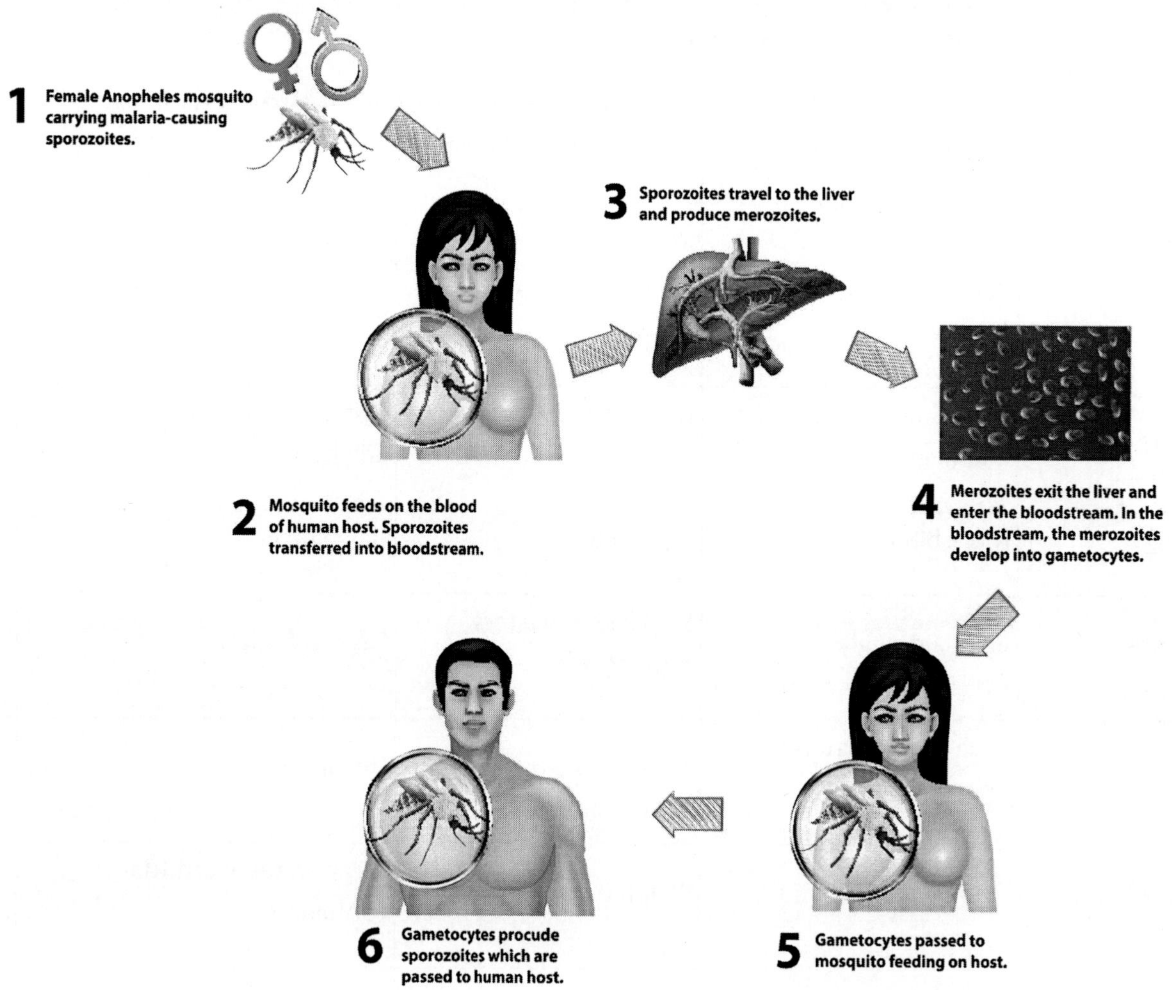

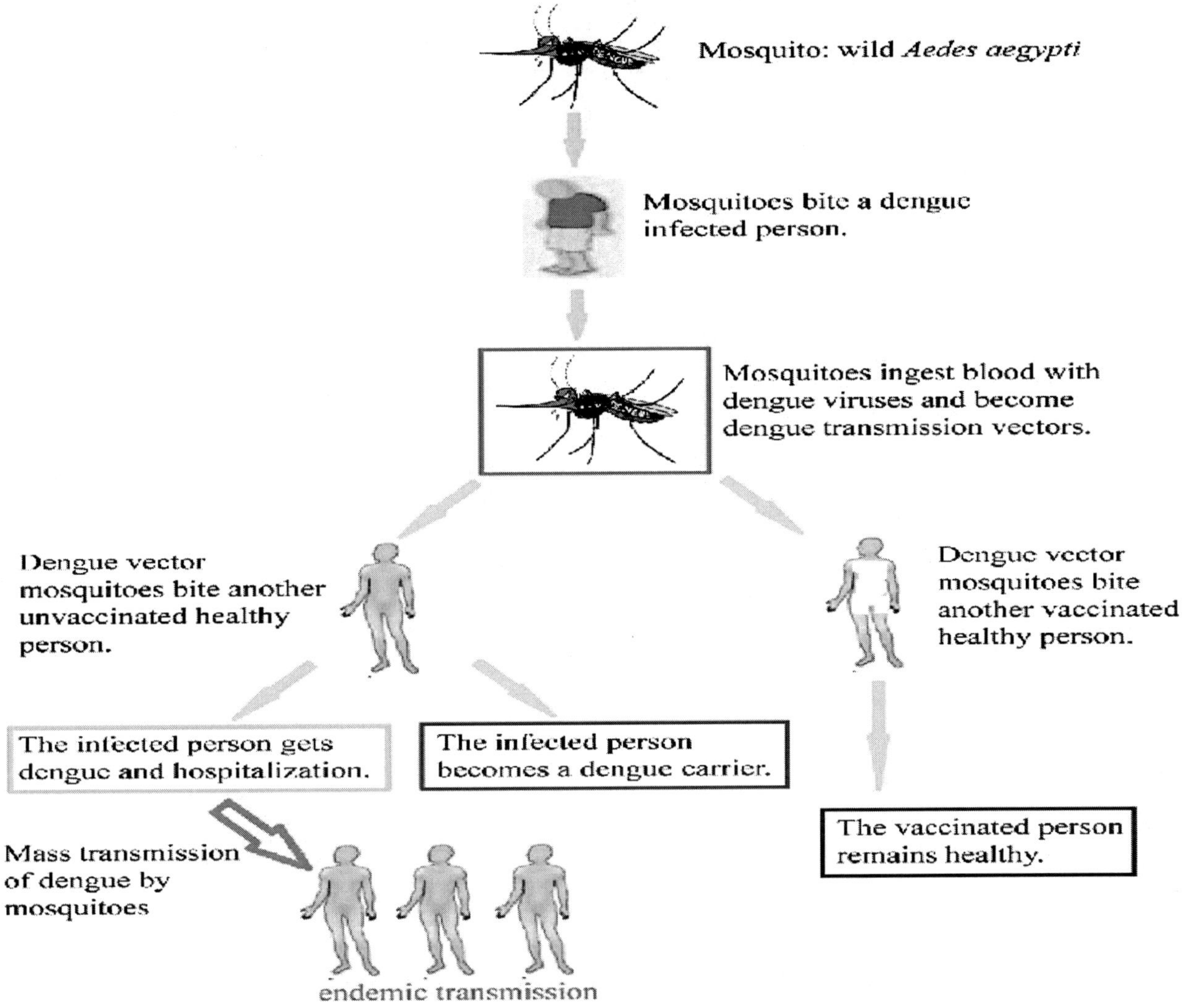

Mosquitoes transmit a wide range of **protozoal and viral diseases** of major public health importance. Each mosquito genus is associated with specific diseases based on its feeding behavior habitat preference and biological compatibility with the pathogen. Knowledge of diseases transmitted by mosquitoes is essential for diagnosis epidemiology and prevention.

Diseases transmitted by major mosquito genera

Mosquito genus	Type of pathogen transmitted	Diseases transmitted
Anopheles	Protozoa	Malaria
Culex	Helminths and viruses	Filariasis Japanese encephalitis West Nile fever
Aedes	Viruses	Dengue chikungunya yellow fever Zika infection

Explanation

Anopheles mosquitoes transmit malaria by introducing malaria parasites into the human bloodstream during blood feeding. Only the female mosquito is responsible for transmission. Malaria remains one of the most important mosquito borne diseases worldwide.

Culex mosquitoes transmit filarial worms and several viral infections. These mosquitoes usually bite at night and breed in stagnant polluted water. Their role in filariasis makes them important vectors in tropical regions.

Aedes mosquitoes are aggressive day time biters and are responsible for several viral epidemics. Their ability to breed in small artificial water collections brings them into close contact with humans. This behavior explains frequent outbreaks of dengue and chikungunya in urban areas.

Prevention and Control of Mosquitoes

Method of control	Measures included	Purpose
Environmental control	Drainage of stagnant water, filling of pits and ditches, covering water storage containers, proper disposal of waste	Elimination of mosquito breeding sites
Larval control	Use of larvicides, oiling of water surfaces, introduction of larvivorous fish such as Gambusia and guppy	Destruction of mosquito larvae before adulthood
Adult mosquito control	Indoor residual spraying, fogging, use of insecticide sprays	Reduction of adult mosquito population
Personal protective measures	Use of bed nets, repellents, protective clothing, window and door screens	Prevention of mosquito bites
Community participation	Health education, public awareness, community cleanliness drives	Sustained and effective mosquito control
Integrated control approach	Combination of environmental, chemical, biological, and personal measures	Long term reduction of mosquito borne diseases

10. Arthropods as Vectors of Disease

Introduction

Arthropods play a major role in the **transmission of human diseases** and are therefore of great medical importance. They act as vectors by carrying disease producing organisms from one host to another. Unlike mosquitoes, which form a uniform and well defined group, arthropod vectors include **diverse organisms** such as ticks lice fleas mites sandflies and flies. For this reason, they are studied together under a separate unit.

From a medical zoology perspective, arthropods may transmit pathogens in two principal ways. In some cases, the pathogen undergoes **development or multiplication within the arthropod**, making it a biological vector. In other cases, the arthropod merely carries the pathogen on its body surface or mouthparts, acting as a mechanical vector.

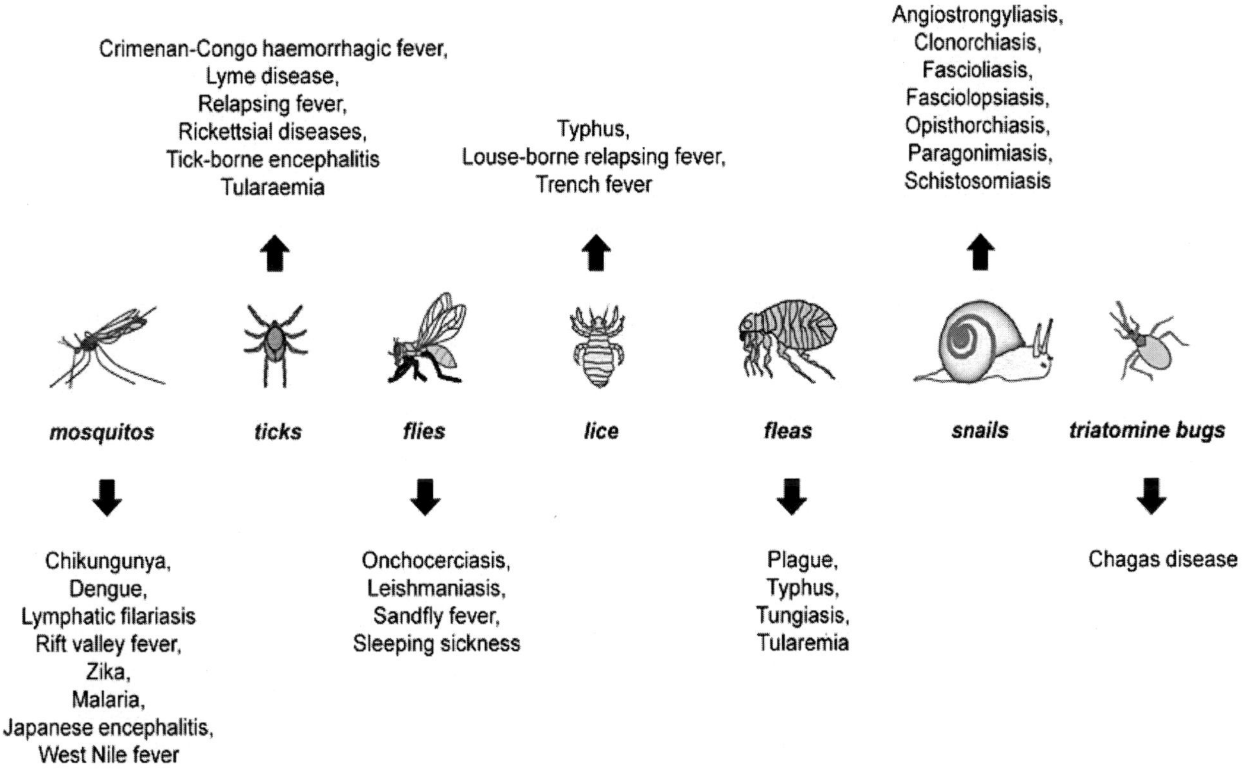

vectors are responsible for transmission of **protozoal helminthic bacterial and viral diseases**. Their importance lies not only in disease transmission but also in their close association with human habitations living conditions hygiene and environment. Control of arthropod vectors therefore plays a crucial role in public health.

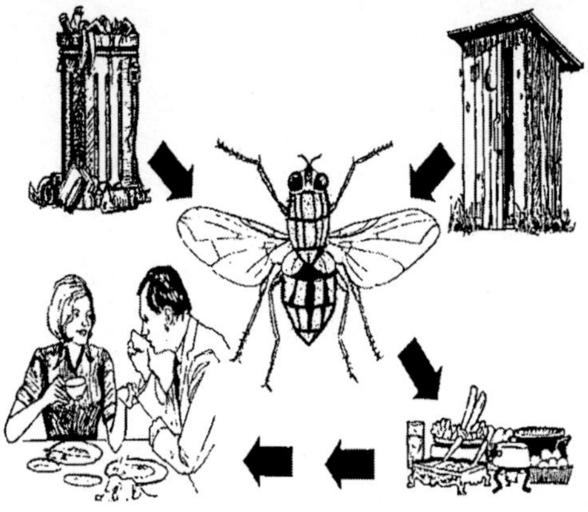

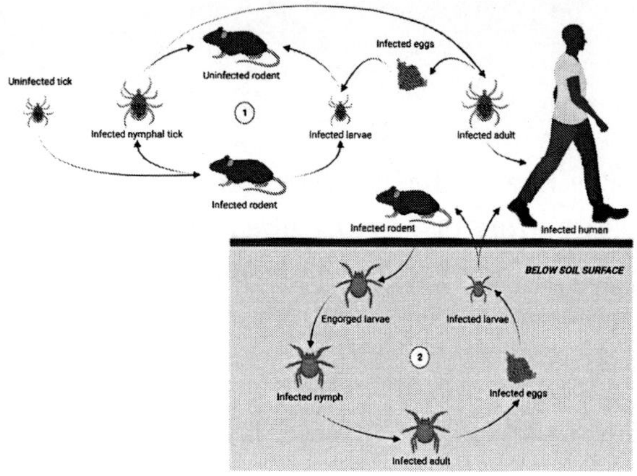

Types of Arthropod Vectors

Arthropods transmit disease producing organisms in **two basic ways**. Understanding these types is essential for linking vector biology with epidemiology and control strategies.

Classification based on mode of transmission

Type of vector	Definition	Role of arthropod	Examples of diseases
Biological vector	Pathogen undergoes development or multiplication inside the arthropod	Essential part of life cycle of pathogen	Malaria filariasis sleeping sickness leishmaniasis
Mechanical vector	Pathogen does not develop inside the arthropod and is carried passively	Acts only as a carrier	Cholera typhoid dysentery

Explanation

In **biological transmission**, the arthropod is an essential host for the pathogen. The disease producing organism develops or multiplies inside the vector before being transmitted to humans. Without the arthropod, transmission cannot occur. This type of transmission is highly specific and depends on close biological adaptation between pathogen and vector.

In **mechanical transmission**, the arthropod simply carries infectious material on its body surface mouthparts or gut. There is no development of the pathogen inside the vector. Transmission occurs through contamination of food water or wounds.

*Most serious vector borne diseases are transmitted through **biological vectors**, which makes control more challenging. Mechanical vectors mainly reflect **poor sanitation and hygiene**.*

Classification of Arthropods of Medical Importance

Arthropods of medical importance are classified based on their **taxonomic group and role in disease transmission**. This classification helps students organize diverse vectors in a logical manner and link each group with the diseases they transmit.

Classification based on major arthropod groups

Arthropod group	Important examples	Diseases transmitted or caused
Insects	Mosquitoes sandflies lice fleas houseflies	Malaria dengue filariasis leishmaniasis typhus plague mechanical transmission of enteric diseases
Arachnids	Ticks mites	Relapsing fever Lyme disease scrub typhus scabies
Crustaceans	Cyclops	Dracunculiasis

Explanation

Insects form the largest and most important group of arthropod vectors. They are responsible for transmission of a wide range of protozoal helminthic bacterial and viral diseases. Their close association with humans makes them highly significant from a public health point of view.

Arachnids include ticks and mites. These arthropods are important vectors of bacterial and rickettsial diseases. Some also cause direct skin infestations and allergic reactions.

Crustaceans, though fewer in number, play an important role in transmission of certain parasitic diseases. Cyclops acts as an intermediate host in dracunculiasis.

This classification provides a ***framework for studying individual arthropods*** *in detail. Each group will be discussed separately with respect to morphology life cycle diseases transmitted and control measures.*

Ticks of Medical Importance

Ticks are **blood sucking arachnids** of great medical importance. They act as **biological vectors** of several bacterial viral and protozoal diseases and may also cause direct harm to humans through blood loss skin irritation and toxin mediated effects. Ticks are larger than most insect vectors and remain attached to the host for prolonged periods during feeding.

Ticks belong to the class Arachnida and therefore possess **four pairs of legs in the adult stage**. Their body is dorsoventrally flattened and adapted for firm attachment to the host skin.

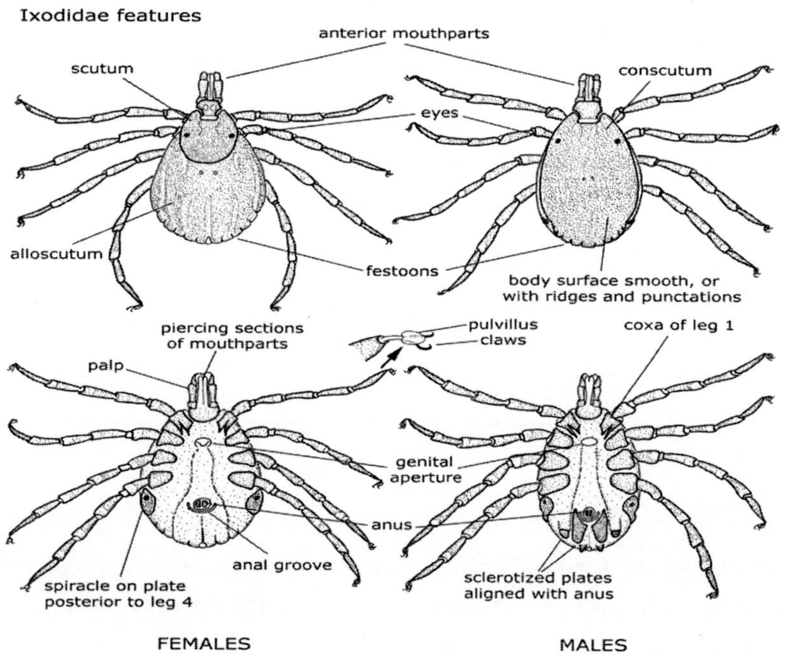
Ixodidae features
anterior mouthparts
scutum
conscutum
eyes
alloscutum
festoons
body surface smooth, or
with ridges and punctations
piercing sections
of mouthparts
pulvillus
claws
coxa of leg 1
palp
genital
aperture
anus
anal groove
spiracle on plate
posterior to leg 4
sclerotized plates
aligned with anus
FEMALES
MALES

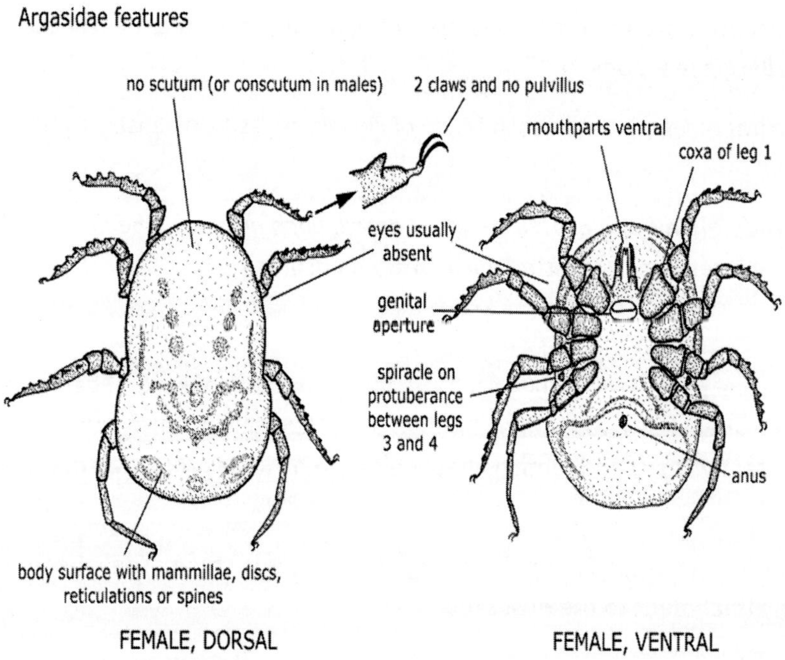
Argasidae features
no scutum (or conscutum in males)
2 claws and no pulvillus
mouthparts ventral
coxa of leg 1
eyes usually
absent
genital
aperture
spiracle on
protuberance
between legs
3 and 4
anus
body surface with mammillae, discs,
reticulations or spines
FEMALE, DORSAL
FEMALE, VENTRAL

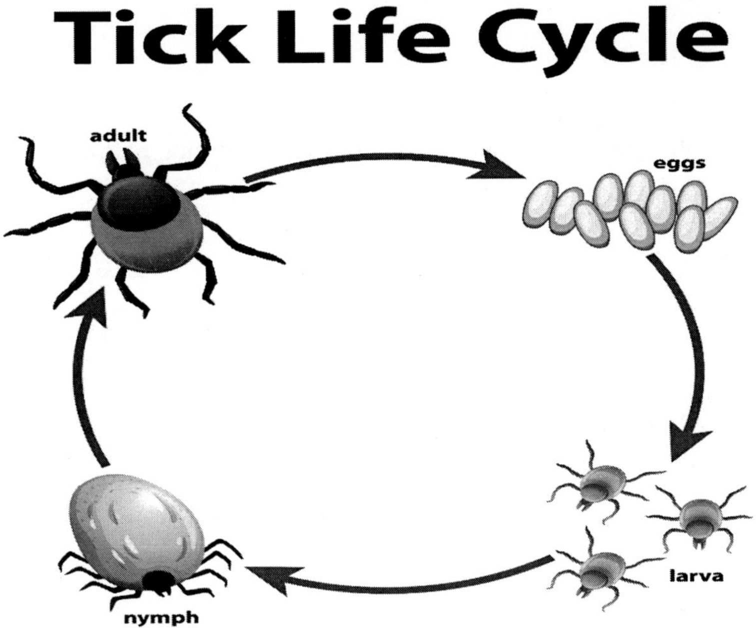

General characteristics of ticks

Ticks have a **tough cuticle** and a specialized mouthpart structure called the capitulum, which is adapted for piercing skin and sucking blood. Both male and female ticks feed on blood, unlike mosquitoes where only females feed.

Ticks undergo **incomplete metamorphosis** and pass through egg larva nymph and adult stages. All active stages require blood meals. Ticks are usually found in grassy areas forests animal shelters and cracks in walls.

Classification of ticks

Ticks of medical importance are broadly divided into two groups.

Feature	Hard ticks	Soft ticks
Family	Ixodidae	Argasidae
Body covering	Hard dorsal shield present	No hard shield
Mouthparts	Clearly visible from above	Not visible from above
Feeding duration	Long lasting feeding	Short repeated feeding
Habitat	Vegetation and animal hosts	Animal shelters cracks and crevices

Diseases transmitted by ticks

Ticks transmit a variety of diseases due to their prolonged blood feeding and ability to maintain pathogens for long periods.

Disease type	Examples
Bacterial diseases	Lyme disease relapsing fever
Viral diseases	Tick borne encephalitis hemorrhagic fevers
Protozoal diseases	Babesiosis
Toxin mediated effects	Tick paralysis

Ticks may also act as **reservoirs of infection**, maintaining pathogens in nature even in the absence of human hosts.

Medical importance of ticks

Ticks are of considerable medical importance because they cause disease through multiple mechanisms. They act as vectors by **transmitting infectious agents** such as bacteria viruses and protozoa to humans during blood feeding. Their prolonged attachment to the host also leads to **local skin reactions**, including inflammation irritation and secondary infection at the site of bite. Repeated or heavy infestation may result in **significant blood loss**, which can cause anemia, especially in children and debilitated individuals. Some tick species release **toxins during feeding**, which may lead to neuromuscular dysfunction and result in tick paralysis in susceptible hosts. The medical importance of ticks is further increased by their **wide host range**, as they infest domestic animals wildlife and humans, allowing maintenance and spread of infections across different species.

Lice of Medical Importance

Lice are **small wingless blood sucking insects** that live as **permanent ectoparasites on humans**. They belong to the order Anoplura and are of medical importance because they transmit certain bacterial diseases and also cause direct irritation and skin lesions. Lice show close host specificity and spend their entire life cycle on the human body or clothing.

Lice have a **flattened body** adapted for life among hair or clothing fibers. They possess three pairs of short legs with strong claws that help them cling firmly to the host. Both male and female lice feed on blood several times a day.

Types of lice infesting humans

Humans are infested by three types of lice.

Head louse lives on the scalp and hair
Body louse lives in clothing seams and moves to skin for feeding
Pubic louse lives in coarse hair of pubic region and axilla

Among these, the **body louse** is the most important from a disease transmission point of view.

Medical importance of lice

Lice are important medically because they act as **biological vectors** of certain bacterial infections. Body lice transmit diseases such as epidemic typhus trench fever and relapsing fever. Transmission usually occurs when infected louse feces contaminate skin abrasions produced by scratching.

In addition to disease transmission, lice cause **intense itching and irritation** due to repeated bites. Continuous scratching may lead to secondary bacterial infection thickening of skin and pigmentation changes. Heavy infestation may result in weakness and anemia especially in children.Lice infestation is closely associated with **poor personal hygiene overcrowding and poverty**, making it an important public health problem in disadvantaged populations.

Fleas of Medical Importance

Fleas are **small wingless insects** that act as **temporary ectoparasites** of humans and animals. They belong to the order Siphonaptera and are of medical importance because they transmit serious bacterial diseases and also cause direct skin irritation. Fleas are laterally compressed, which allows easy movement between hair and clothing fibers.

Both male and female fleas feed on blood. They possess strong hind legs that enable them to jump long distances. Fleas usually live on animals such as rats dogs and cats but may bite humans when their natural hosts are unavailable.

Medical importance of fleas

Fleas are medically important because they act as **biological vectors of bacterial diseases**. The most important disease transmitted by fleas is **plague**, which is caused by Yersinia pestis. The rat flea plays a key role in transmitting infection from rodents to humans. Fleas also transmit **endemic typhus** in certain regions.

In addition to disease transmission, flea bites produce **local skin reactions** such as itching redness and swelling. Repeated bites may cause allergic reactions and secondary bacterial infection due to scratching. Heavy infestation may lead to discomfort sleep disturbance and anemia in vulnerable individuals.

Fleas also serve as **intermediate hosts** for some parasitic worms. Their ability to infest both animals and humans increases their importance in maintaining infection cycles in nature.

The medical importance of fleas is closely related to their association with rodents domestic animals and human habitations. Control of flea infestation is therefore essential for prevention of flea borne diseases.

Educational significance

Fleas are important arthropods from a medical education perspective because they act as vectors of serious bacterial diseases and also cause direct harm to humans. Their role in transmission of plague and endemic typhus highlights their public health importance. In addition, their ability to infest both animals and humans helps maintain infection cycles in nature. Understanding flea biology and behavior is therefore essential for correlating disease transmission with rodent control, environmental hygiene, and preventive strategies.

Mites of Medical Importance

Mites are **very small arachnids** that are closely related to ticks. They are of medical importance because some species act as **vectors of disease**, while others cause **direct infestation of skin** leading to dermatological conditions. Mites are usually microscopic and may live on the skin, in hair follicles, or in the environment such as dust and vegetation.

Mites possess a **rounded body** and four pairs of legs in the adult stage. Their small size allows them to remain unnoticed for long periods. Some mites are free living, while others are obligate parasites of humans or animals.

Medical importance of mites

Mites cause disease in humans mainly by **direct infestation** rather than by transmission of multiple pathogens. The most important condition caused by mites is **scabies**, which results from infestation of the skin. The female mite burrows into the superficial layers of skin and lays eggs, leading to intense itching and characteristic skin lesions.

Certain mites also act as **vectors of rickettsial diseases**. In scrub typhus, mites transmit infection to humans during feeding. These mites normally parasitize rodents, and humans become accidental hosts when exposed to mite infested environments.

In addition, mites present in house dust may cause **allergic reactions** such as asthma and dermatitis. These reactions are due to mite allergens rather than infection.

Clinical and public health significance

Mites are of considerable clinical and public health importance because they cause **widespread skin infestation and discomfort**, particularly in overcrowded communities. Infestation leads to intense itching that is usually worse at night, resulting in scratching and frequent secondary bacterial infections. The characteristic distribution of skin lesions and high transmissibility make mite infestation a common problem in families hostels and institutions. From a public health perspective, mites are important because they are responsible for transmission of scrub typhus in endemic areas and are closely associated with poor hygiene and living conditions. Effective control therefore requires early diagnosis treatment of affected individuals and improvement in personal and environmental hygiene.

Sandflies of Medical Importance

Sandflies are **small delicate insects** of medical importance because they act as **biological vectors** of important protozoal and viral diseases. They belong mainly to the genus **Phlebotomus** in the Old World and are closely associated with human habitations in endemic areas.

Sandflies are much smaller than mosquitoes and are silent fliers. Both male and female sandflies feed on plant juices, but **female sandflies require blood meals** for egg development. Biting usually occurs during evening and night hours. Because of their small size, sandflies can pass through ordinary mosquito nets.

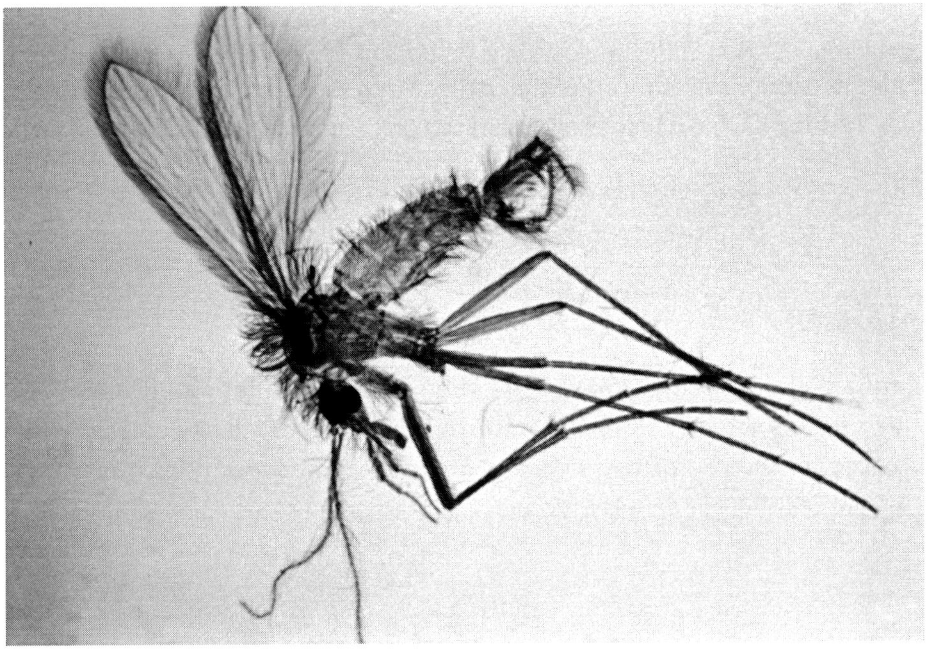

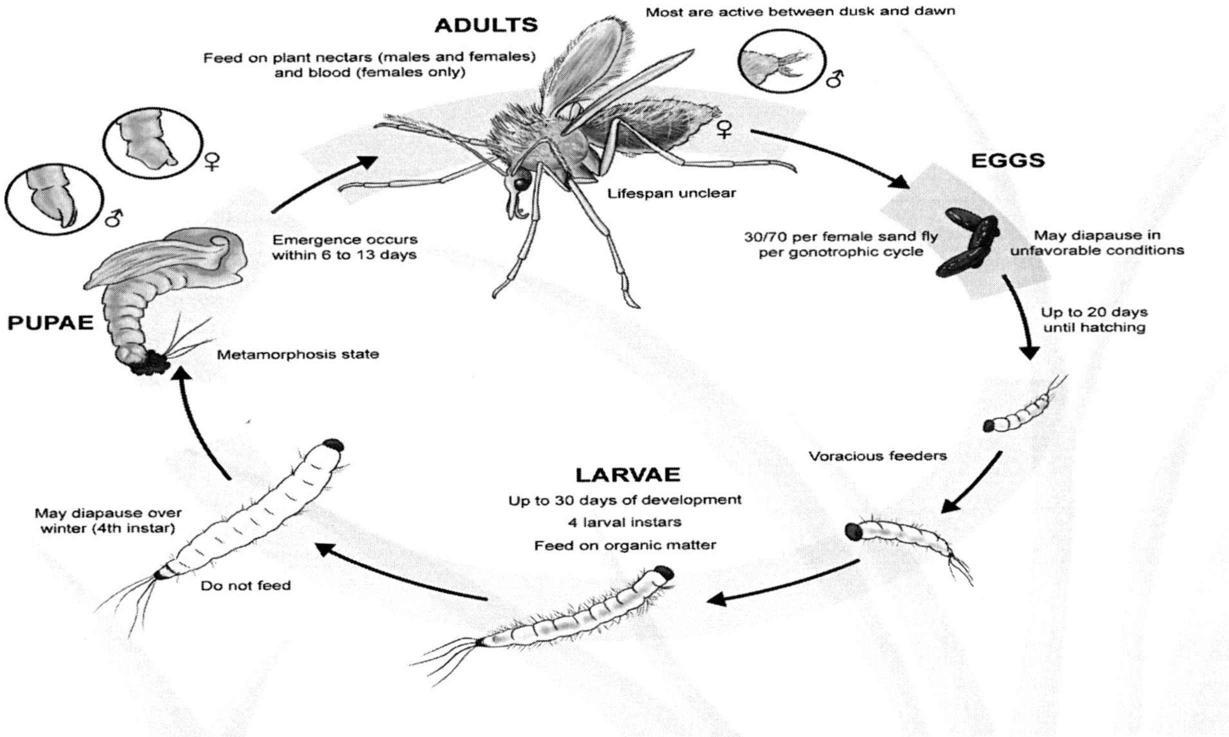
ADULTS
Most are active between dusk and dawn
Feed on plant nectars (males and females) and blood (females only)
♂
♀
Lifespan unclear
EGGS
30/70 per female sand fly per gonotrophic cycle
May diapause in unfavorable conditions
Up to 20 days until hatching
Voracious feeders
LARVAE
Up to 30 days of development
4 larval instars
Feed on organic matter
Do not feed
May diapause over winter (4th instar)
PUPAE
Metamorphosis state
Emergence occurs within 6 to 13 days
♀
♂

Medical importance of sandflies

Sandflies are the **vectors of leishmaniasis**, a group of diseases caused by species of **Leishmania**. During blood feeding, the infected female sandfly introduces infective forms of the parasite into the human skin. This leads to different clinical forms such as visceral leishmaniasis cutaneous leishmaniasis and mucocutaneous leishmaniasis.

Sandflies also transmit certain viral infections in some regions. Their role in disease transmission is strongly influenced by environmental factors such as poor housing cracks in walls presence of organic matter and close contact with animal reservoirs.

Clinical and public health significance

Sandflies are important clinically because the diseases they transmit are often **chronic debilitating and difficult to treat**. Visceral leishmaniasis affects vital organs and may be fatal if untreated. From a public health point of view, sandfly borne diseases are closely linked to poverty malnutrition overcrowding and poor housing. Control of sandflies therefore requires improvement of living conditions early diagnosis of human cases and vector control measures.

Houseflies as Mechanical Vectors of Disease

Houseflies are **common insects closely associated with human habitations** and are of medical importance because they act as **mechanical vectors of disease**. Unlike mosquitoes or sandflies, houseflies do not transmit pathogens through biting. Instead, they carry disease producing organisms from contaminated sources to food and surfaces used by humans.

Houseflies breed in **decaying organic matter**, garbage, feces, and sewage. Their body surface, legs, and mouthparts easily become contaminated with pathogenic organisms. When flies settle on uncovered food or utensils, they deposit these organisms through contact, regurgitation, or defecation.

Medical importance

Houseflies play an important role in the spread of **intestinal infections**. They mechanically transmit bacteria responsible for diseases such as cholera typhoid dysentery and diarrhea. They may also carry cysts of intestinal protozoa and eggs of intestinal worms, contributing to parasitic infections.

The transmission is purely mechanical, as the pathogen does not undergo any development or multiplication inside the fly. The presence of houseflies therefore reflects **poor sanitation and hygiene**, and their role in disease spread is closely linked to environmental conditions.

Clinical and public health significance

From a clinical and public health perspective, houseflies are important because they facilitate **rapid spread of enteric infections**, especially in crowded areas. Outbreaks of diarrheal diseases are commonly associated with high fly density and improper food handling. Control of houseflies through sanitation waste management and food protection is therefore an essential component of disease prevention.

Educational significance

Houseflies serve as a classic example of **mechanical transmission of disease**. Their study helps students clearly differentiate between biological and mechanical vectors and emphasizes the importance of environmental hygiene in disease control.

11. Helminths of Medical Importance

Introduction

Helminths are **multicellular parasitic worms** that cause a wide range of diseases in humans. They are of major medical importance because they produce **chronic infections**, nutritional deficiencies, tissue damage, and long term morbidity. Helminthic infections are especially common in tropical and subtropical regions where sanitation, hygiene, and health awareness are limited.

From a medical zoology perspective, helminths are important because they show **complex body organization**, diverse life cycles, and varied modes of transmission. Unlike protozoa, helminths do not multiply within the human host in most cases. Disease is mainly produced by **mechanical damage, toxic metabolites, immune reactions, and nutritional competition**.

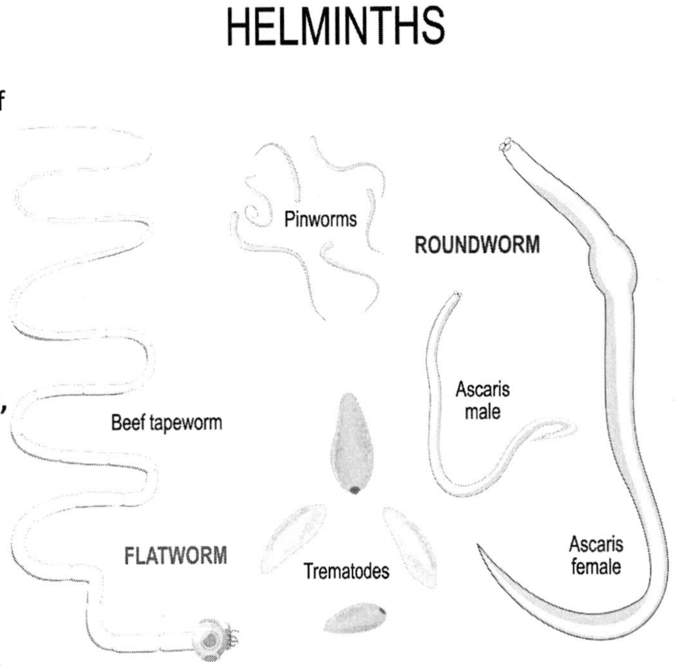

Helminths may live in different sites of the human body such as the **intestine, blood, lymphatic system, liver, lungs, muscles, and other tissues**. Infection is acquired through ingestion of eggs or larvae, penetration of skin, or transmission through insect vectors, depending on the species.

Helminths of medical importance are broadly classified into **roundworms, tapeworms, and flukes**. Each group shows distinct morphological features, life cycle patterns, and disease manifestations. Understanding these groups helps students correlate parasite structure with clinical effects and methods of control.

Classification of Helminths of Medical Importance

Helminths of medical importance are classified based on **body shape, internal structure, and life cycle characteristics**. This classification helps in systematic study and provides a clear framework for understanding morphology, mode of transmission, disease produced, laboratory diagnosis, and control measures.

From a medical zoology point of view, helminths are divided into **three major groups**.

1. Nematodes/ Roundworms

Nematodes are **elongated cylindrical worms** with a smooth body surface. The body is unsegmented and covered by a tough cuticle. The alimentary canal is complete with mouth and anus. Sexes are usually separate, and males are generally smaller than females.

Most nematodes infect the **intestinal tract**, though some live in blood or tissues. Transmission commonly occurs through ingestion of eggs or larvae, or by penetration of larvae through skin.

Examples include intestinal roundworms and filarial worms.

2. Cestodes/Tapeworms

Cestodes are **flat ribbon like worms** with a segmented body. The body consists of a head region called scolex, followed by a series of segments known as proglottids. They lack an alimentary canal and absorb nutrients through their body surface.

Cestodes usually live in the **intestinal tract** of humans in the adult stage. Humans may act as definitive or intermediate hosts depending on the species. Infection is commonly acquired by ingestion of larvae present in undercooked meat or fish.

Examples include beef tapeworm and pork tapeworm.

3. Trematodes/Flukes

Trematodes are **leaf shaped flat worms** with an incomplete digestive system. They possess suckers that help in attachment to host tissues. Most trematodes are hermaphrodites, except blood flukes which have separate sexes.

They usually require **one or more intermediate hosts**, commonly snails, to complete their life cycle. Infection may occur through ingestion of contaminated food or water, or by skin penetration of larvae.

Examples include liver flukes and blood flukes.

Educational significance

Classification of helminths is of great educational importance because it provides a clear and logical framework for studying parasitic worms of medical relevance. By grouping helminths into nematodes cestodes and trematodes, students can easily understand differences in body structure life cycle patterns mode of transmission and disease manifestations. This systematic approach helps in correlating morphology with clinical features laboratory diagnosis and preventive measures, thereby strengthening conceptual clarity and improving examination performance.

General Characteristics of Helminths

Helminths are **multicellular parasitic worms** that show a high degree of structural organization compared with protozoa. They are usually **elongated or flattened** and large enough to be seen with the naked eye in many cases. Their complex body structure enables them to survive for long periods within the human host.Most helminths do **not multiply within the human body**. Disease is produced mainly by the presence of adult worms or migrating larvae, which cause mechanical obstruction tissue damage and inflammatory reactions. Chronic infection often leads to nutritional deficiency anemia and impaired growth, especially in children.

Helminths exhibit **well defined organ systems**. Nematodes possess a complete digestive system with mouth and anus, while cestodes lack a digestive tract and absorb nutrients through the body surface. Trematodes have an incomplete digestive system and are equipped with suckers for attachment to host tissues.The **life cycle of helminths is complex** and often involves one or more intermediate hosts. Transmission to humans occurs through ingestion of eggs or larvae penetration of skin or via insect vectors depending on the species. Environmental factors such as sanitation hygiene and climate play a major role in transmission.

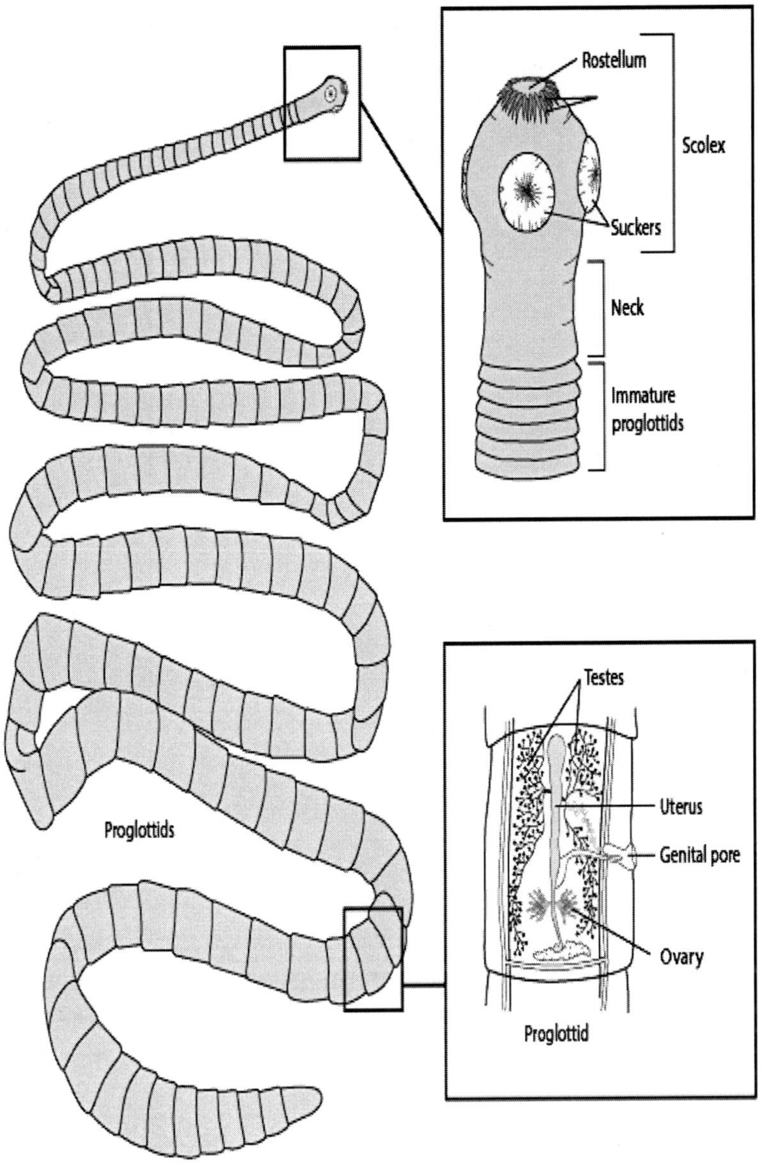
Rostellum
Scolex
Suckers
Neck
Immature
proglottids
Testes
Uterus
Genital pore
Ovary
Proglottid
Proglottids

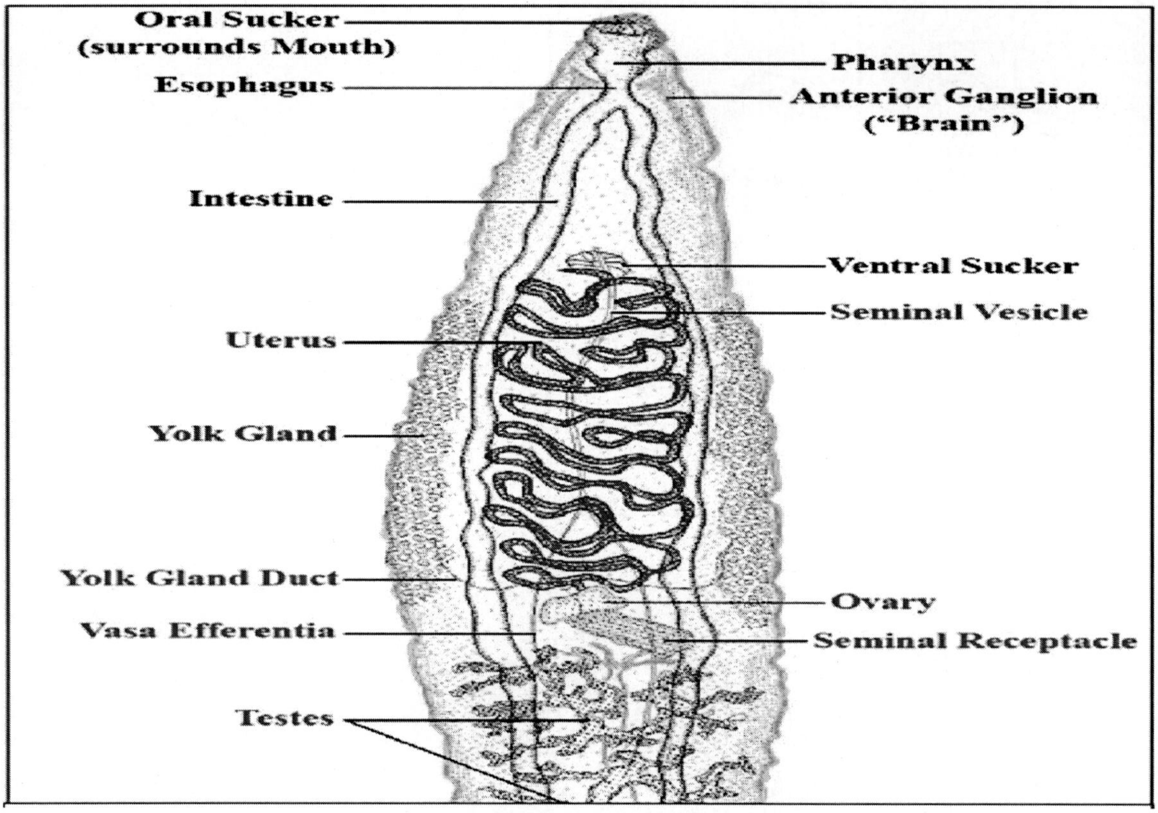

Helminths produce disease by several mechanisms. These include **mechanical injury**, secretion of toxic metabolites, induction of immune mediated reactions, and competition for host nutrients. Long standing infection may result in fibrosis obstruction of organs and hypersensitivity reactions.Thus, helminths are medically important parasites because of their complex biology chronic disease pattern and significant public health impact. Understanding these general characteristics forms the foundation for studying individual helminths their life cycles clinical features diagnosis and control measures.

Nematodes of Medical Importance

Introduction

Nematodes are commonly known as **roundworms** and constitute an important group of helminths of medical significance. They are responsible for a wide variety of human infections affecting the intestine blood lymphatic system and tissues. Nematode infections are especially common in regions with poor sanitation inadequate hygiene and favorable climatic conditions.

From a medical zoology perspective, nematodes are important because they possess a **simple elongated cylindrical body** with a complete digestive system. The body is unsegmented and covered by a protective cuticle. Sexes are usually separate and sexual dimorphism is commonly observed with females being larger than males.

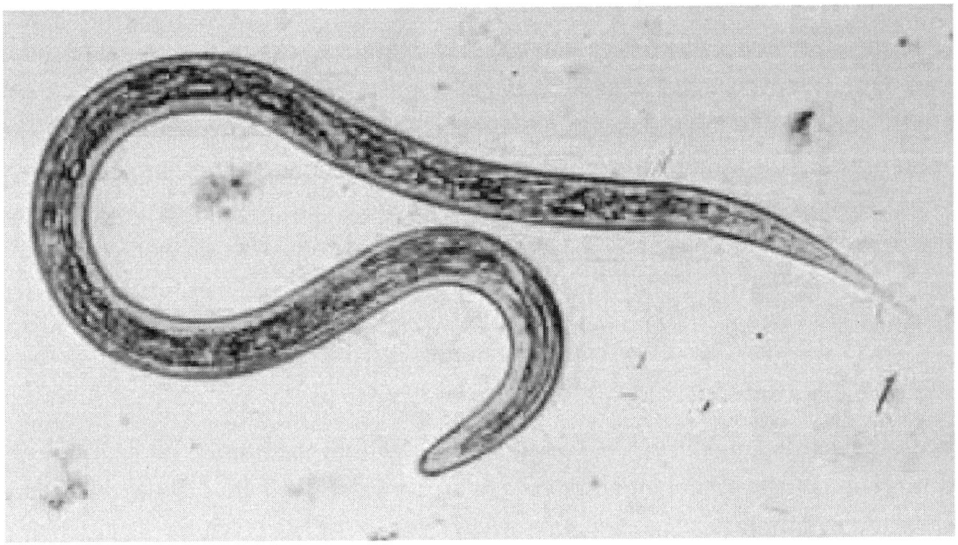

Most nematodes infect the **intestinal tract**, where they may cause abdominal pain malnutrition anemia and growth retardation. Some nematodes live in blood and lymphatic vessels producing chronic conditions such as lymphatic filariasis. Others migrate through tissues and organs causing inflammatory reactions and tissue damage.

Transmission of nematode infections occurs by different mechanisms depending on the species. Humans may acquire infection through ingestion of eggs or larvae present in contaminated food or water penetration of larvae through the skin or transmission by insect vectors. The life cycles of nematodes may be direct or indirect and often involve migration of larvae through various organs of the human body.

Disease caused by nematodes results from **mechanical obstruction tissue injury toxic secretions and immune responses** of the host. Chronic infections may persist for years and contribute significantly to morbidity rather than mortality.

The study of nematodes of medical importance is essential for understanding intestinal parasitic infections blood borne helminthic diseases and public health problems related to sanitation and hygiene.

General Characteristics of Nematodes

Nematodes are **elongated cylindrical worms** with a smooth unsegmented body that is circular in cross section. The body is covered by a **tough protective cuticle**, which helps the parasite resist digestive enzymes and host immune responses. This cuticle is periodically shed during growth in larval stages.Nematodes possess a **complete digestive system** with a mouth at the anterior end and an anus at the posterior end. The alimentary canal is well developed and adapted for ingestion and digestion of host contents. This feature clearly distinguishes nematodes from cestodes, which lack a digestive tract.Sexes in nematodes are **separate**, and sexual dimorphism is commonly observed. Females are usually larger and longer than males. In many species, the male has a curved posterior end with copulatory structures, while the female has a straight posterior end and a larger reproductive system capable of producing a large number of eggs.

Nematodes show **high reproductive capacity**, which contributes to widespread infection and transmission. Eggs or larvae are often passed in feces and contaminate soil, water, or food. Some nematodes produce larvae that actively penetrate the skin, while others require ingestion to establish infection.

The life cycle of nematodes may be **direct or indirect**. In direct life cycles, no intermediate host is required, and infection spreads from one human to another through the environment. In indirect life cycles, insect vectors or intermediate hosts are involved.Pathogenicity of nematodes is due to **mechanical damage**, obstruction of organs, tissue migration of larvae, secretion of toxic substances, and immune mediated reactions. Chronic infection may lead to anemia malnutrition growth retardation and impaired physical development.Thus, nematodes are medically important parasites because of their simple body structure efficient reproduction diverse modes of transmission and significant impact on human health. Understanding these general characteristics forms the basis for studying individual nematode infections in detail.

Classification of Nematodes of Medical Importance

Nematodes of medical importance are classified mainly on the basis of **habitat within the human body**, **mode of transmission**, and **life cycle pattern**. This classification helps students relate structure and life cycle with clinical presentation laboratory diagnosis and prevention.

Classification based on habitat

Group	Site of localization	Examples
Intestinal nematodes	Intestine	Ascaris lumbricoides Hookworm Enterobius vermicularis Trichuris trichiura
Tissue nematodes	Tissues and organs	Trichinella spiralis Dracunculus medinensis
Blood and lymphatic nematodes	Blood and lymph vessels	Wuchereria bancrofti Brugia malayi

Classification based on mode of transmission

Mode of transmission	Description	Examples
Ingestion of eggs	Eggs swallowed with contaminated food or water	Ascaris lumbricoides Trichuris trichiura
Skin penetration by larvae	Infective larvae penetrate intact skin	Hookworm Strongyloides stercoralis
Vector borne transmission	Larvae transmitted by insect vectors	Wuchereria bancrofti

Classification based on life cycle

Life cycle type	Characteristics	Examples
Direct life cycle	No intermediate host required	Ascaris lumbricoides Enterobius vermicularis
Indirect life cycle	One or more intermediate hosts or vectors involved	Wuchereria bancrofti Dracunculus medinensis

Educational significance

Classification of nematodes is important for systematic learning because it links **site of infection, route of entry,** and **life cycle pattern** with disease manifestations and control measures. This approach helps students organize information logically and improves understanding for examinations and clinical correlation.

Ascaris lumbricoides

Ascaris lumbricoides is the **largest intestinal nematode parasite of humans** and is responsible for a common helminthic infection known as ascariasis. The parasite has a worldwide distribution and is especially prevalent in tropical and subtropical regions where sanitation and hygiene are inadequate. Because of its large size high egg output and simple mode of transmission, Ascaris lumbricoides holds a central place in the study of nematodes of medical importance.

From a medical zoology perspective, this parasite is important because it demonstrates a **direct life cycle**, intestinal habitat, and extensive larval migration within the human body. Adult worms reside in the small intestine, while larval stages migrate through liver lungs and trachea before returning to the intestine. This migration is responsible for many clinical manifestations of the disease.

Infection occurs through **ingestion of embryonated eggs** present in contaminated food water or soil. Poor personal hygiene open defecation and use of untreated human feces as fertilizer contribute significantly to transmission. Children are commonly affected due to frequent exposure to contaminated environments.

Disease caused by Ascaris lumbricoides ranges from asymptomatic infection to severe intestinal and systemic complications. The parasite causes disease by **mechanical obstruction nutritional deprivation toxic effects and immune mediated reactions**. Heavy worm burden may lead to intestinal obstruction biliary complications and impaired growth in children.

Ascaris lumbricoides

Morphology

Ascaris lumbricoides is a **large cylindrical roundworm** with a smooth tapering body adapted for life in the

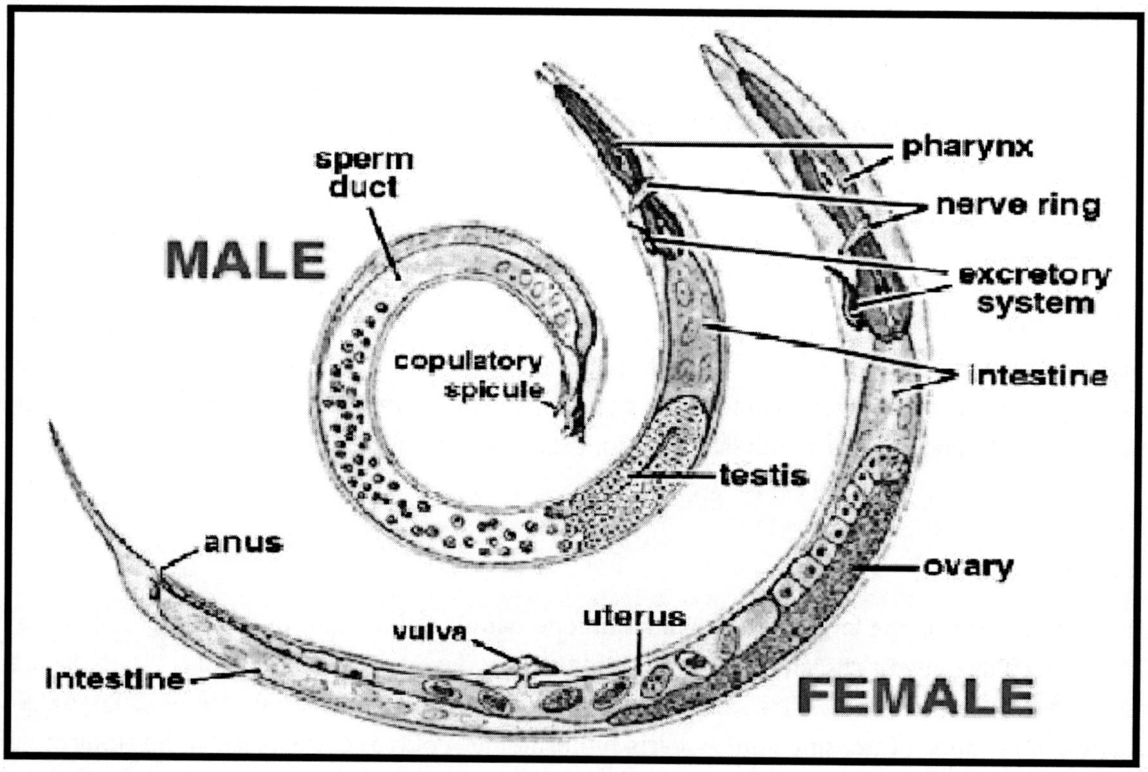

human intestine. The adult worm is creamy white or pale pink in color and shows clear **sexual dimorphism**, with females being larger than males

The **adult female** measures approximately **twenty to thirty five centimeters in length** and is thicker than the male. The posterior end of the female is straight and blunt. The female reproductive system is well developed and produces a very large number of eggs daily, which contributes to widespread transmission.

The **adult male** is smaller, measuring about **fifteen to thirty centimeters in length**. The posterior end of the male is characteristically **curved ventrally** and bears copulatory structures used during mating. This curved posterior end Is an Important identifying feature.

The **anterior end** of the worm bears a mouth surrounded by **three prominent lips**, one dorsal and two ventral. These lips help in ingestion of intestinal contents. Sensory papillae are present on the lips.

The body wall consists of a **thick cuticle**, which protects the worm from digestive enzymes of the host. Beneath the cuticle lie muscle layers that enable the worm to move actively within the intestinal lumen.

The **eggs** of Ascaris lumbricoides are of great diagnostic importance. Fertilized eggs are oval with a thick shell and an outer mammillated albuminous coat. They are brown in color due to bile staining. Unfertilized eggs are larger elongated and have a thinner shell with irregular contents.

Thus, the morphology of Ascaris lumbricoides includes large sexually dimorphic adults with characteristic lips and thick cuticle, and distinctive eggs that are easily identified microscopically. Understanding morphology is essential for diagnosis and correlation with life cycle and disease manifestations.

Life Cycle of Ascaris lumbricoides

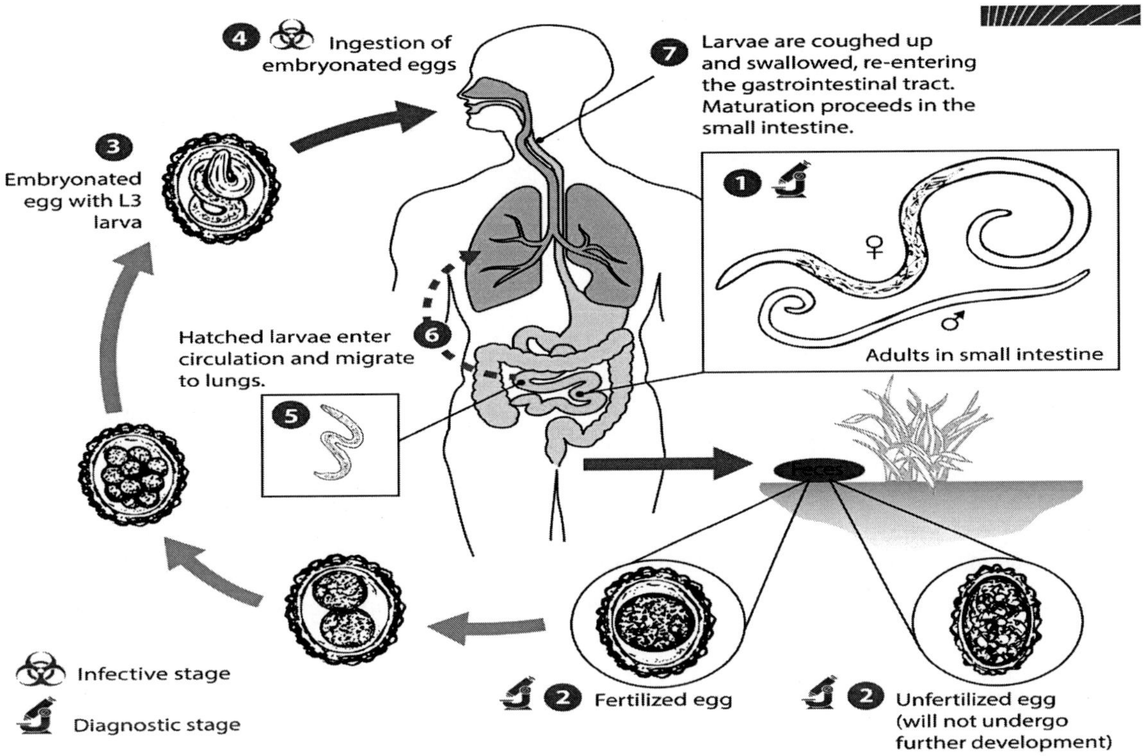

The life cycle of Ascaris lumbricoides is **direct**, meaning no intermediate host is required. Human beings are the **only definitive host**. Infection occurs through ingestion of infective eggs, and the parasite completes its development within the human body after a characteristic larval migration.

Adult worms live in the **small intestine** of humans. Fertilized female worms produce a very large number of eggs daily, which are passed out with feces. These eggs are **not infective at the time of passage**.

When eggs reach the soil under suitable conditions of moisture warmth and oxygen, they undergo development. Inside the egg, the embryo develops into a **second stage larva**. This process is called **embryonation**. The embryonated egg containing the larva is the **infective stage** for humans.

Humans acquire infection by **ingestion of embryonated eggs** through contaminated food water or hands. After ingestion, the eggs hatch in the **small intestine**, releasing larvae.

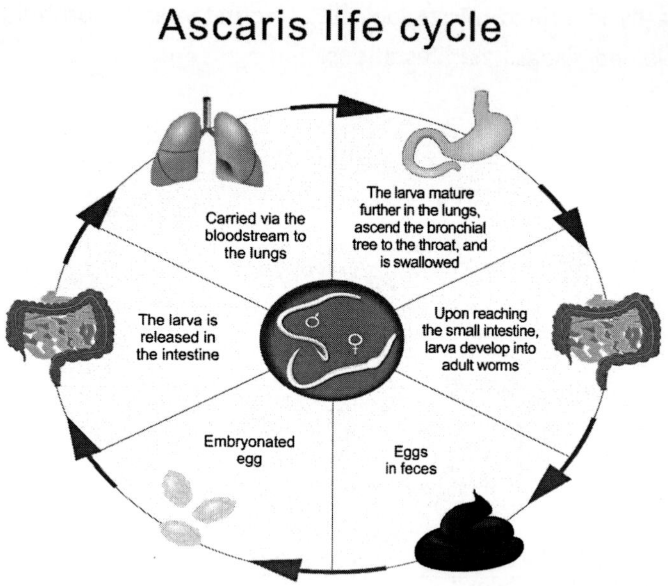

The larvae penetrate the intestinal wall and enter the bloodstream. They are carried first to the **liver**, then to the **heart**, and finally to the **lungs**. In the lungs, larvae break into the alveoli and continue their development.

From the alveoli, the larvae migrate up the bronchi and trachea to reach the throat. They are then **swallowed** and return to the small intestine. This phase is known as **larval migration** and is responsible for respiratory symptoms seen in some patients.

Once back in the small intestine, the larvae mature into **adult worms**. The adults live freely in the intestinal lumen and begin producing eggs, thus completing the life cycle.

Educational significance

The life cycle of Ascaris lumbricoides is of great educational importance because it clearly demonstrates the relationship between poor sanitation and transmission of intestinal helminthic infections. It explains how ingestion of embryonated eggs leads to intestinal infection and how larval migration through the lungs produces respiratory manifestations before the worms return to the intestine. Understanding this life cycle helps students correlate clinical features with parasite development and highlights the importance of hygiene safe disposal of feces and health education in prevention of ascariasis.

Ascaris lumbricoides

Pathogenicity and Clinical Features

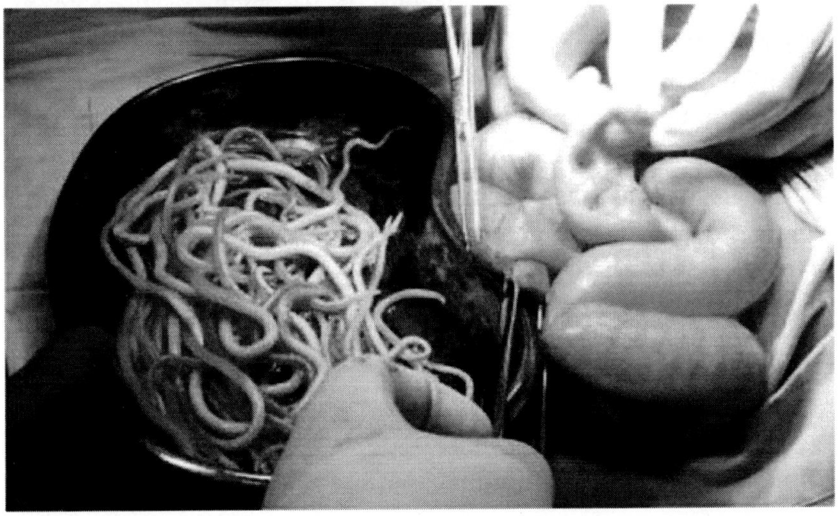

Disease caused by Ascaris lumbricoides is known as **ascariasis**. The pathogenicity of this parasite depends on the **number of worms present**, their **migration through tissues**, and the **host immune response**. Many infections are mild or asymptomatic, but heavy infestation may lead to serious complications.Pathogenic effects occur during **two main phases**, the larval migration phase and the intestinal phase.

During the **larval migration phase**, larvae pass through the lungs after entering the bloodstream. This may produce respiratory symptoms such as cough wheezing breathlessness and fever. In some individuals, an allergic type reaction develops in the lungs, leading to transient pulmonary infiltrates and eosinophilia. This condition is often referred to as Loffler syndrome.During the **intestinal phase**, adult worms residing in the small intestine cause symptoms related to mechanical irritation and nutritional competition. Common symptoms include abdominal pain nausea vomiting loss of appetite and weight loss. In children, chronic infection may result in malnutrition anemia and impaired physical growth.

Heavy worm burden may lead to **intestinal obstruction**, especially in children. Worms may also migrate into abnormal sites such as the bile duct appendix or pancreatic duct, producing complications like biliary colic obstructive jaundice appendicitis or pancreatitis.The immune response to the parasite often results in **eosinophilia**, which is a common laboratory finding in ascariasis. Secondary bacterial infection may occur due to tissue damage caused by migrating larvae or adult worms.Thus, Ascaris lumbricoides produces disease through larval tissue migration mechanical effects of adult worms nutritional deprivation and immune mediated reactions. Understanding these clinical features helps in early recognition diagnosis and prevention of complications.

Laboratory diagnosis

Laboratory diagnosis of ascariasis is based mainly on **demonstration of eggs in stool**, supported by clinical features and relevant laboratory findings. Diagnosis is usually straightforward in intestinal infection because adult female worms produce a large number of eggs.

The **stool examination** is the most important diagnostic method. Microscopic examination of stool reveals **fertilized or unfertilized eggs** of Ascaris lumbricoides. Fertilized eggs are oval with a thick shell and an outer mammillated coat stained brown by bile. Unfertilized eggs are larger elongated and have a thinner shell with irregular granular contents. Identification of these characteristic eggs confirms the diagnosis.In cases where only male worms are present, eggs may be absent in stool. In such situations, diagnosis is suggested by clinical features and other supportive findings. Occasionally, **adult worms may be passed in stool or vomitus**, which provides direct evidence of infection.During the **larval migration phase**, stool examination may be negative. At this stage, laboratory findings often show **eosinophilia in peripheral blood**, which reflects an allergic response to migrating larvae. Sputum examination may occasionally demonstrate larvae in patients with prominent respiratory symptoms.Other laboratory findings such as mild anemia and raised eosinophil count support the diagnosis but are **not specific**. Imaging studies may help detect complications but do not replace parasitological diagnosis.Thus, laboratory diagnosis of ascariasis relies primarily on **microscopic detection of eggs in stool**, supported by blood findings and clinical correlation. Understanding these diagnostic methods helps students correlate parasite biology with disease presentation and prevention strategies.

Treatment of ascariasis

Drug name	Usual oral dose	Duration	Educational note
Albendazole	400 mg single dose	One day	Effective against adult intestinal worms
Mebendazole	100 mg twice daily	Three days	Alternative drug for intestinal ascariasis
Pyrantel pamoate	As per body weight	Single dose	Causes paralysis of worms

Supportive care may be required in heavy infection or complications. In cases of intestinal obstruction or biliary involvement, specialized management may be necessary. Drug therapy is most effective when combined with preventive measures.

Prevention of ascariasis

Prevention is based on **breaking the cycle of transmission**, which mainly occurs through soil contamination and poor hygiene.

- Important preventive measures include
- Proper disposal of human feces
- Use of sanitary latrines
- Washing hands before meals and after defecation
- Thorough washing of vegetables and fruits
- Health education regarding personal hygiene
- Periodic deworming programs in endemic areas

Educational significance

Understanding treatment and prevention of Ascaris lumbricoides helps students correlate parasite life cycle with control strategies. It highlights the role of sanitation hygiene and public health measures in reducing helminthic infections and emphasizes that medical management alone is not sufficient without environmental control.

Enterobius vermicularis

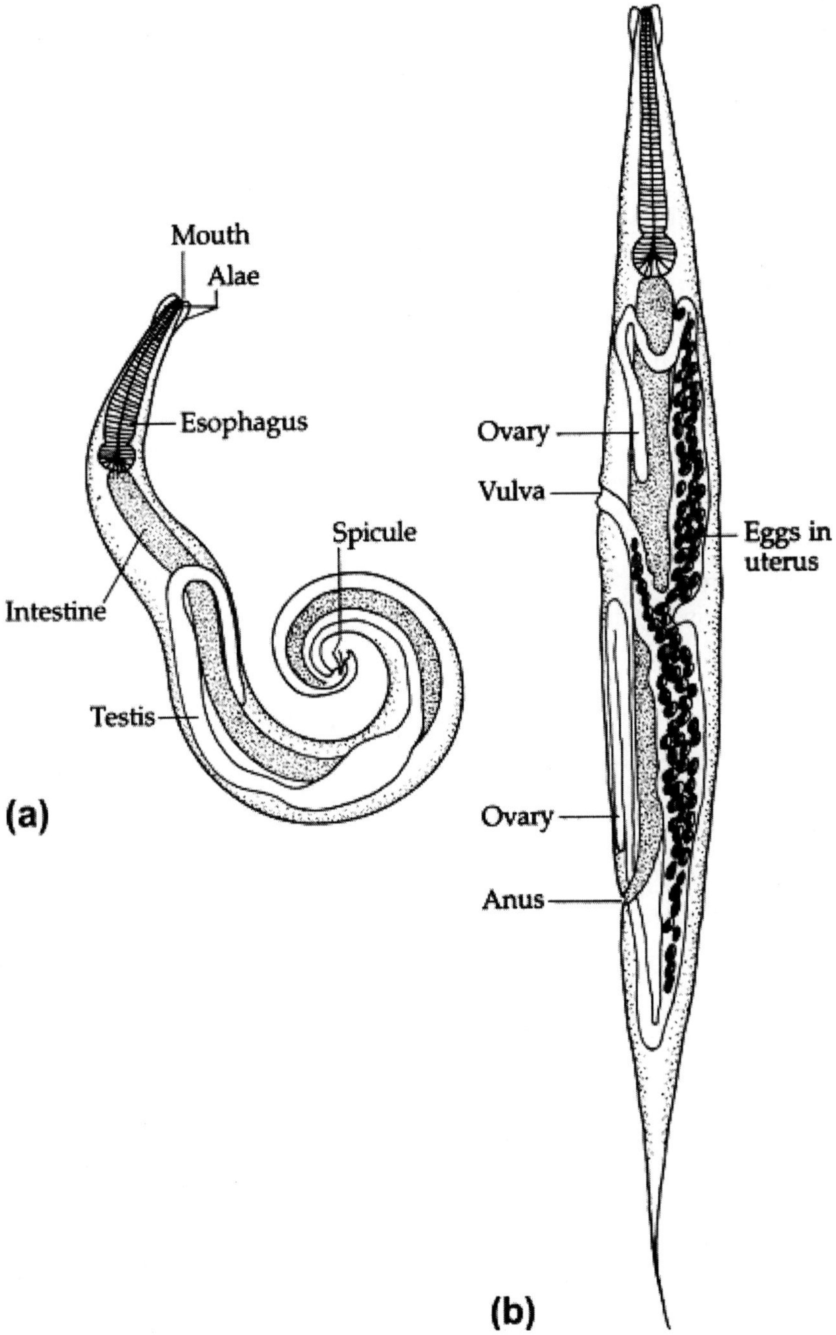

Enterobius vermicularis commonly known as the **pinworm** is a small intestinal nematode parasite of humans. It is one of the **most common helminthic infections worldwide**, particularly affecting children. Unlike many other nematodes, enterobiasis is closely related to **personal hygiene and close human contact** rather than soil contamination.

The parasite primarily inhabits the **cecum appendix and colon**. Female worms migrate to the perianal region at night to lay eggs, producing intense itching. Because of this behavior, enterobiasis spreads easily among family members school children and institutional populations.

Morphology

Enterobius vermicularis is a **small white thread like worm**. The adult female measures about eight to thirteen millimeters in length and is longer than the male. The posterior end of the female is **long pointed and pin like**, which gives the parasite its common name.

The male worm is smaller and measures about two to five millimeters in length. The posterior end of the male is curved ventrally. The anterior end of the worm bears **lateral alae**, which appear as wing like expansions of the cuticle and are important identifying features.

The eggs are **oval flattened on one side and colorless**. They have a thin transparent shell and contain a partially developed larva. These eggs become infective within a few hours of being laid.

Life cycle

The life cycle of Enterobius vermicularis is **direct** and simple. Humans are the only host. Adult worms live in the large intestine. At night, gravid females migrate out through the anus and deposit eggs on the perianal skin.

The eggs become infective rapidly. Infection occurs by **ingestion or inhalation of eggs**, which may contaminate fingers clothing bedding toys and dust. After ingestion, eggs hatch in the small intestine and larvae migrate to the large intestine where they mature into adults.

Auto infection is common due to scratching of the perianal area and transfer of eggs to the mouth. Reinfection maintains the cycle in the absence of effective hygiene measures.

Pathogenicity and clinical features

The most prominent symptom of enterobiasis is **intense perianal itching**, especially at night. Scratching leads to disturbed sleep irritability restlessness and secondary bacterial infection of the skin.

In children, chronic infection may cause poor concentration loss of appetite and behavioral disturbances. Occasionally worms may migrate to abnormal sites such as the female genital tract causing vulvovaginitis.

Eosinophilia is usually mild or absent because larval tissue migration does not occur.

Laboratory diagnosis

Diagnosis is made by **demonstration of eggs**, not by routine stool examination. The most reliable method is the **perianal adhesive tape technique**, in which a transparent adhesive tape is pressed against the perianal skin in the early morning and examined microscopically for eggs.

Adult worms may sometimes be seen in the perianal region or in stool.

Treatment and prevention

For educational purpose only

Drug name	Usual oral dose	Duration
Albendazole	400 mg single dose	One day
Mebendazole	100 mg single dose	One day

Repeat dosing after two weeks is often advised in teaching texts to prevent reinfection.

Prevention depends on **personal hygiene measures**, including regular hand washing trimming of fingernails daily bathing washing of clothes and bedding and treatment of all household contacts.

Educational significance

Enterobius vermicularis is an excellent example of a helminth infection related to **behavior hygiene and close contact** rather than environmental contamination. Its study helps students understand direct life cycles auto infection and the importance of non pharmacological preventive measures in parasitic diseases.

Hookworm Infection

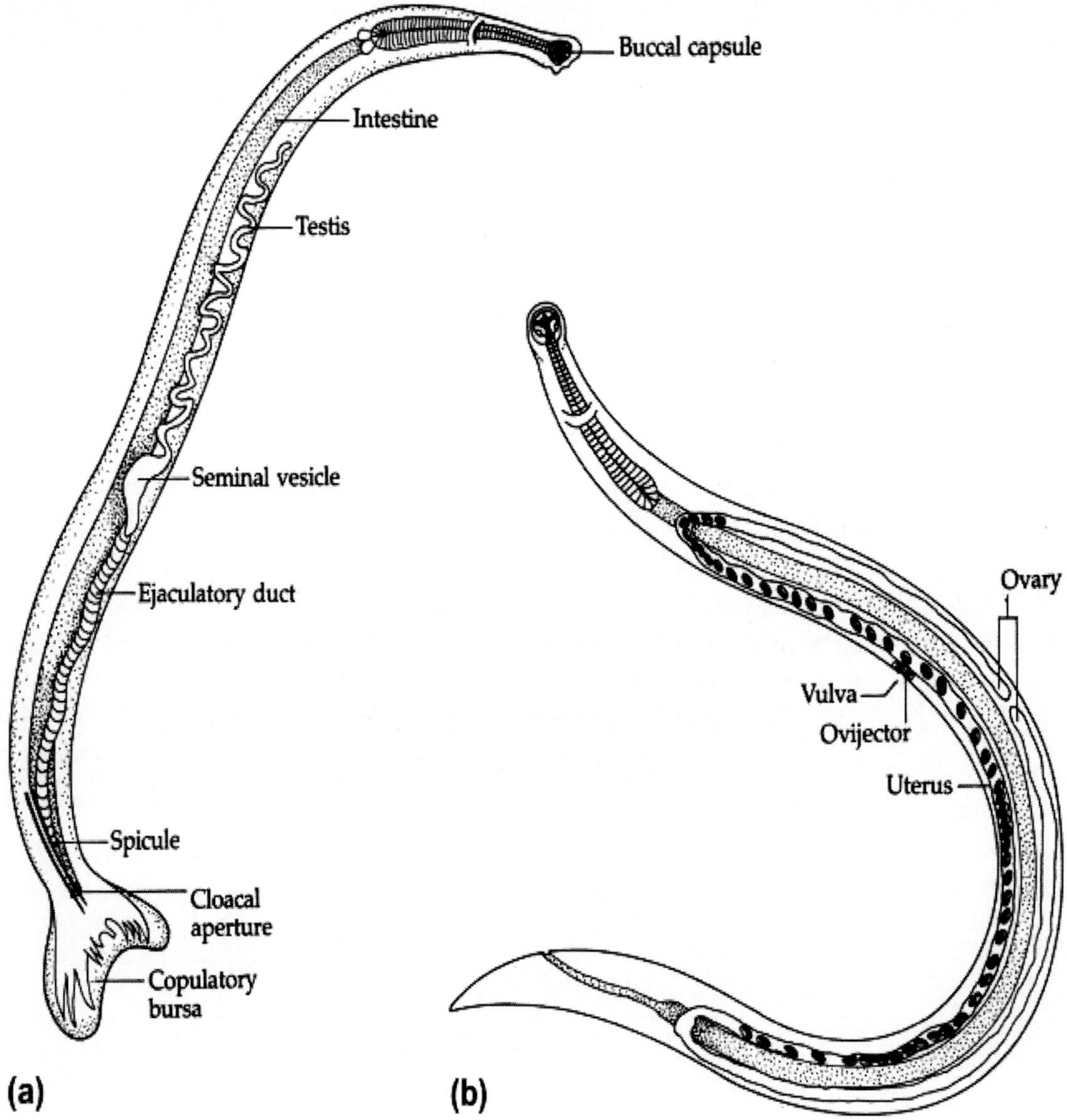

(a) (b)

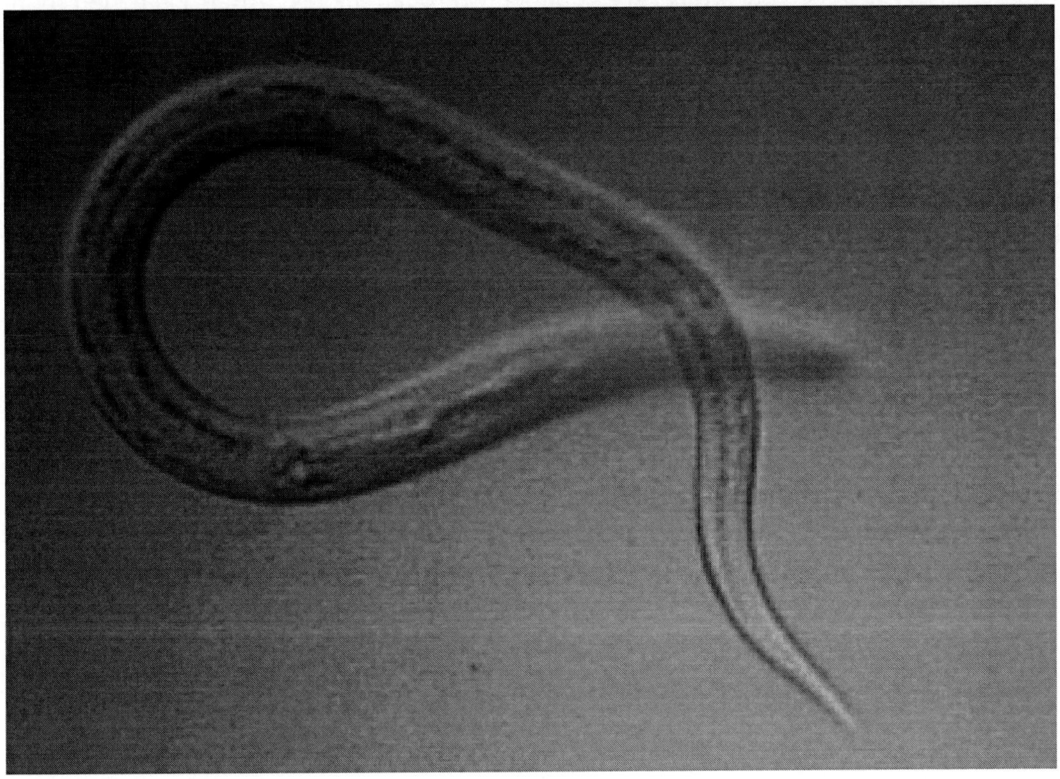

Hookworm infection is an important **intestinal nematode disease** affecting millions of people worldwide, particularly in tropical and subtropical regions. The disease is mainly associated with **poor sanitation barefoot walking and contaminated soil**. Hookworms attach to the intestinal mucosa and feed on blood, leading to chronic blood loss and anemia.

The two principal hookworms infecting humans are **Ancylostoma duodenale** and **Necator americanus**. Adult worms reside in the small intestine where they cause continuous blood loss. Infection is common among agricultural workers miners and children who come in contact with contaminated soil.

Morphology

Adult hookworms are **small cylindrical worms** with a curved anterior end that gives a hook like appearance. The body is grayish white and much smaller than Ascaris.

The anterior end bears a **buccal capsule** adapted for attachment to intestinal mucosa. Ancylostoma possesses teeth within the buccal capsule, while Necator has cutting plates. These structures are responsible for firm attachment and blood feeding.

Sexes are separate. The male is smaller and has a copulatory bursa at the posterior end. The female is larger and produces eggs that are passed in feces.

The eggs are **oval thin shelled and colorless**, containing a segmented ovum. They are usually detected in stool examination.

Life cycle

The life cycle of hookworms is **direct**. Humans are the definitive host. Eggs passed in feces hatch in soil under favorable conditions of moisture and warmth. The larvae develop into **infective filariform larvae**.

Infection occurs when infective larvae **penetrate intact skin**, commonly through the feet. After skin penetration, larvae enter the bloodstream and are carried to the lungs. They migrate through alveoli bronchi and trachea and are swallowed.

Larvae reach the small intestine where they mature into adult worms and attach to the mucosa. Adult worms begin feeding on blood and producing eggs, completing the life cycle.

Pathogenicity and clinical features

Pathogenicity of hookworm infection is mainly due to **chronic blood loss**. At the site of skin penetration, itching and rash may occur, commonly called ground itch.

During lung migration, mild respiratory symptoms such as cough may be seen. The most significant effects occur in the intestinal phase. Adult worms feed on blood and cause continuous bleeding from attachment sites.

Clinical features include **iron deficiency anemia weakness fatigue pallor and breathlessness**. In children, chronic infection leads to poor growth delayed development and reduced learning capacity. Severe anemia may occur in heavy infection.

Laboratory diagnosis

Diagnosis is made by **microscopic examination of stool** showing characteristic hookworm eggs. The eggs of Ancylostoma and Necator are morphologically similar and cannot be differentiated by routine microscopy.

Blood examination often shows **microcytic hypochromic anemia** and eosinophilia, which supports the diagnosis.

Treatment and prevention

For educational purpose only

Treatment aims at elimination of adult worms and correction of anemia.

Albendazole is commonly mentioned in teaching texts as a single oral dose. Mebendazole is an alternative option. Iron supplementation is important in anemic patients.

Prevention

Prevention of hookworm infection is based on interrupting transmission from contaminated soil to humans. This includes the **use of sanitary latrines** and **proper disposal of human feces** to prevent soil contamination with hookworm eggs. **Wearing footwear** is an important protective measure, as it prevents skin penetration by infective larvae present in soil. In addition, **health education** regarding personal hygiene and environmental sanitation, along with **periodic deworming programs** in endemic areas, plays a crucial role in reducing the prevalence of hookworm infection.

Educational significance

Hookworm infection clearly demonstrates the relationship between **parasitic infection nutrition and socioeconomic factors**. Its study helps students understand skin penetration as a mode of transmission chronic blood loss as a mechanism of disease and the importance of environmental sanitation and footwear in prevention.

Trichuris trichiura

Trichuris trichiura commonly known as the **whipworm** is an intestinal nematode parasite of humans. The name whipworm is derived from the characteristic shape of the adult worm, which resembles a whip, with a thin anterior portion and a thicker posterior portion. Infection with this parasite is called **trichuriasis** and is widely prevalent in tropical and subtropical regions where sanitation and hygiene are poor.

Transmission occurs through **ingestion of embryonated eggs** present in contaminated soil food or water. Children are commonly affected because of frequent exposure to contaminated environments and inadequate hand hygiene. Trichuriasis often occurs along with other soil transmitted helminthic infections.

Disease severity depends on the **worm burden**. Light infections may be asymptomatic, whereas heavy infections can lead to significant intestinal symptoms anemia and growth retardation in children. Because of its chronic nature, trichuriasis contributes substantially to long term morbidity rather than mortality.

The study of Trichuris trichiura is important for understanding **soil transmitted helminth infections**, characteristic egg morphology, and the role of sanitation in disease prevention.

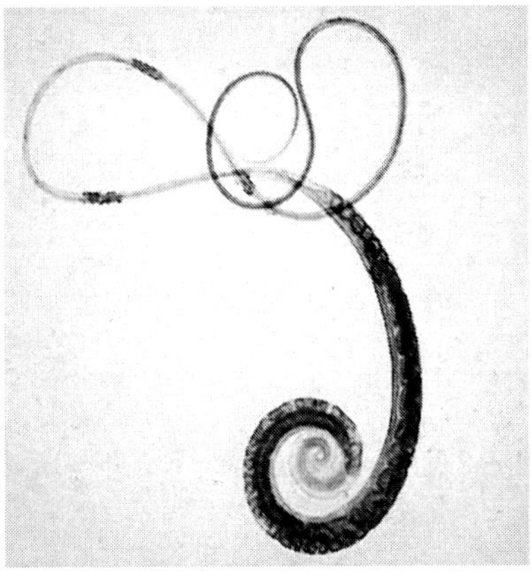

Trichuris trichiura (Eggs)

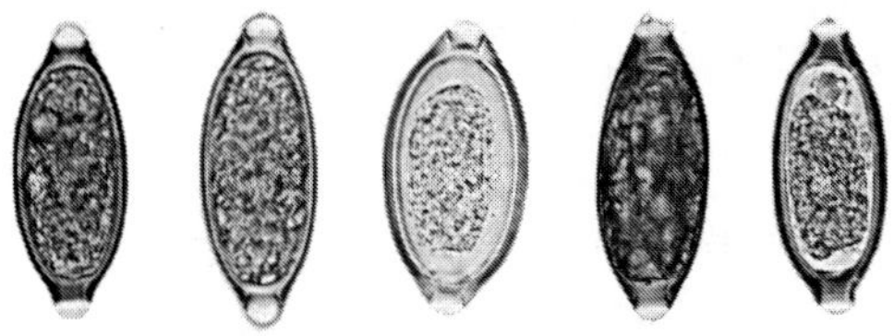

Morphology

TRICHURIS TRICHIURA

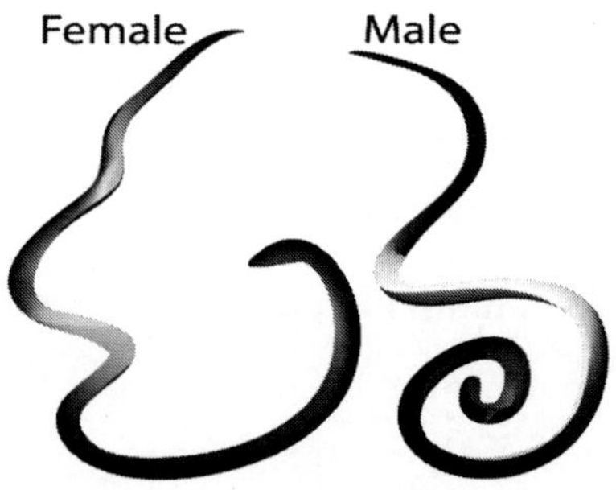

ADULT TRICHURIS TRICHIURA

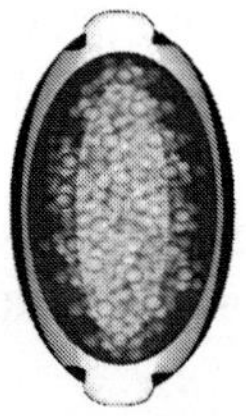

EGG TRICHURIS TRICHIURA

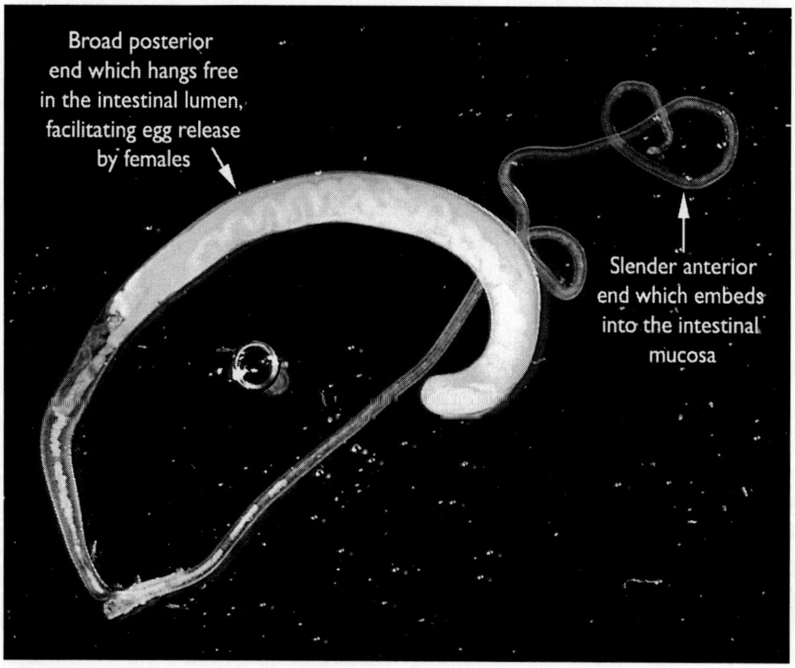

Trichuris trichiura is a **slender whip shaped nematode**, and its morphology is distinctive and useful for identification. The adult worm shows a characteristic division of the body into two unequal parts. The **anterior two thirds** of the body is long thin and thread like, while the **posterior one third** is thicker and broader. This whip like appearance gives the parasite its common name whipworm.

The **adult male** measures approximately **thirty to forty five millimeters** in length. Its posterior end is **coiled ventrally** and contains the copulatory structures. The male is generally smaller than the female.The **adult female** is larger and measures about **thirty five to fifty millimeters** in length. The posterior end of the female is straight and blunt. The female produces a large number of eggs that are passed out with feces.The **anterior thin portion** of the worm is embedded deeply into the intestinal mucosa. This portion contains the esophagus and helps the parasite anchor firmly to the intestinal wall, causing local tissue damage and inflammation.

The **eggs of Trichuris trichiura** are highly characteristic and are of great diagnostic importance. They are **barrel shaped or lemon shaped**, brown in color, and possess **prominent bipolar mucus plugs** at both ends. The shell is thick and smooth. These eggs are unembryonated when passed in feces and require development in soil to become infective.

Thus, the morphology of Trichuris trichiura includes a whip shaped adult worm with clear sexual dimorphism and distinctive eggs with bipolar plugs. Recognition of these features is essential for laboratory diagnosis and understanding of disease pathology.

Life Cycle of Trichuris trichiura

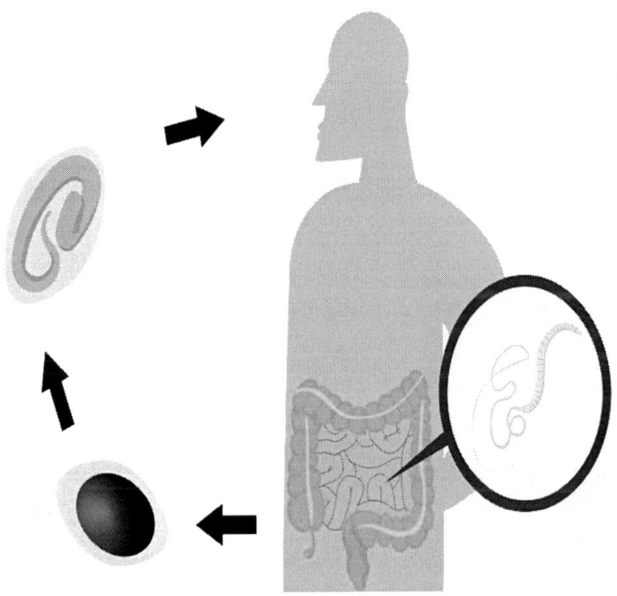

The life cycle of Trichuris trichiura is **direct**, and humans are the only definitive host. No intermediate host is required. Transmission occurs through ingestion of infective eggs present in contaminated soil food or water.

Adult worms live in the **cecum and ascending colon** of humans. Fertilized female worms lay eggs that are passed out with feces. The eggs are **not infective when freshly passed**.When the eggs reach soil under suitable conditions of moisture temperature and oxygen, they undergo development. Inside the egg, the embryo gradually develops into a larval stage. This process takes about **2 to 3 weeks**. The **embryonated egg** containing the larva is the infective stage for humans.

Human infection occurs by **ingestion of embryonated eggs**, usually through contaminated hands food or drinking water. After ingestion, the eggs hatch in the **small intestine**, releasing larvae.

The larvae then migrate to the **large intestine**, particularly the cecum and colon. Here they embed their anterior thin portion into the intestinal mucosa and mature into adult worms. There is **no lung migration** in the life cycle of Trichuris trichiura, which distinguishes it from Ascaris and hookworm.Adult worms may live for several years in the intestine and continue to produce eggs, which are passed in feces and contaminate the environment, thus completing the life cycle.

Educational significance

The life cycle of Trichuris trichiura is important for understanding soil transmitted helminth infections. It explains why poor sanitation and ingestion of contaminated food play a key role in transmission and why respiratory symptoms are absent in this infection. Knowledge of this life cycle helps students correlate intestinal pathology with preventive measures such as hygiene and proper disposal of human waste.

Laboratory Diagnosis

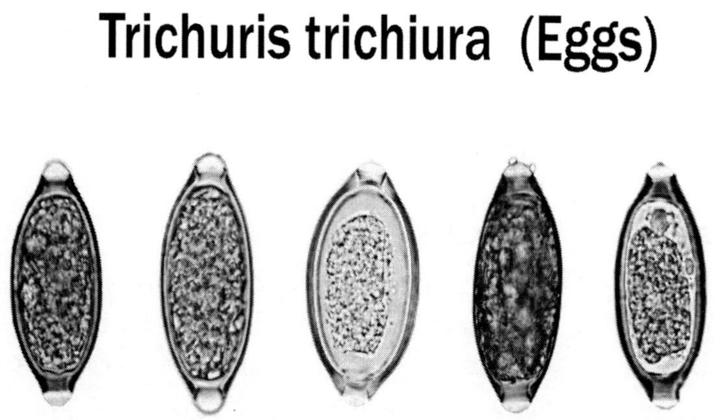

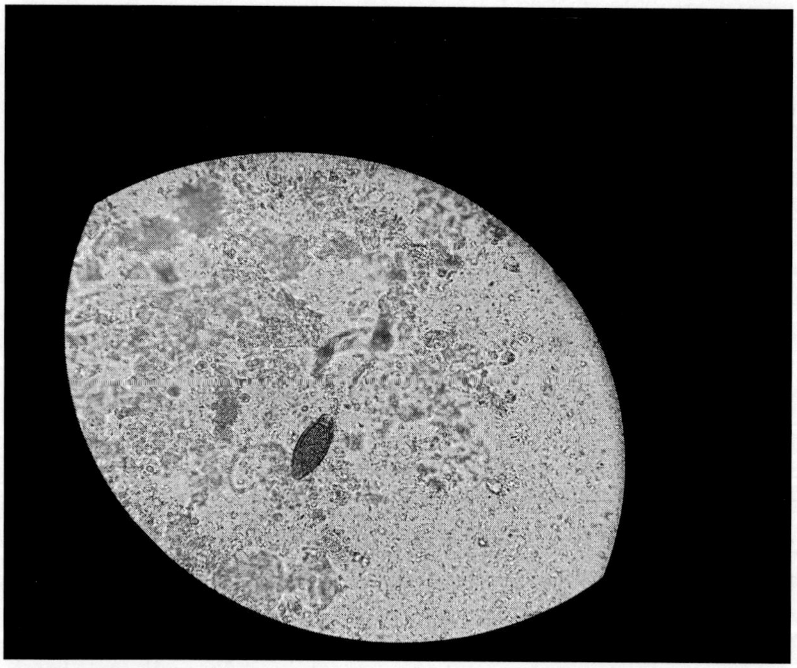

Laboratory diagnosis of trichuriasis is based primarily on **demonstration of characteristic eggs in stool samples**. Because adult worms reside in the large intestine and continuously shed eggs, stool examination is usually reliable in established infection.The **routine stool microscopy** reveals the eggs of Trichuris trichiura, which are highly distinctive. The eggs are **barrel shaped or lemon shaped**, brown in color, and possess **prominent bipolar mucus plugs** at both ends. The shell is thick and smooth. These characteristic features make identification straightforward even at undergraduate level.In light infections, egg output may be low. In such cases, **concentration techniques** improve the sensitivity of stool examination. Repeated stool examination on different days may be required for confirmation.Occasionally, **adult worms may be visualized** during proctoscopic or colonoscopic examination, especially in cases presenting with rectal prolapse. The thin anterior ends of worms may be seen embedded in the mucosa.Laboratory findings may also show **mild anemia** in moderate to heavy infection due to chronic blood loss. Eosinophilia is usually mild or absent because larval tissue migration does not occur in this infection.Thus, laboratory diagnosis of Trichuris trichiura relies mainly on stool microscopy demonstrating characteristic eggs, supported by clinical findings in heavy infection.

Treatment and Prevention

For educational purpose only

Management of trichuriasis aims at **elimination of adult worms**, improvement of nutritional status, and prevention of reinfection. The information below is provided **for academic understanding and teaching correlation**, not for clinical use.

Treatment of trichuriasis

Drug name	Usual oral dose	Duration	Educational note
Albendazole	400 mg once daily	3 days	Commonly mentioned first line drug in teaching texts
Mebendazole	100 mg twice daily	3 days	Alternative option for intestinal infection

In heavy infections, repeated treatment courses may be discussed in textbooks to improve cure rates. Correction of anemia and nutritional deficiency is an important supportive measure.

Prevention

Prevention of trichuriasis is based on **breaking the cycle of fecal contamination and ingestion of infective eggs**. Proper disposal of human feces and use of sanitary latrines reduce soil contamination. Regular hand washing before meals and after defecation is essential, especially in children. Washing vegetables and fruits thoroughly before consumption helps prevent ingestion of eggs. Health education and periodic deworming programs in endemic areas play a major role in reducing disease burden.

Educational significance

Understanding treatment and prevention of Trichuris trichiura helps students correlate parasite life cycle with control strategies. It emphasizes that improvement in sanitation hygiene and community level interventions are as important as drug therapy in reducing soil transmitted helminth infections.

Strongyloides stercoralis

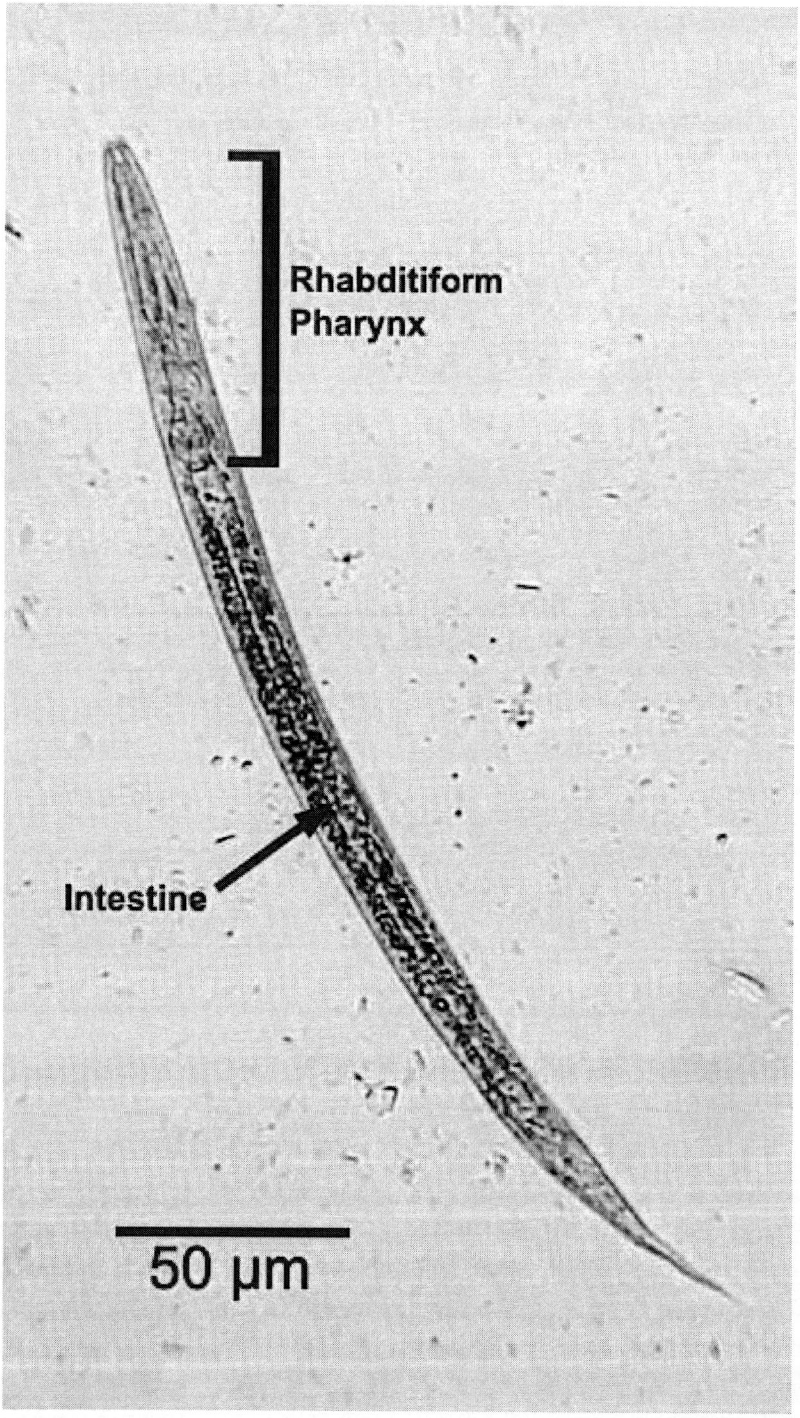

L_1: rhabditiform

b: oral cavity
es: oesophagus
i: midgut
A: anus
gp: genitale Primordium

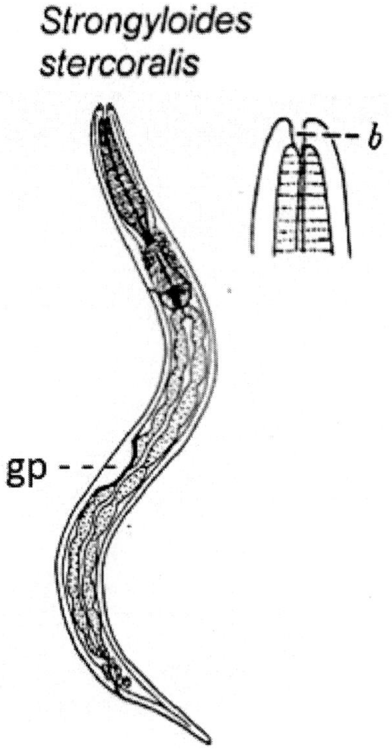

Strongyloides stercoralis is a **small intestinal nematode** of major medical importance because of its **unique life cycle and ability to cause autoinfection**. The infection produced by this parasite is known as strongyloidiasis. It is commonly seen in tropical and subtropical regions and is closely associated with poor sanitation and soil contamination.Unlike most other intestinal nematodes, Strongyloides stercoralis has both a **parasitic cycle in humans** and a **free living cycle in soil**. This biological feature allows the parasite to persist in the environment and also maintain infection within the human host for long periods. Chronic infection may remain asymptomatic for years.

The adult parasitic worm lives embedded in the **mucosa of the small intestine**, particularly the duodenum and jejunum. Only the female worm is parasitic and reproduces by parthenogenesis. Eggs usually hatch inside the intestinal mucosa, releasing larvae rather than eggs into the stool.Transmission occurs mainly through **skin penetration by infective larvae** present in contaminated soil. Barefoot walking is a common risk factor. In some cases, the parasite can complete its life cycle entirely within the human host through **autoinfection**, leading to persistent infection and potentially severe disease in immunocompromised individuals.

Disease manifestations range from mild intestinal symptoms to severe disseminated infection. Because of its ability to multiply within the host, Strongyloides stercoralis is considered one of the most dangerous intestinal nematodes under conditions of reduced immunity.The study of Strongyloides stercoralis is important for understanding **soil transmitted helminths**, autoinfection mechanisms, chronic parasitism, and the interaction between parasitic infection and host immunity.

Strongyloides stercoralis

Morphology

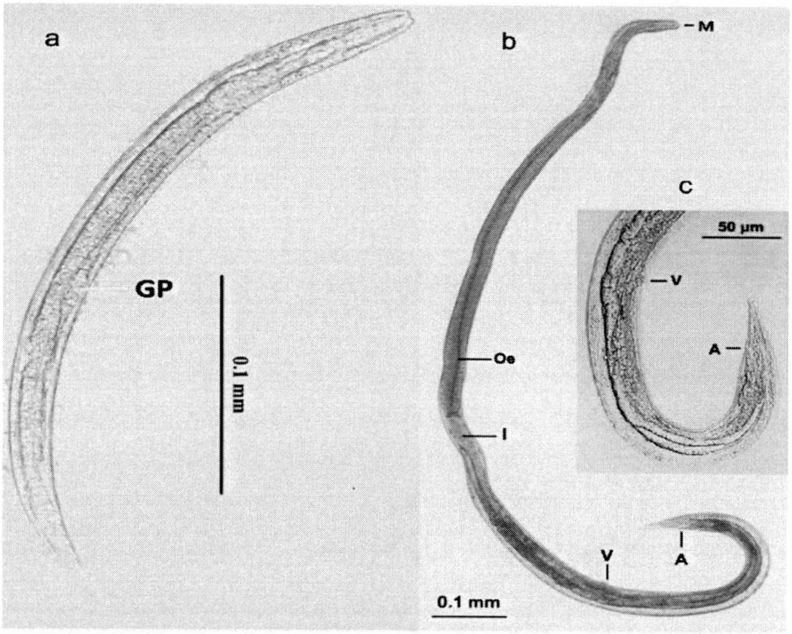

Strongyloides stercoralis is a **small delicate nematode** with distinct morphological features seen in adult and larval stages. The morphology is of great importance because **larvae rather than eggs are detected in stool**, which differentiates this parasite from most other intestinal nematodes.

The **adult parasitic form** is a slender female worm that lives embedded in the mucosa of the small intestine. The adult female measures approximately two to three millimeters in length. The anterior end is tapered, and the posterior end is pointed. The reproductive system is well developed, and reproduction occurs without fertilization. Male worms are not seen in the parasitic stage.

The **rhabditiform larva** is the form commonly found in fresh stool samples. It has a short buccal cavity and a prominent genital primordium. This larval form is non infective and may either develop into infective larvae or continue the free living cycle in soil.

The **filariform larva** is the infective stage. It is longer and more slender than the rhabditiform larva and has a long esophagus. This larva actively penetrates human skin and initiates infection. The filariform larva is responsible for both primary infection and autoinfection.

Eggs of Strongyloides stercoralis are rarely seen in stool because they usually hatch within the intestinal mucosa. Therefore, identification of larvae is the key morphological feature for diagnosis.

Thus, the morphology of Strongyloides stercoralis includes a small parasitic female adult and two distinct larval forms with characteristic features. Recognition of these forms is essential for laboratory diagnosis and understanding the unique biology of this parasite.

Strongyloides stercoralis

Life Cycle

The life cycle of Strongyloides stercoralis is **complex and unique** among intestinal nematodes because it includes **parasitic free living and autoinfection cycles**. Human beings act as the definitive host, and no intermediate host is required.

Adult parasitic female worms live embedded in the **mucosa of the small intestine**. These females produce eggs that **hatch within the intestinal mucosa**, releasing **rhabditiform larvae**. As a result, eggs are rarely seen in stool, and larvae are the diagnostic stage.

The rhabditiform larvae pass into the intestinal lumen and are excreted in feces. Once in the environment, these larvae may follow **two different developmental pathways**. In one pathway, the larvae directly develop into **infective filariform larvae**. In the other pathway, they develop into **free living adult male and female worms** in the soil. These free living adults mate and produce eggs, which hatch into rhabditiform larvae that later transform into infective filariform larvae.

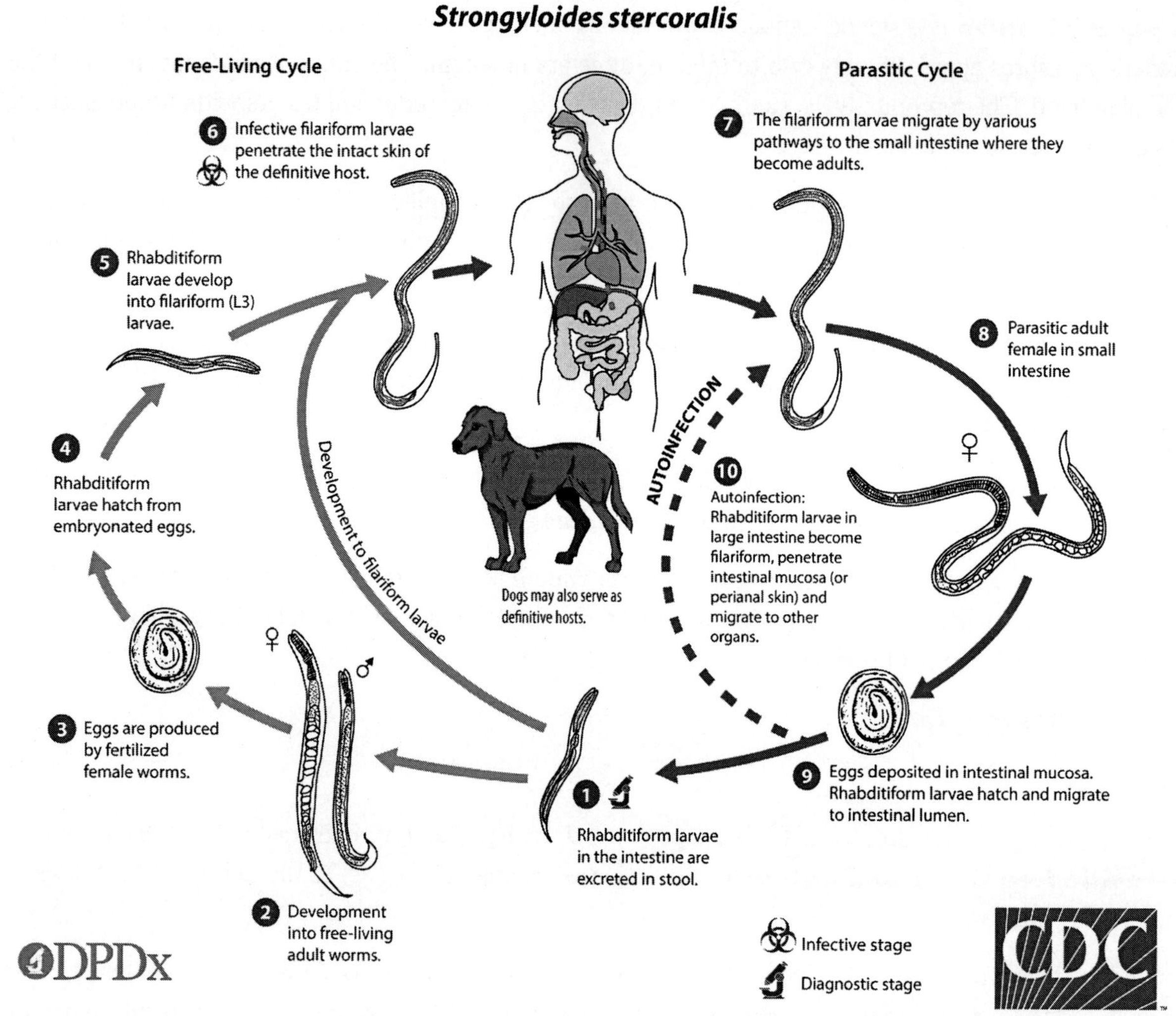

Human infection occurs when **infective filariform larvae penetrate intact skin**, usually through bare feet. After skin penetration, the larvae enter the bloodstream and are carried to the **lungs**. They penetrate the alveoli, migrate up the bronchi and trachea, and are swallowed.

After reaching the small intestine, the larvae mature into adult parasitic females and embed in the intestinal mucosa, completing the parasitic cycle.

A unique and clinically important feature of Strongyloides stercoralis is **autoinfection**. Some rhabditiform larvae transform into infective filariform larvae **within the intestine or perianal region**. These larvae penetrate the intestinal wall or perianal skin and re enter the circulation. Autoinfection allows the parasite to persist in the host for many years and may lead to severe disseminated infection in individuals with reduced immunity.

Educational significance

The life cycle of Strongyloides stercoralis is educationally important because it explains the persistence of infection, the occurrence of autoinfection, and the risk of severe disease in immunocompromised individuals. Understanding this life cycle helps students correlate parasite biology with chronic infection patterns and emphasizes the importance of early detection and preventive hygiene measures.

Pathogenicity and Clinical Features

Disease caused by Strongyloides stercoralis is known as **strongyloidiasis**. The pathogenicity of this parasite is related to **skin penetration by larvae, migration through lungs, intestinal mucosal invasion,** and the unique ability to cause **autoinfection**. Clinical manifestations vary widely from asymptomatic infection to severe life threatening disease.

During the **skin penetration phase**, infective filariform larvae produce local irritation at the site of entry. This may present as itching redness and a serpiginous rash. Repeated penetration during autoinfection can cause recurrent skin lesions.

During **larval migration through the lungs**, patients may develop cough wheezing breathlessness and fever. In some cases, pulmonary infiltrates and eosinophilia are observed. These respiratory symptoms resemble those seen in other nematode infections with lung migration.

The **intestinal phase** is characterized by inflammation of the intestinal mucosa. Adult female worms embedded in the mucosa cause abdominal pain diarrhea nausea vomiting and malabsorption. Chronic infection may result in weight loss and nutritional deficiency.

A distinctive feature of strongyloidiasis is **autoinfection**, which allows the parasite to persist for years. In individuals with normal immunity, infection may remain mild. However, in **immunocompromised patients**, autoinfection may become uncontrolled, leading to **hyperinfection syndrome**. In this condition, large numbers of larvae disseminate to organs such as lungs liver and brain, producing severe systemic manifestations.Eosinophilia is commonly present in uncomplicated infection but may be absent in severe disseminated disease. Secondary bacterial infection may occur due to translocation of intestinal bacteria carried by migrating larvae.Thus, Strongyloides stercoralis produces disease through tissue invasion chronic intestinal infection and autoinfection. Its ability to cause severe disease in immunocompromised individuals makes it one of the most clinically significant intestinal nematodes.

Laboratory diagnosisof Strongyloides stercoralis

Laboratory diagnosis of strongyloidiasis is based mainly on **demonstration of larvae**, as eggs are rarely seen in stool. Accurate diagnosis is important because infection may persist for many years and may become severe in individuals with reduced immunity.The **stool examination** is the most commonly used method. Fresh stool samples may show **rhabditiform larvae**, which are the diagnostic stage. These larvae have a short buccal cavity and a prominent genital primordium. Because larval output may be low and intermittent, repeated stool examination on different days improves detection.

Concentration techniques increase diagnostic yield. The Baermann technique is particularly useful, as it allows active larvae to migrate into warm water where they can be collected and examined microscopically. Agar plate culture is another sensitive method in which larvae migrate over the agar surface, leaving visible tracks.

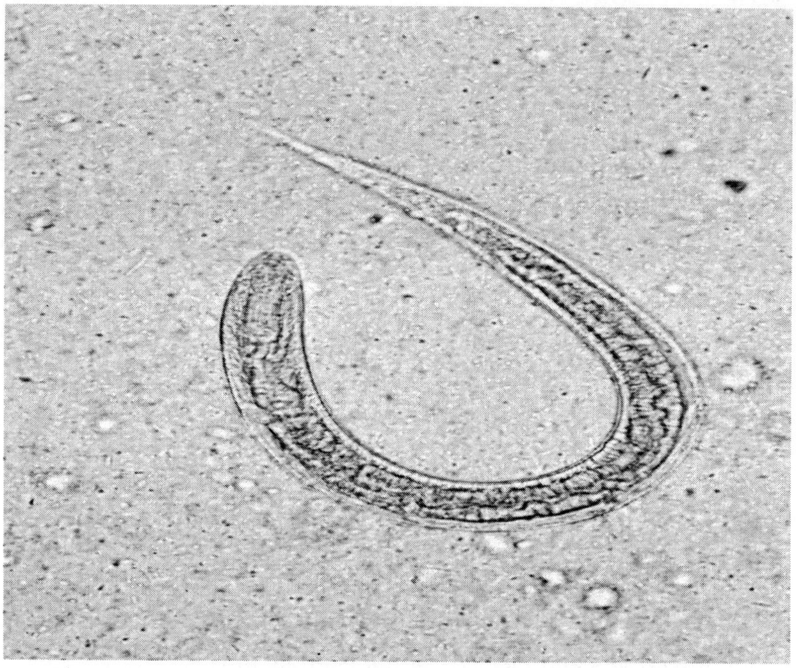

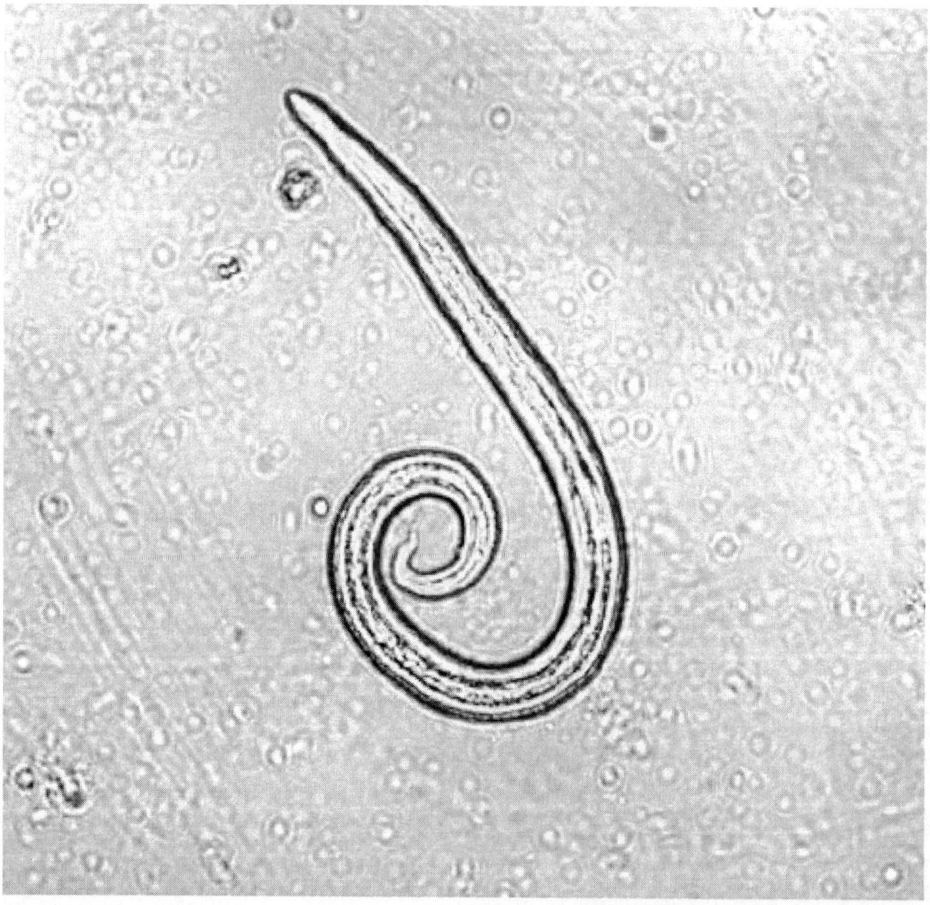

.

During the **pulmonary phase**, larvae may occasionally be detected in sputum in patients with respiratory symptoms. This finding supports the diagnosis but is not routinely used.

Blood examination often reveals **eosinophilia** in uncomplicated infection. However, eosinophilia may be absent in severe disseminated disease, especially in immunocompromised patients.

Serological tests are mentioned in teaching texts as supportive tools, especially in chronic infection when larvae are difficult to demonstrate. These tests help indicate exposure but do not distinguish past from active infection.

Thus, laboratory diagnosis of Strongyloides stercoralis relies primarily on **detection of larvae in stool**, supported by concentration methods and clinical correlation. Understanding these diagnostic principles is essential because early detection prevents severe complications related to autoinfection.

Treatment and Prevention

For educational purpose only

Management of strongyloidiasis aims at **elimination of the parasite**, prevention of autoinfection, and avoidance of severe disseminated disease. The following information is provided **strictly for academic understanding** and **not for clinical use**.

Treatment of strongyloidiasis

Drug name	Usual oral dose	Duration	Educational note
Ivermectin	200 microgram per kilogram body weight	One to two days	Drug of choice mentioned in standard teaching texts
Albendazole	400 mg twice daily	Seven days	Alternative option with lower efficacy

In severe infection or hyperinfection states, prolonged therapy is discussed in advanced textbooks. Management of associated bacterial infection and supportive care are essential in complicated cases.

Prevention

Prevention of strongyloidiasis focuses on **interrupting transmission from contaminated soil and preventing autoinfection**. Use of sanitary latrines and proper disposal of human feces reduce soil contamination. Wearing footwear prevents skin penetration by infective larvae. Health education regarding personal hygiene is important in endemic areas. Screening and treatment of infected individuals before initiation of immunosuppressive therapy is crucial to prevent severe disseminated disease.

Educational significance

Understanding treatment and prevention of Strongyloides stercoralis highlights the importance of early diagnosis because of the parasite's ability to cause lifelong infection through autoinfection. This section helps students appreciate the relationship between parasite biology host immunity and disease severity, and emphasizes preventive strategies in both community health and hospital settings.

Filarial worms of medical importance

Introduction

Filarial worms are **slender thread like nematodes** that inhabit the **blood lymphatic system or subcutaneous tissues** of humans. They are of major medical importance because they cause **chronic disabling diseases**, leading to long term morbidity rather than immediate mortality. Filarial infections are common in tropical and subtropical regions and are closely associated with mosquito transmission.

From a medical zoology perspective, filarial worms are unique among nematodes because they are **vector borne parasites**. Transmission occurs through the bite of infected mosquitoes, which introduce infective larvae into the human host. Inside the human body, adult worms localize mainly in lymphatic vessels or tissues and produce larvae known as microfilariae.Microfilariae circulate in peripheral blood or remain in tissues depending on the species. Their presence and periodic appearance in blood have important implications for **laboratory diagnosis and epidemiology**. Chronic infection leads to obstruction of lymphatic vessels, resulting in conditions such as lymphatic swelling and tissue hypertrophy.Filarial diseases produce significant social and economic burden due to **disfigurement reduced work capacity and psychological impact**. Conditions such as limb swelling scrotal enlargement and recurrent inflammatory episodes are characteristic features of advanced disease.The study of filarial worms is essential for students of life science allied health MBBS and MD courses because it integrates **parasitology vector biology pathology and public health control programs**. This section deals with filarial worms of medical importance in a systematic and simplified manner to build strong conceptual understanding.

Classification of filarial worms

Filarial worms of medical importance are classified mainly on the basis of their **habitat in the human host**, **site of localization of adult worms**, and **circulation pattern of microfilariae**. This classification helps in understanding clinical manifestations laboratory diagnosis and vector control strategies.

Classification based on habitat and site of infection

Group	Site of adult worms	Microfilariae location	Examples
Lymphatic filariae	Lymphatic vessels and lymph nodes	Peripheral blood	Wuchereria bancrofti Brugia malayi
Subcutaneous filariae	Subcutaneous tissues	Skin	Loa loa Onchocerca volvulus
Serous cavity filariae	Body cavities	Peripheral blood	Mansonella species

Explanation

Lymphatic filarial worms inhabit the lymphatic system and are responsible for obstruction of lymph flow. Chronic infection leads to lymphoedema and tissue hypertrophy. Microfilariae circulate in peripheral blood and show periodicity related to vector biting habits.

Subcutaneous filarial worms reside in the subcutaneous tissues. Their microfilariae are usually found in the skin rather than blood. These infections are associated with localized swellings skin lesions and ocular involvement.

Serous cavity filarial worms live in body cavities such as the peritoneal or pleural cavities. Microfilariae circulate in the blood but usually cause milder disease compared to lymphatic filariasis.

Educational significance

Classification of filarial worms provides a clear framework for correlating **site of infection clinical features diagnostic approach and vector transmission**. It helps students understand why different filarial infections present with distinct symptoms and require different methods of diagnosis and control.

Wuchereria bancrofti

Wuchereria bancrofti is the **most important filarial nematode infecting humans** and is the principal cause of **lymphatic filariasis**. The disease produced by this parasite is commonly known as filariasis and is a major public health problem in many tropical and subtropical regions. It causes chronic inflammation and obstruction of lymphatic vessels, leading to progressive swelling and deformity of affected body parts.From a medical zoology perspective, Wuchereria bancrofti is significant because it is a **vector borne helminth** transmitted by mosquitoes. The adult worms reside in the lymphatic vessels and lymph nodes of humans, while their larval forms known as **microfilariae** circulate in the peripheral blood. Transmission occurs when mosquitoes ingest microfilariae during blood feeding and later transmit infective larvae to another human host.The infection is usually acquired in childhood, but clinical manifestations often appear much later. Early infection may remain asymptomatic for years. Chronic disease develops gradually and is characterized by recurrent inflammatory episodes, lymphatic damage, and tissue fibrosis. Advanced stages result in conditions such as **lymphedema hydrocele and elephantiasis**, which cause physical disability and social stigma.

The life cycle of Wuchereria bancrofti involves two hosts, humans as the definitive host and mosquitoes as the intermediate host. This close relationship between parasite biology and vector behavior is essential for understanding disease transmission and control strategies.

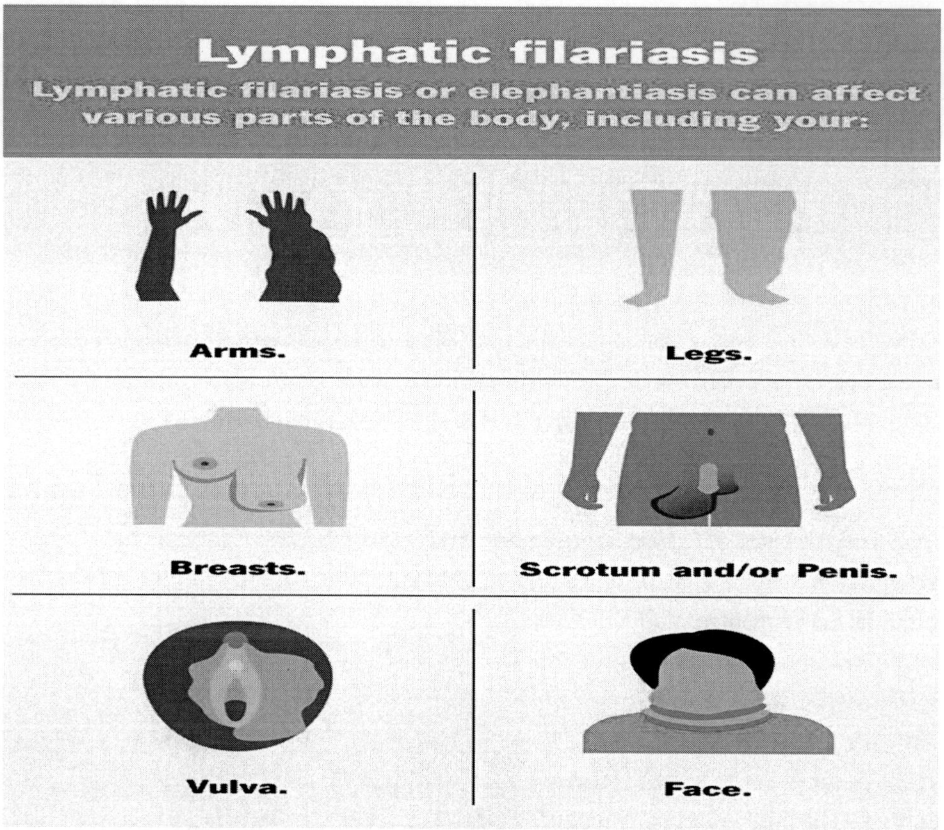

Wuchereria bancrofti

Morphology

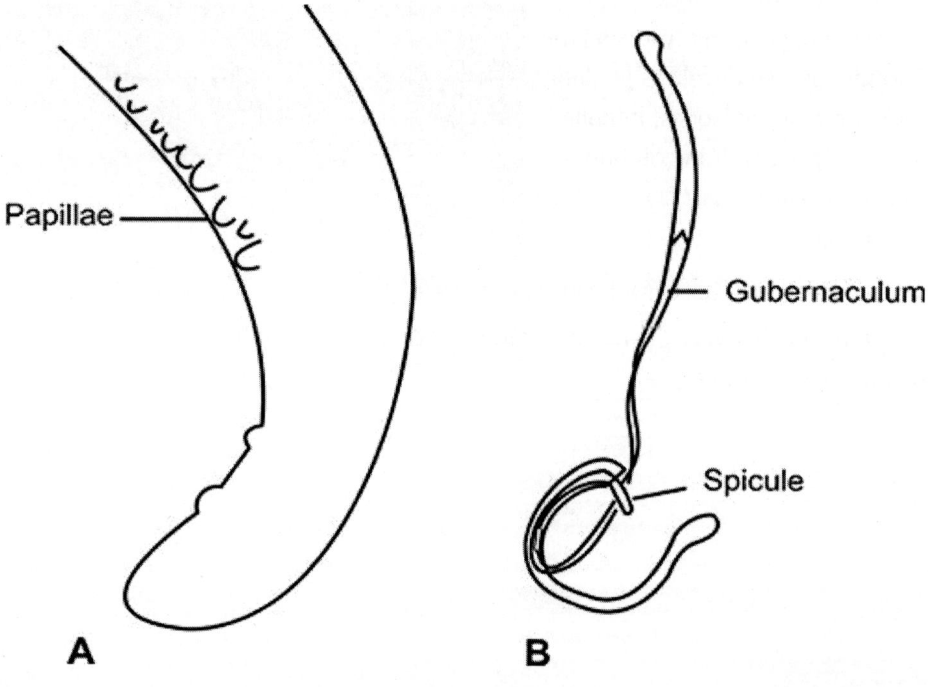

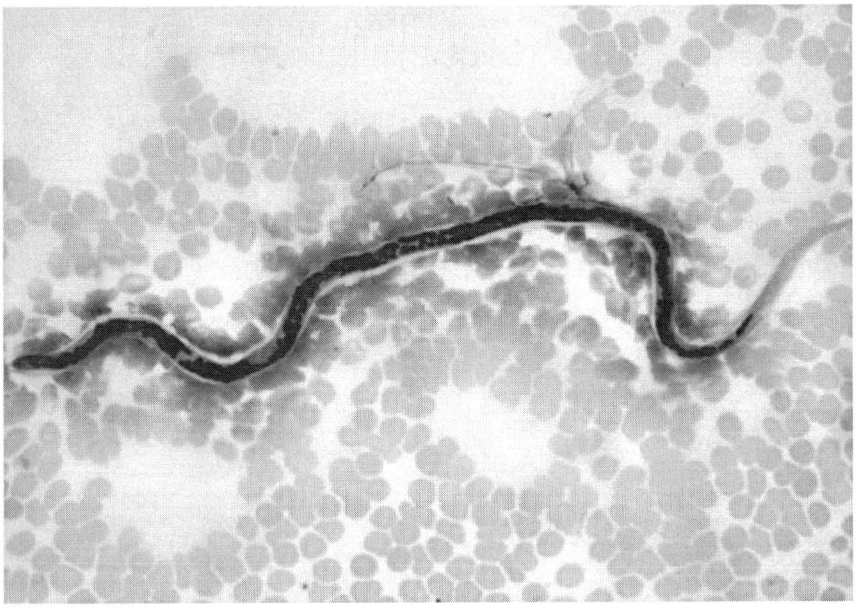

Wuchereria bancrofti is a **slender thread like filarial nematode**. Morphological features are studied mainly in the **adult worms** and the **microfilariae**, as both are important for understanding disease mechanism and laboratory diagnosis.The **adult worms** are long thin and delicate. They are milky white in color and live coiled within the **lymphatic vessels and lymph nodes**. Adult worms are not usually seen in routine clinical practice and are studied mainly from surgical specimens or post mortem findings.The **adult male** is smaller than the female and measures approximately **four centimeters** in length. Its posterior end is curved and contains copulatory structures used during mating.The **adult female** is longer and measures about **eight to ten centimeters** in length. The female produces a large number of larvae called microfilariae, which are released into the lymph and then circulate in the blood.

The **microfilaria** is the most important diagnostic stage. It is a **slender transparent larva** measuring about **two hundred ninety micrometers** in length. The body is gently curved and enclosed within a **delicate sheath**, which is derived from the egg membrane.The microfilaria contains a column of nuclei extending throughout most of the body. A key identifying feature is that the **nuclei do not extend to the tip of the tail**, leaving the tail end free of nuclei. This nuclear pattern helps in differentiating Wuchereria bancrofti from other filarial species.Thus, the morphology of Wuchereria bancrofti includes long thread like adult worms inhabiting lymphatics and sheathed microfilariae circulating in peripheral blood. Recognition of these features is essential for diagnosis and understanding the pathology of lymphatic filariasis.

Wuchereria bancrofti

Life Cycle

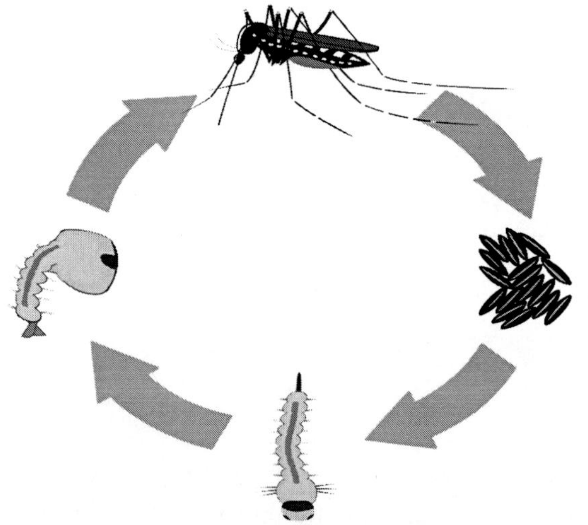

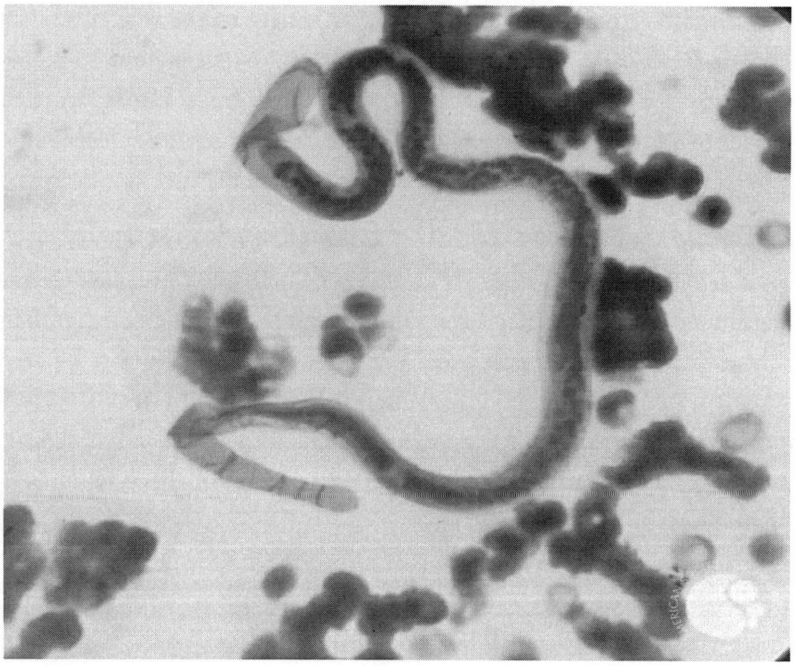

The life cycle of Wuchereria bancrofti is **indirect** and involves **two hosts**, human beings as the definitive host and mosquitoes as the intermediate host. Understanding this life cycle is essential for explaining transmission periodicity clinical features and control strategies.

Life cycle in human host

Adult worms live coiled in the **lymphatic vessels and lymph nodes** of humans. After mating, the gravid female releases large numbers of **microfilariae** into the lymph, which then enter the peripheral blood circulation. These microfilariae do not cause immediate symptoms but are responsible for transmission of infection.A characteristic feature of Wuchereria bancrofti is **nocturnal periodicity**. Microfilariae appear in maximum numbers in peripheral blood during night hours and retreat to deeper vessels during the day. This periodicity corresponds to the night biting habit of mosquito vectors and is important for laboratory diagnosis.

Life cycle in mosquito host

When a mosquito bites an infected person during night hours, it ingests blood containing microfilariae. Inside the mosquito, microfilariae shed their sheath and migrate to the thoracic muscles. Here they undergo development through **first stage larva second stage larva and finally infective third stage larva**.The infective larvae then migrate to the **proboscis of the mosquito**. This developmental process takes about **ten to fourteen days**, depending on environmental conditions.

Transmission to a new human host

During a subsequent blood meal, the infected mosquito deposits infective larvae on the human skin. These larvae actively penetrate the skin and enter the lymphatic system. They migrate to lymphatic vessels where they mature into adult worms over several months, thus completing the life cycle.

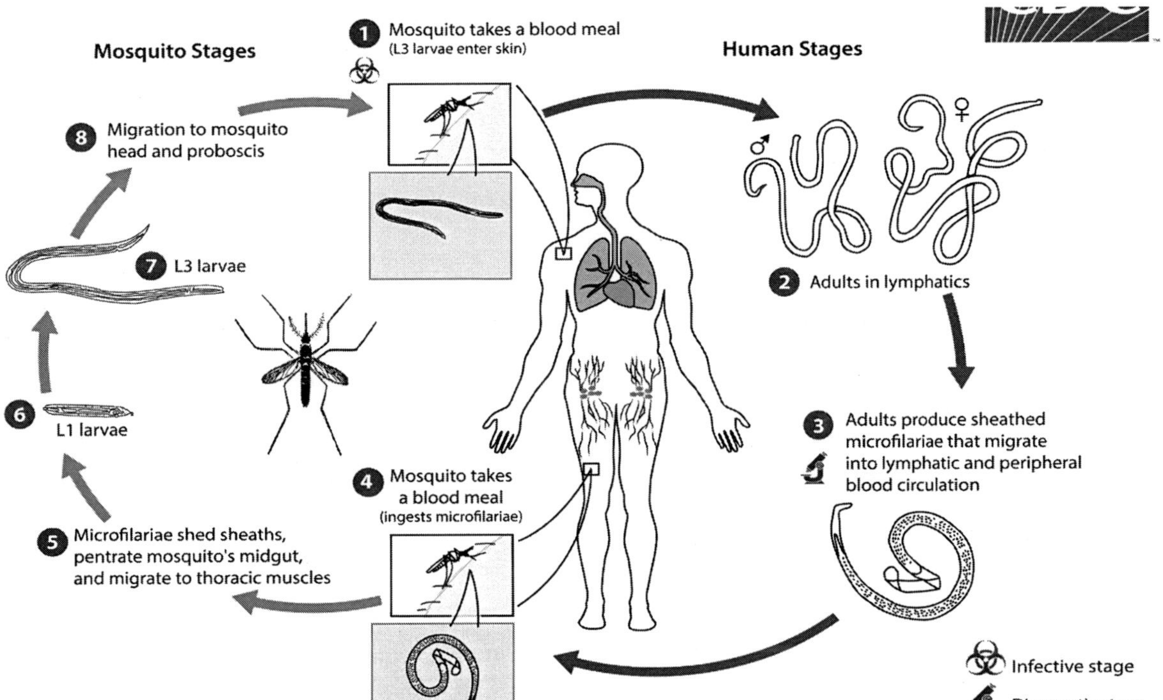

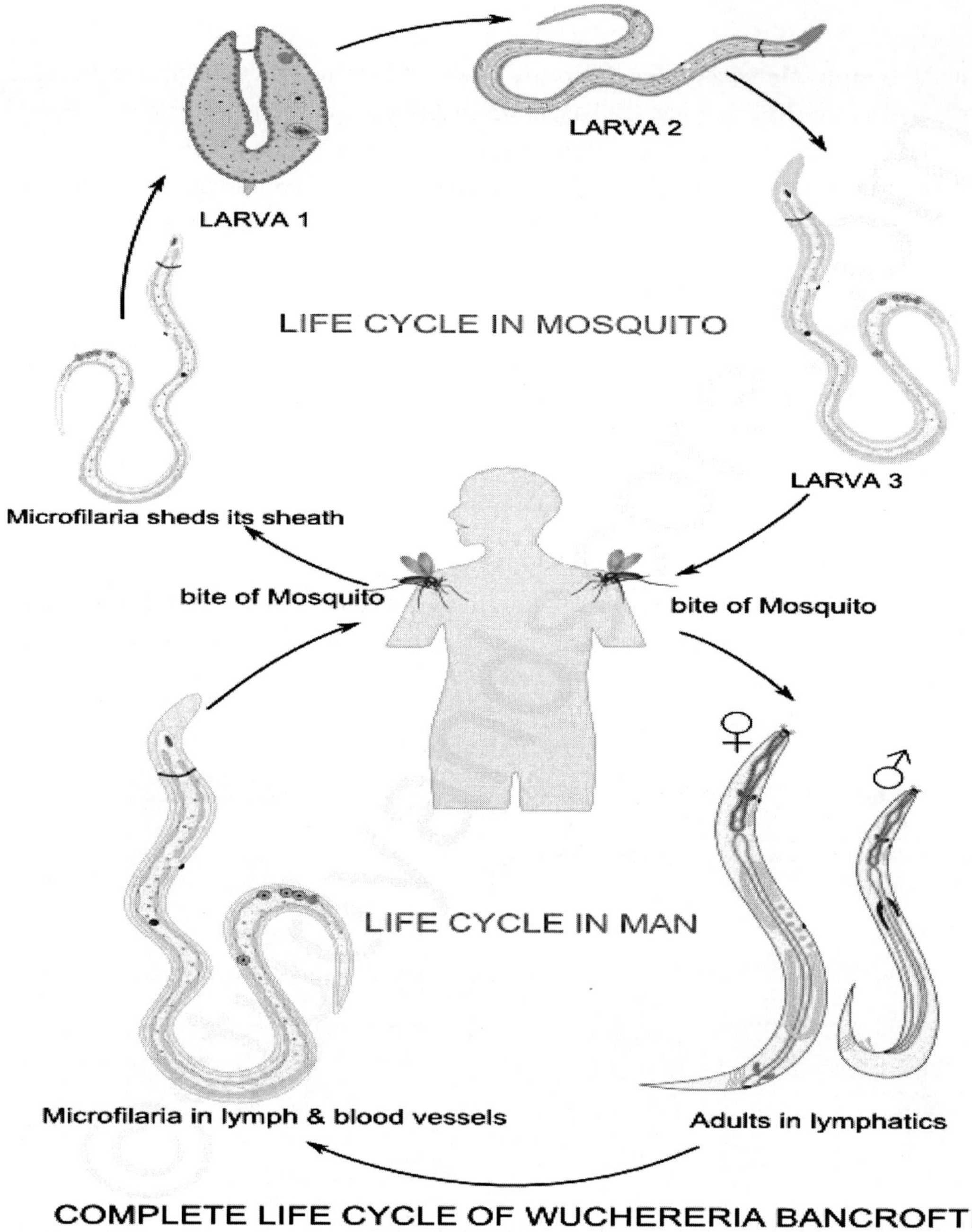

COMPLETE LIFE CYCLE OF WUCHERERIA BANCROFTI

Educational significance

The life cycle of Wuchereria bancrofti explains the role of mosquitoes in disease transmission and the concept of nocturnal periodicity of microfilariae. It helps students correlate parasite biology with diagnostic timing vector control measures and public health programs aimed at elimination of lymphatic filariasis.

Pathogenicity and Clinical Features

Disease caused by Wuchereria bancrofti is known as **lymphatic filariasis**. The pathogenicity of this infection is primarily related to **chronic inflammation obstruction and fibrosis of lymphatic vessels** caused by the presence of adult worms and host immune response. Clinical manifestations usually appear **years after initial infection**, even though infection is often acquired in childhood.

In the **early stage**, many infected individuals remain asymptomatic. However, microscopic damage to lymphatic vessels continues silently. Some patients may experience **acute inflammatory episodes** characterized by fever chills and painful swelling of lymph nodes and lymphatic vessels. These episodes are often referred to as acute filarial lymphangitis.As the disease progresses, repeated inflammation leads to **permanent damage of lymphatic channels**. Obstruction of lymph flow results in accumulation of lymph in tissues, producing **lymphedema**. Commonly affected sites include lower limbs scrotum breasts and arms. Swelling is initially soft but gradually becomes hard due to fibrosis.In advanced stages, long standing lymphatic obstruction leads to **elephantiasis**, characterized by massive enlargement thickening and hardening of skin and underlying tissues. The skin becomes rough nodular and hyperpigmented. These changes are irreversible and cause significant physical disability and social stigma.Male patients may develop **hydrocele**, which is accumulation of fluid in the scrotal sac due to lymphatic obstruction. Recurrent secondary bacterial infections further worsen tissue damage and inflammation.Microfilariae circulating in blood usually produce minimal symptoms. However, immune reactions to dead or dying parasites contribute significantly to tissue damage. Eosinophilia is commonly seen in early stages but may decrease in chronic disease.Thus, Wuchereria bancrofti causes disease through **chronic lymphatic inflammation obstruction fibrosis and immune mediated reactions**. Understanding these pathogenic mechanisms helps students correlate parasite biology with clinical presentation long term complications and the need for early detection and preventive public health measures.

Laboratory Diagnosis

Laboratory diagnosis of Wuchereria bancrofti infection is based on **demonstration of microfilariae**, detection of **filarial antigens**, and supportive laboratory findings. Diagnosis requires correlation with clinical features and timing of sample collection.

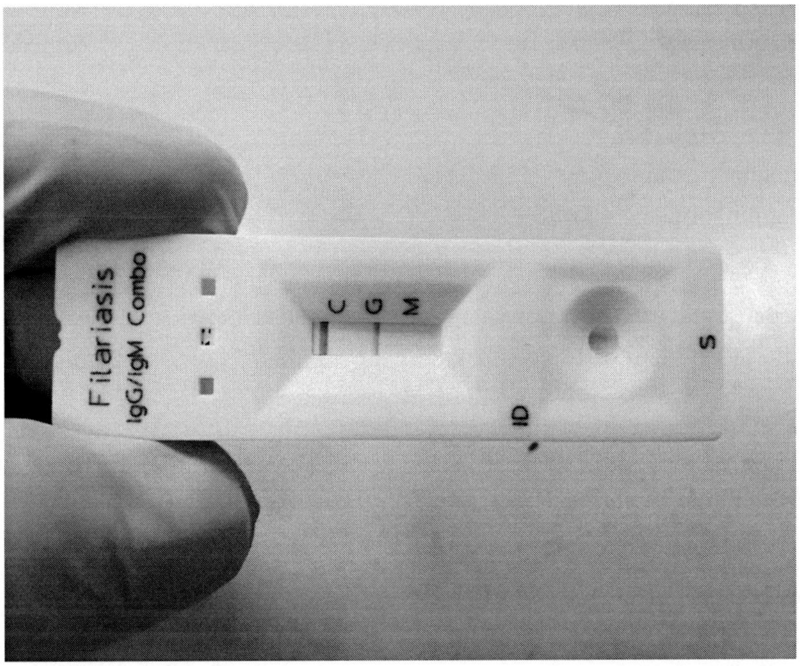

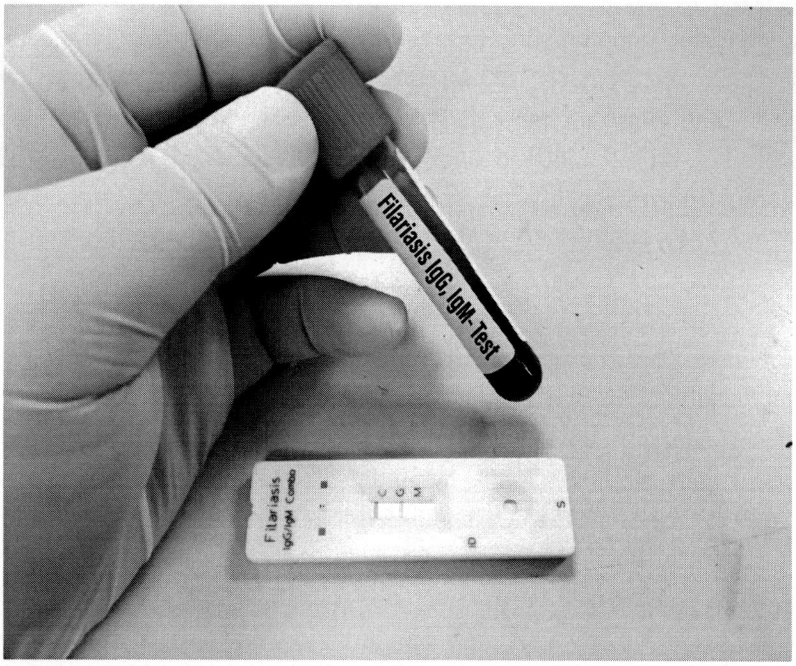

The most classical method is **microscopic examination of peripheral blood**. Blood samples are collected preferably **at night**, because microfilariae show **nocturnal periodicity** and are present in maximum numbers in peripheral circulation during night hours. A stained blood smear reveals **sheathed microfilariae** with a gently curved body and a column of nuclei that do not extend to the tip of the tail. This nuclear pattern is a key diagnostic feature.

In cases where microfilarial density is low, **concentration techniques** improve detection. Thick blood smear examination increases sensitivity. Repeated night blood examinations may be required in suspected cases.

Detection of **circulating filarial antigens** provides an important diagnostic tool. These tests can detect adult worm antigens even in the absence of microfilariae in blood. Antigen detection is particularly useful in chronic cases and in monitoring control programs.

Ultrasonography may demonstrate **movement of adult worms within dilated lymphatic vessels**, a finding often referred to as the filarial dance sign. Although imaging does not replace laboratory diagnosis, it supports confirmation in selected cases.

Additional laboratory findings include **eosinophilia**, especially in early infection. Raised immunological markers may be present but are not specific.

Thus, laboratory diagnosis of Wuchereria bancrofti relies on timed blood examination for microfilariae, antigen detection methods, and supportive imaging findings. Understanding these diagnostic principles helps students correlate parasite biology with clinical practice and public health screening programs.

Treatment and Prevention

For educational purpose only

Management of lymphatic filariasis aims at **reducing microfilarial load**, preventing progression of lymphatic damage, and interrupting transmission. The information below is provided **strictly for academic understanding and teaching correlation**, not for clinical use.

Treatment of lymphatic filariasis

Drug name	Usual oral dose	Duration	Educational note
Diethylcarbamazine	As per body weight	12 days	Reduces microfilariae and affects adult worms
Albendazole	400 mg	Single dose with other drugs	Used in combination therapy in control programs
Ivermectin	As per body weight	Single dose	Reduces microfilarial density

In chronic cases with established lymphedema or elephantiasis, drug therapy has limited effect on existing tissue changes. Supportive care and management of complications are essential.

Prevention

Prevention of Wuchereria bancrofti infection focuses on **breaking the mosquito human transmission cycle** and reducing community microfilarial load. Control of mosquito vectors through elimination of breeding sites use of insecticide treated bed nets and indoor spraying helps reduce transmission. **Mass drug administration programs** play a major role in endemic areas by reducing microfilariae in the population. Personal protective measures such as avoiding mosquito bites and improving housing conditions further support prevention. Health education and community participation are essential for long term success of elimination efforts.

Educational significance

Understanding treatment and prevention of Wuchereria bancrofti highlights the importance of **integrated public health approaches** combining chemotherapy vector control and community participation. This section helps students appreciate why lymphatic filariasis control requires sustained efforts over many years and why early intervention is critical to prevent irreversible lymphatic damage.

Brugia malayi

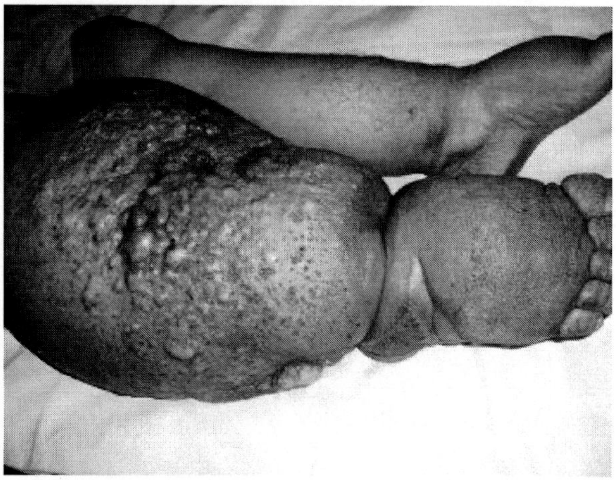

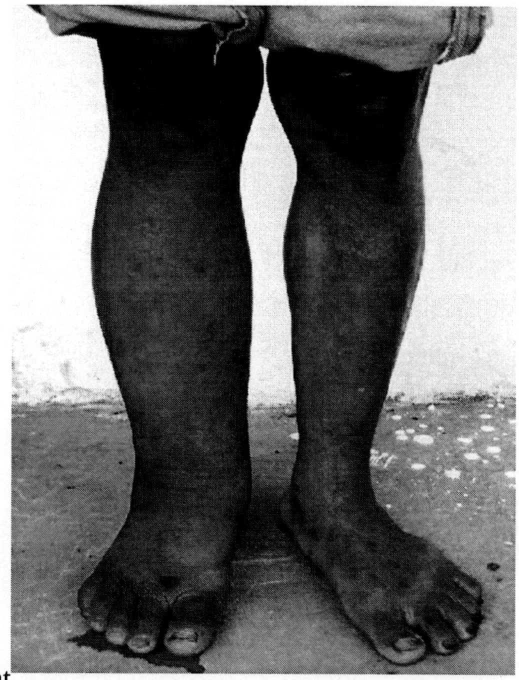

Brugia malayi is an important **lymphatic filarial nematode** that causes **brugian filariasis**, a disease closely resembling infection produced by Wuchereria bancrofti. It is of major medical importance in certain endemic regions of Asia and contributes significantly to chronic lymphatic disease and disability.

From a medical zoology perspective, Brugia malayi is important because it shares many biological and clinical features with other lymphatic filariae, yet shows **distinct morphological and epidemiological characteristics**. Adult worms inhabit the **lymphatic vessels and lymph nodes**, while their larval forms known as **microfilariae** circulate in peripheral blood.Transmission occurs through the bite of infected mosquitoes, particularly species of **Mansonia** and **Anopheles**. As in other filarial infections, humans act as the definitive host and mosquitoes serve as the intermediate host. Infection is usually acquired early in life, but clinical manifestations appear gradually over years.

The disease produced by Brugia malayi mainly affects the **lymphatic system of limbs**. Swelling of lower limbs is common, while involvement of genital organs is less frequent compared with bancroftian filariasis. Chronic infection leads to lymphatic obstruction fibrosis and tissue hypertrophy, resulting in long term morbidity.

The study of Brugia malayi is essential for students because it helps in **comparative understanding of lymphatic filariasis**, differentiation between filarial species, and appreciation of regional variations in disease pattern and vector biology.

Morphology

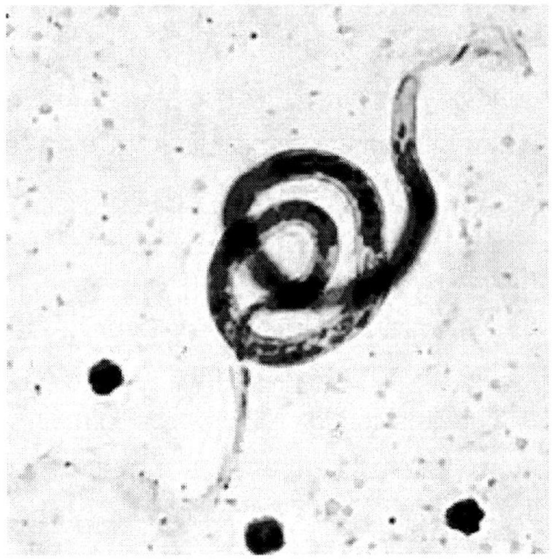

Brugia malayi is a **slender filarial nematode** whose morphology is studied mainly in the **microfilarial stage**, as adult worms are rarely recovered in routine practice. Morphological identification is important for differentiation from other lymphatic filariae.

The **adult worms** are thin thread like and creamy white in color. They reside in the **lymphatic vessels and lymph nodes** of the human host. Adult males are smaller than females. Females are longer and produce large numbers of microfilariae that enter the peripheral circulation.

The **microfilaria of Brugia malayi** is the diagnostic stage. It is a **sheathed larva** measuring approximately **one hundred seventy to two hundred thirty micrometers** in length. The body is gently curved and enclosed in a delicate sheath derived from the egg membrane.A key identifying feature lies in the **nuclear pattern**. The nuclei are arranged in a continuous column but **two distinct nuclei are present at the tip of the tail**, separated from the rest of the nuclear column. This feature is of great importance in differentiating Brugia malayi from Wuchereria bancrofti, in which nuclei do not extend to the tail tip.The microfilariae show **nocturnal periodicity**, appearing in peripheral blood mainly at night. This periodicity corresponds to the biting habits of mosquito vectors and is important for proper timing of blood sample collection.Thus, the morphology of Brugia malayi includes thread like adult worms in lymphatics and sheathed microfilariae with characteristic terminal nuclei. Recognition of these features is essential for laboratory diagnosis and for comparative understanding of lymphatic filariasis.

Life Cycle

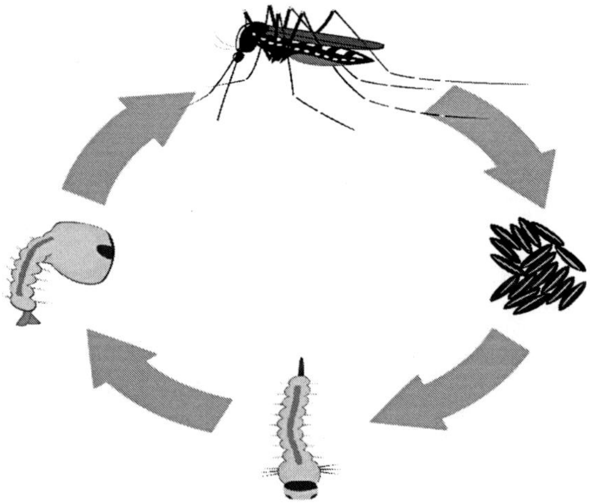

The life cycle of Brugia malayi is **indirect** and requires **two hosts**, human beings as the definitive host and mosquitoes as the intermediate host. The life cycle closely resembles that of Wuchereria bancrofti, with certain epidemiological and vector related differences.

Life cycle in human host

Adult worms live in the **lymphatic vessels and lymph nodes**, mainly of the lower limbs. After fertilization, the female worm releases **microfilariae** into the lymph, which then enter the peripheral blood circulation. These microfilariae show **nocturnal periodicity**, appearing in maximum numbers in peripheral blood during night hours. This periodicity corresponds to the night biting habit of mosquito vectors.Microfilariae circulating in blood do not mature further in humans. They remain infective only for mosquitoes and are responsible for continuation of transmission.

Life cycle in mosquito host

When an infected mosquito bites a human host during night hours, it ingests blood containing microfilariae. Inside the mosquito, the microfilariae shed their sheath and migrate to the thoracic muscles. Here they undergo a series of developmental changes and transform into **infective third stage larvae**.After development, the infective larvae migrate to the **proboscis of the mosquito**. This developmental process takes about **ten to fourteen days**, depending on environmental conditions such as temperature and humidity.

Transmission to new human host

During a subsequent blood meal, the infected mosquito deposits infective larvae on the skin of a human host. The larvae actively penetrate the skin and migrate through tissues to reach the lymphatic system. Over several months, they mature into adult worms within lymphatic vessels, thus completing the life cycle.

Educational significance

The life cycle of Brugia malayi helps students understand mosquito borne transmission of lymphatic filariasis and the concept of nocturnal periodicity of microfilariae. It also explains why vector control and mass drug administration programs are essential components of filariasis control strategies.

Pathogenicity and Clinical Features

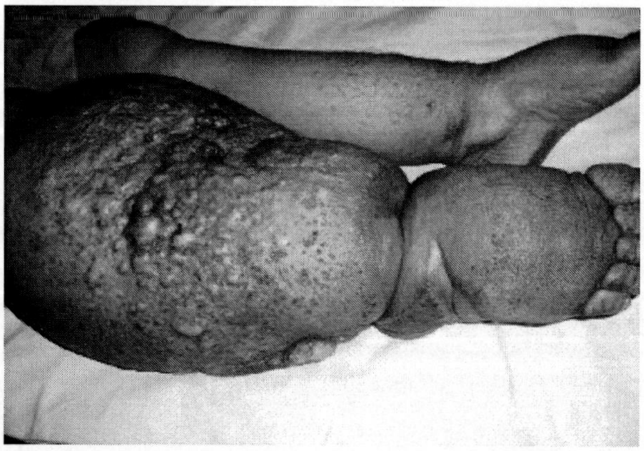

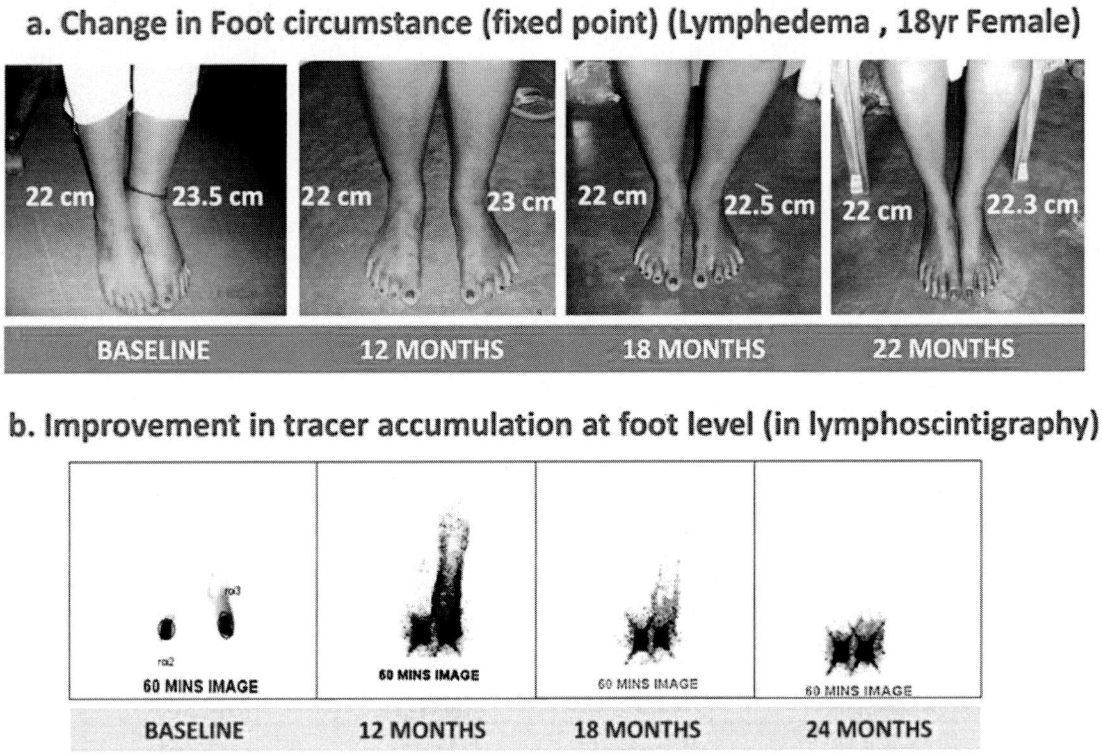

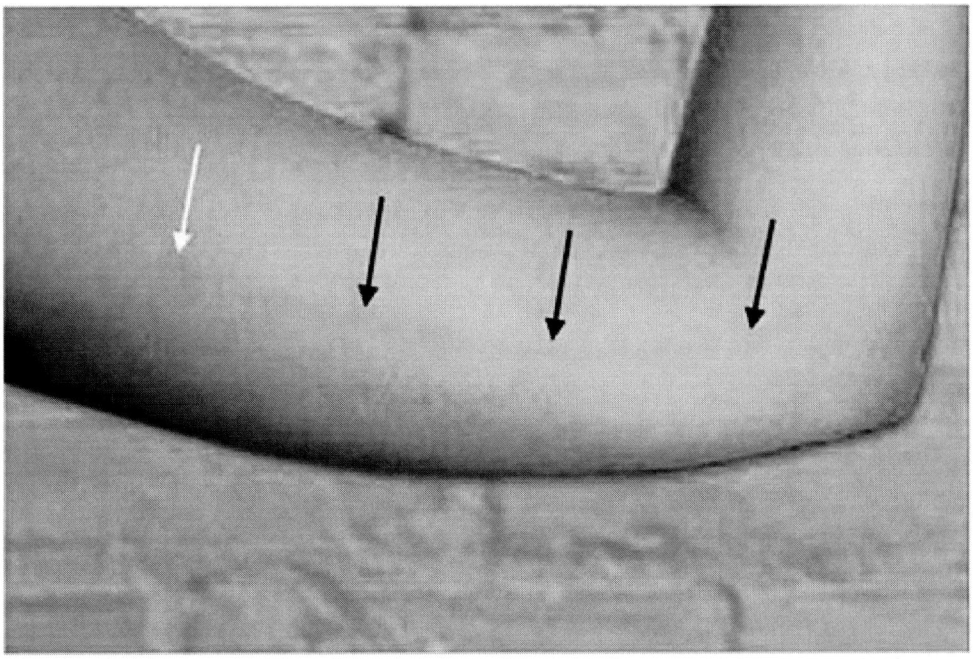

Disease caused by Brugia malayi is known as **brugian filariasis**. The pathogenicity of this infection is mainly due to **chronic inflammation and obstruction of lymphatic vessels** produced by adult worms and the host immune response to the parasite. Clinical manifestations develop slowly and usually appear **years after initial infection**.

In the **early stage**, most infected individuals remain asymptomatic. However, microscopic damage to lymphatic vessels continues silently. Some patients experience **acute inflammatory episodes** characterized by fever pain and tenderness along lymphatic vessels and lymph nodes. These attacks may recur and are often associated with secondary bacterial infection.With progression of disease, repeated inflammation leads to **permanent lymphatic damage**. Obstruction of lymph flow results in **lymphedema**, most commonly involving the lower limbs. Swelling is initially soft and pitting but gradually becomes firm due to fibrosis of tissues.

In advanced stages, long standing lymphatic obstruction produces **elephantiasis**, characterized by gross enlargement thickening and hardening of the affected limb. Skin becomes rough hyperpigmented and nodular. Compared with bancroftian filariasis, involvement of **genital organs is uncommon** in brugian filariasis, which is an important distinguishing feature.Microfilariae circulating in blood usually produce minimal symptoms. However, immune reactions to dead or degenerating worms contribute significantly to tissue damage. Eosinophilia is commonly present in early stages but may be less prominent in chronic disease.Thus, Brugia malayi causes disease through **chronic lymphatic inflammation obstruction fibrosis and immune mediated reactions**. Understanding these clinical features helps students differentiate brugian filariasis from other forms of lymphatic filariasis and appreciate the long term public health impact of the disease.

Laboratory Diagnosis

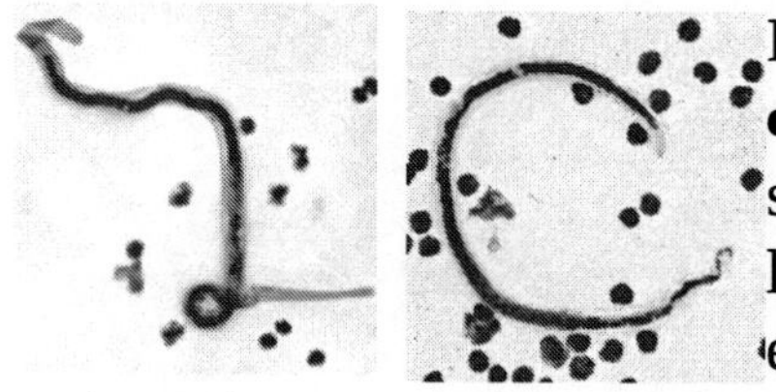

Laboratory diagnosis of Brugia malayi infection is based on **demonstration of microfilariae in peripheral blood**, supported by clinical findings and epidemiological history. As in other lymphatic filarial infections, correct timing of sample collection is essential.

The **peripheral blood examination** is the classical diagnostic method. Because microfilariae show **nocturnal periodicity**, blood samples should be collected preferably **at night**. Microscopic examination of stained blood smears reveals **sheathed microfilariae** with characteristic morphological features.

The most important diagnostic feature is the **nuclear pattern of the microfilaria**. In Brugia malayi, the nuclei extend up to the tail and **two distinct terminal nuclei are present at the tip of the tail**, separated from the rest of the nuclear column. This feature differentiates it from Wuchereria bancrofti, in which the tail tip is free of nuclei.

Thick blood smear examination increases sensitivity, especially in cases with low microfilarial density. Repeated night blood examinations may be required in suspected cases.In chronic cases where microfilariae are absent from blood, diagnosis may be supported by **serological tests** that detect filarial antigens or antibodies. These tests are useful for epidemiological surveys and screening programs but do not always distinguish active from past infection.Additional laboratory findings may include **eosinophilia** in early stages of infection. Imaging studies such as ultrasonography may occasionally demonstrate adult worms in lymphatic vessels, but these are supportive rather than primary diagnostic methods.Thus, laboratory diagnosis of Brugia malayi relies mainly on **microscopic identification of characteristic sheathed microfilariae in night blood samples**, with emphasis on tail nuclear pattern for species differentiation.

Treatment and Prevention

For educational purpose only

Management of brugian filariasis aims at **reducing microfilarial load**, preventing progression of lymphatic damage, and interrupting transmission in endemic areas. The information below is provided **strictly for academic understanding and teaching correlation**, not for clinical use.

Treatment of brugian filariasis

Drug name	Usual oral dose	Duration	Educational note
Diethylcarbamazine	As per body weight	12 days	Reduces microfilariae and affects adult worms
Albendazole	400 mg	Single dose in combination	Used in mass drug administration programs
Ivermectin	As per body weight	Single dose	Effective in reducing microfilarial density

In chronic cases with established lymphedema or elephantiasis, drug therapy has limited effect on existing tissue changes. Management focuses on prevention of secondary infection limb hygiene physiotherapy and supportive care.

Prevention

Prevention of Brugia malayi infection depends on **breaking the mosquito human transmission cycle**. Control of mosquito vectors through elimination of breeding sites use of insecticide treated bed nets and indoor spraying reduces transmission. **Mass drug administration programs** in endemic areas help lower community microfilarial load and prevent new infections. Personal protective measures to avoid mosquito bites improvement of housing conditions and health education play an essential role in long term control.

Educational significance

Understanding treatment and prevention of Brugia malayi emphasizes the importance of **integrated public health strategies** combining chemotherapy vector control and community participation. This section helps students appreciate why lymphatic filariasis elimination requires sustained efforts and why early intervention is essential to prevent irreversible lymphatic damage.

12.Intestinal Nematodes

Introduction

Intestinal nematodes are **roundworms that primarily inhabit the human intestinal tract** and are responsible for a large proportion of helminthic infections in humans. These parasites are of major medical and public health importance because they commonly affect children and contribute to chronic morbidity such as malnutrition anemia growth retardation and reduced learning capacity.

Transmission of intestinal nematodes is closely linked with **poor sanitation and inadequate personal hygiene**. Eggs or larvae passed in human feces contaminate soil food and water, leading to infection of new hosts. Some species infect humans through ingestion of infective eggs, while others enter the body by penetration of larvae through intact skin. Due to this close association with environmental contamination, intestinal nematodes are commonly referred to as soil transmitted helminths.

Biologically, intestinal nematodes have a **simple cylindrical body with a complete digestive system and high reproductive potential**. Adult worms usually live in the intestine, whereas eggs or larvae are passed in feces. In some species, larvae migrate through tissues such as lungs before returning to the intestine, which explains the presence of systemic symptoms in addition to intestinal complaints.

This chapter presents intestinal nematodes in a **comparative and summarized manner**. Detailed morphology life cycle and pathogenic mechanisms have already been discussed briefly in **Chapter 11**. Students should refer to Chapter 11 for descriptive background wherever required.

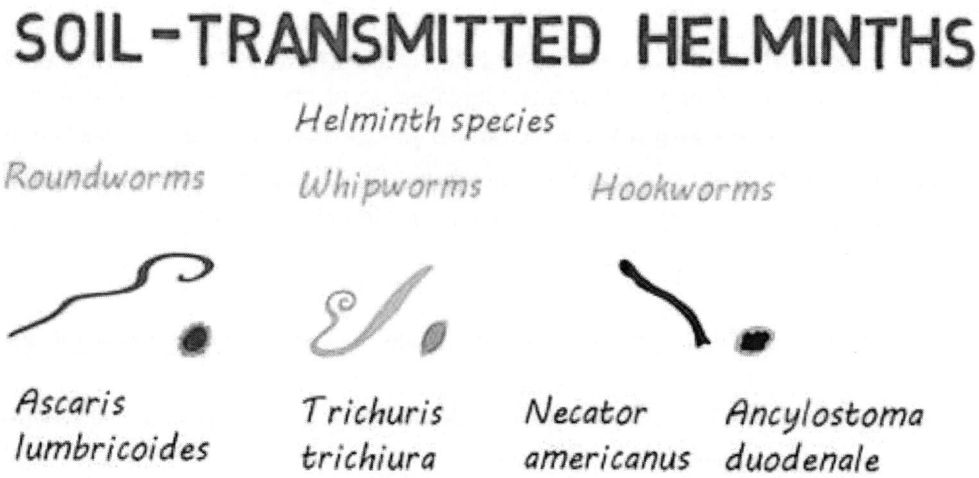

Comparative table of intestinal nematodes of medical importance

Name of parasite	Site of infection	Mode of transmission	Major clinical features	Diagnostic stage	Public health importance
Ascaris lumbricoides	Small intestine	Ingestion of embryonated eggs from contaminated food or water	Abdominal pain malnutrition intestinal obstruction respiratory symptoms during larval migration	Eggs in stool	Highly prevalent soil related infection especially in children
Enterobius vermicularis	Cecum colon and perianal region	Ingestion or inhalation of eggs with auto infection	Perianal itching disturbed sleep irritability	Eggs on perianal skin detected by adhesive tape method	Common household and school related infection
Hookworms	Small intestine	Skin penetration by infective larvae from contaminated soil	Iron deficiency anemia weakness fatigue	Eggs in stool	Major cause of anemia in tropical regions
Trichuris trichiura	Cecum and colon	Ingestion of embryonated eggs from contaminated soil	Chronic diarrhea anemia rectal prolapse in heavy infection	Eggs with bipolar plugs in stool	Chronic infection contributing to malnutrition
Strongyloides stercoralis	Small intestine	Skin penetration by infective larvae with possibility of autoinfection	Abdominal pain diarrhea larva currens hyperinfection in immune suppressed individuals	Larvae in stool	Persistent infection with potential for severe disease

Educational significance

Intestinal nematodes represent a major group of parasitic infections that primarily affect populations living in conditions of poor sanitation and hygiene. Studying these parasites in a comparative manner helps students understand how differences in site of infection mode of transmission and life cycle influence clinical manifestations and public health impact. This chapter emphasizes conceptual clarity rather than repetition of descriptive details, which have already been addressed in Chapter 11. Such an approach strengthens integration between basic parasitology and applied aspects such as diagnosis prevention and control discussed in subsequent chapters.

13.Tissue Nematodes

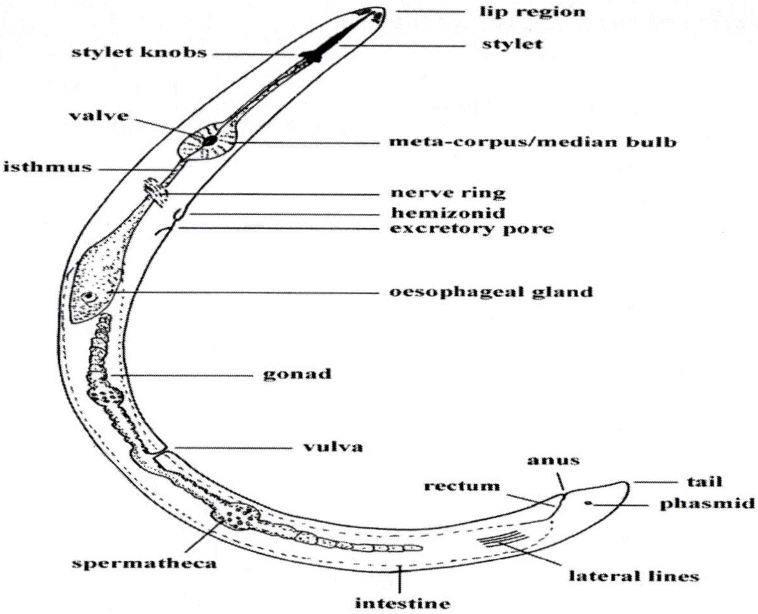

Introduction

Tissue nematodes are **roundworms that primarily inhabit tissues, lymphatic vessels, or body spaces** rather than the intestinal lumen. These parasites are of major medical importance because they produce **chronic progressive disease**, often leading to long term disability, deformity, and social stigma. Unlike intestinal nematodes, tissue nematode infections are usually **vector borne** and develop slowly over many years.

In tissue nematode infections, adult worms are located deep within tissues such as lymphatic vessels or subcutaneous spaces, while their larval forms circulate in blood or remain in tissues. Because of this localization, early infection is often **asymptomatic**, and clinical disease appears only after prolonged lymphatic damage or immune mediated reactions.

From a public health point of view, tissue nematodes are important because they affect large populations in endemic areas and require **community based control measures** rather than individual treatment alone. In India, lymphatic filariasis caused by tissue nematodes remains a significant health problem in many regions.

This chapter presents tissue nematodes in a **comparative and summarized manner**, as their detailed morphology life cycle pathogenicity and diagnosis have already been explained briefly in Chapter 11. Students are advised to refer to Chapter 11 for additional descriptive background where required.

Comparative overview of tissue nematodes of medical importance

Name of parasite	Site of adult worms	Mode of transmission	Major clinical features	Diagnostic stage	Public health importance
Wuchereria bancrofti	Lymphatic vessels and lymph nodes	Bite of infected mosquito	Lymphangitis lymphedema hydrocele elephantiasis	Microfilariae in night blood	Major cause of lymphatic filariasis in India
Brugia malayi	Lymphatic vessels mainly of limbs	Bite of infected mosquito	Limb lymphedema elephantiasis genital involvement uncommon	Microfilariae in night blood	Regional cause of lymphatic filariasis in India

Explanatory note

Both Wuchereria bancrofti and Brugia malayi are **lymphatic tissue nematodes** transmitted by mosquitoes. Adult worms damage lymphatic vessels gradually, leading to obstruction fibrosis and swelling of affected body parts. Microfilariae circulate in peripheral blood with nocturnal periodicity, which has direct relevance for laboratory diagnosis and vector transmission.

Other tissue nematodes such as Loa loa and Onchocerca volvulus are geographically restricted outside India and are therefore not discussed in detail in this text.

Educational significance

Tissue nematodes are responsible for some of the most disabling parasitic diseases due to their chronic course and irreversible tissue damage. Understanding their tissue localization mode of transmission and long term clinical effects is essential for appreciating the need for early detection vector control and community based prevention programs. This chapter provides a concise comparative framework, while detailed descriptive aspects have already been covered in **Chapter 11.** Together, these chapters build a strong conceptual base for advanced topics such as laboratory diagnosis zoonotic infections and prevention strategies discussed later in the book.

14.Cestodes of Medical Importance

Cestodes are parasitic flatworms commonly known as tapeworms. They belong to the phylum Platyhelminthes and class Cestoda under Kingdom Animalia. Cestodes are multicellular, bilaterally symmetrical, and dorsoventrally flattened organisms that are adapted for endoparasitic life within the intestine or tissues of vertebrate hosts.The term cestode is derived from the **Greek word meaning belt or ribbon,** which describes their elongated and flat body structure. Unlike nematodes, cestodes do not possess a cylindrical body. Instead, they are flat and segmented.Cestodes are characterized by the absence of a digestive system. They absorb nutrients directly from the host intestine through their body surface. This adaptation allows them to survive efficiently in the nutrient rich environment of the gastrointestinal tract.

Most cestodes are hermaphroditic, meaning each segment contains both male and female reproductive organs. Their body is divided into three main parts:

1. Scolex
2.Neck
3.Strobila

Some cestodes remain confined to the intestine, while others produce larval stages that invade tissues such as liver, brain, muscles, and lungs. Because of this dual organ localization, cestodes are of major medical importance.From a biological perspective, cestodes are obligate parasites. They cannot complete their life cycle without a host. Most species require one or more intermediate hosts to complete development.Thus, cestodes represent a highly specialized group of helminths that show structural simplification in digestion but extreme development of reproductive capacity and host adaptation.

2. General Morphology of Cestodes

Cestodes show a characteristic ribbon like, segmented body organization. Their morphology is highly specialized for parasitic life.

The body of a typical cestode is divided into three distinct regions:

1. Scolex

The scolex is the anterior end or head of the worm. It is not a true head in the anatomical sense because it does not contain a mouth or digestive organs. Its primary function is attachment to the host intestinal wall.

Depending on the species, the scolex may possess:

• Suckers
• Hooks
• Both suckers and hooks
• Grooves in some species

These attachment organs prevent the worm from being dislodged by intestinal peristalsis.

2. Neck

The neck is a short, narrow, unsegmented region located just behind the scolex. It is the growth zone of the worm.New segments are continuously formed from the neck by a process called strobilation. This allows the worm to increase in length progressively.

3. Strobila

The strobila forms the main body of the tapeworm. It consists of a chain of segments called proglottids.

Each proglottid contains:

- Male reproductive organs
- Female reproductive organs

Thus, each segment is functionally hermaphroditic.

Proglottids are arranged in three stages:

Immature proglottids
Mature proglottids
Gravid proglottids

Gravid segments contain fertilized eggs and detach from the body to release eggs into the environment.

Additional Morphological Features

- Body is dorsoventrally flattened
- Body cavity is absent
- Alimentary canal is absent
- Nutrition occurs by absorption through body surface
- Body is covered by a specialized tegument resistant to digestive enzymes

This structural design reflects evolutionary adaptation for parasitic existence inside the host intestine.

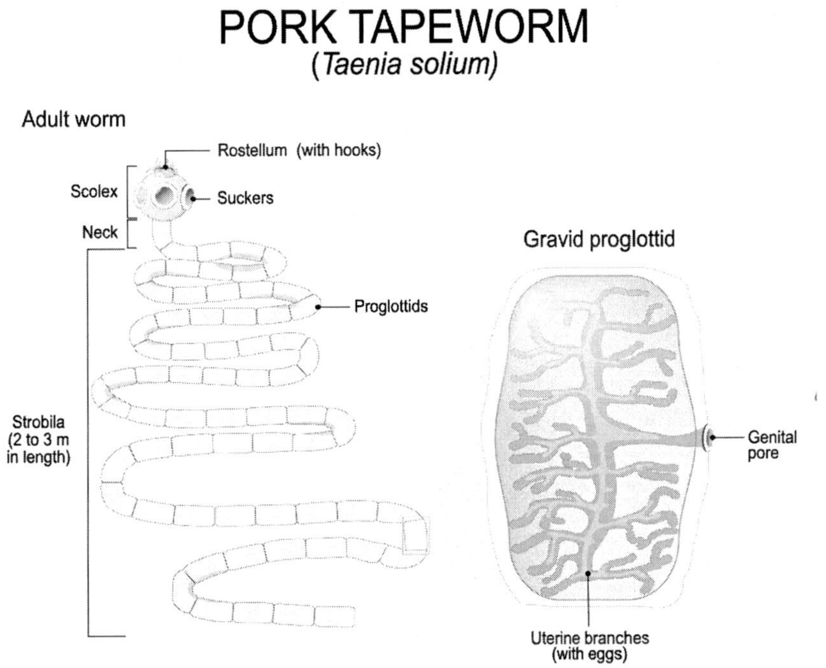

TAPEWORMS

SEXUALLY MATURED PROGLOTTID

GRAVID PROGLOTTID

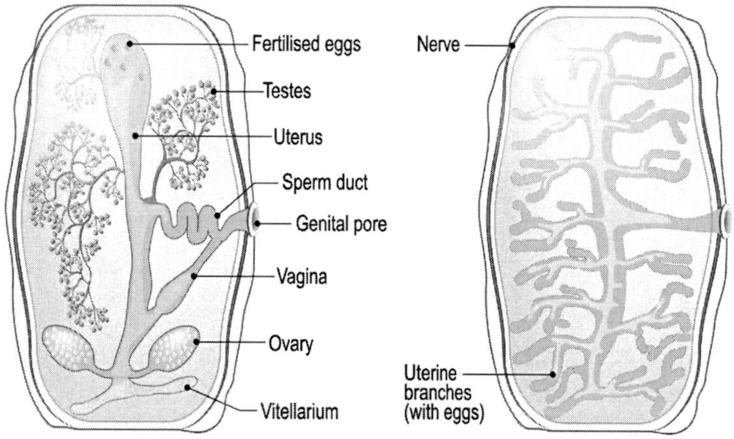

Revise with the help of Diagram

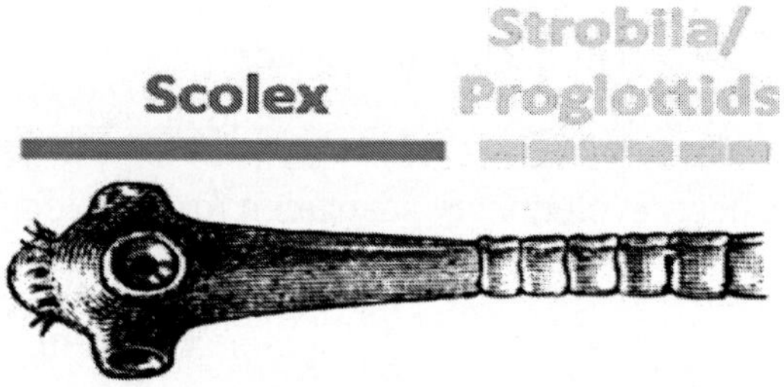

1. **Scolex**
   Attachment organ
   May contain suckers
   May contain hooks in some species such as Taenia solium
   No mouth present
2. **Neck**
   Growth region
   New proglottids formed continuously
3. **Strobila**
   Chain of segments called proglottids
4. **Types of Proglottids**
   Immature segment, reproductive organs not fully developed
   Mature segment, male and female organs well developed
   Gravid segment, filled with fertilized eggs

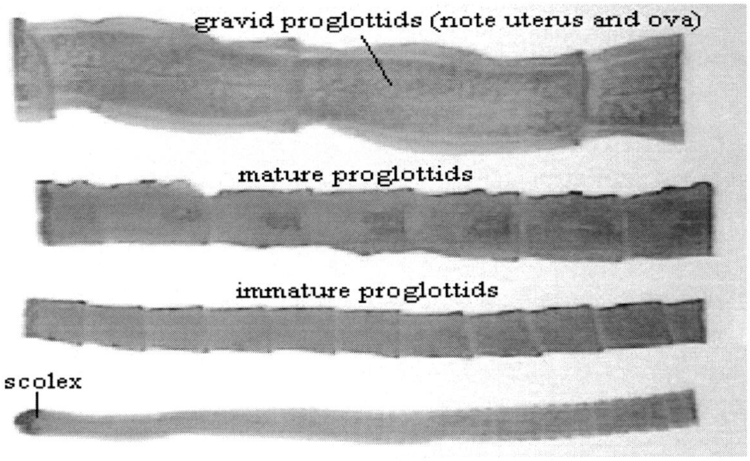

5. **Tegument**
   Specialized outer covering
   Absorbs nutrients directly from host intestine
   Resistant to digestive enzymes

3. Classification of Cestodes

Cestodes belong to **Kingdom Animalia**, **Phylum Platyhelminthes**, and **Class Cestoda**. They are parasitic flatworms characterised by a segmented body and absence of an alimentary canal.

From a medical point of view, cestodes are mainly classified into two important orders:

Order Cyclophyllidea
Order Pseudophyllidea

This classification is based on differences in scolex structure, egg morphology, and life cycle pattern.

Order Cyclophyllidea

This is the most important order in medical zoology.

Characteristics:

• Scolex usually possesses four suckers
• Rostellum may be present and may bear hooks
• Eggs are spherical and non operculated
• Life cycle generally involves one intermediate host
• Larval forms include cysticercus, hydatid cyst, and cysticercoid

Examples of medical importance:

Taenia solium
Taenia saginata

Echinococcus granulosus
Hymenolepis nana

Most medically important human tapeworms belong to Order Cyclophyllidea.

Order Pseudophyllidea

This order differs structurally and developmentally from Cyclophyllidea.

Characteristics:

- Scolex bears two slit like grooves called bothria instead of suckers
- Eggs are operculated
- Life cycle usually involves two intermediate hosts
- Larval stage includes plerocercoid

Example of medical importance:

Diphyllobothrium latum

Presence of operculated eggs and two intermediate hosts are key identifying features of Pseudophyllidea.

Conceptual Understanding

The classification of cestodes is not arbitrary. It is based on structural and developmental differences that influence transmission, organ localisation, and disease pattern.

4. Life Cycle Pattern of Cestodes

The life cycle of cestodes is typically indirect and involves one or more hosts.

Most medically important cestodes require at least one intermediate host to complete their development.

The life cycle can be understood under the following components:

1. Definitive Host

The definitive host is the host in which the adult worm lives and undergoes sexual reproduction.In most human tapeworm infections, **humans act as the definitive host**, harbouring the adult worm in the intestine.Gravid proglottids release eggs into the environment through faeces, thus continuing the transmission cycle.

2. Intermediate Host

The intermediate host harbours the larval stage of the parasite.Eggs ingested by the intermediate host hatch in the intestine and release an embryo called the oncosphere.The oncosphere penetrates the intestinal wall and migrates through the bloodstream to specific organs such as liver, muscle, lungs, or brain, where it develops into a larval form.

The intermediate host plays a crucial role in maintaining transmission in nature.

3. Larval Forms of Cestodes

Different cestodes produce different larval stages. These larval forms are of major pathological importance.

Important larval types include:

Cysticercus
Hydatid cyst
Cysticercoid
Plerocercoid

Each larval form has a characteristic structure and organ localisation.

In many cestode infections, the larval stage produces more severe disease than the adult worm.

4. Modes of Human Infection

Humans may acquire infection by:

- Ingestion of larval cysts in undercooked meat
- Ingestion of eggs through contaminated food or water
- Autoinfection in certain species

Depending on the stage ingested, humans may act as:

Definitive host
Intermediate host
Accidental host

When humans ingest eggs instead of larval cysts, they may become intermediate hosts, leading to tissue infection rather than intestinal infection.

Conceptual Summary

The life cycle of cestodes explains:

Organ localisation
Pathogenesis
Mode of transmission
Public health importance

Understanding the life cycle is essential for diagnosis, prevention, and control of cestode infections.

Taenia solium

Common name, Pork tapeworm

Taenia solium is one of the most medically important cestodes because it can produce both intestinal infection and serious tissue infection in humans.

Taenia solium is unique because humans can act as both definitive and intermediate host.

1. Morphology

Adult worm

The adult worm is long, flat, and segmented, measuring approximately 2 to 7 metres in length.

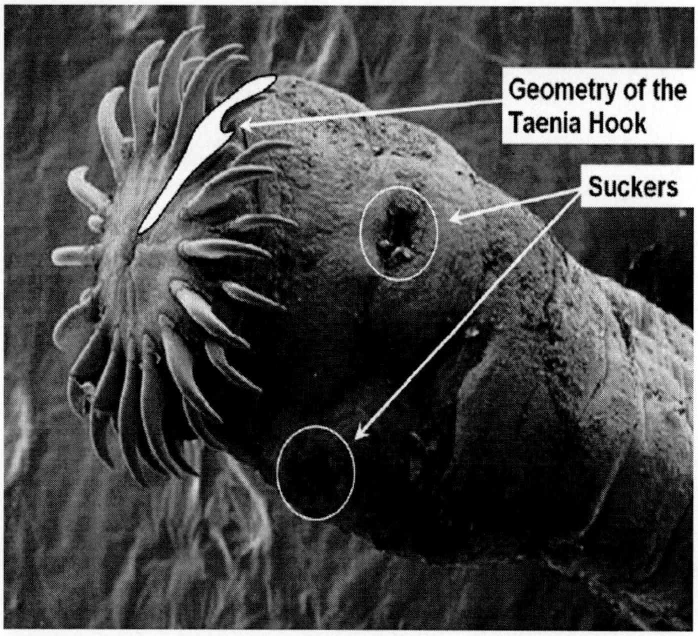

The scolex is globular and contains:

- Four suckers
- A protrusible rostellum
- A double row of hooklets

Presence of hooks on the scolex is the key identifying feature of Taenia solium.

Neck

The neck is short and narrow and acts as the growth region.

Strobila

The body consists of numerous proglottids arranged in immature, mature, and gravid stages.

Gravid proglottids contain a central uterus with 7 to 13 lateral branches on each side.

Number of uterine branches is an important differentiating point from Taenia saginata.

Egg

Eggs are spherical, non operculated, and contain a hexacanth embryo with six hooklets.

Eggs of Taenia solium and Taenia saginata are morphologically indistinguishable.

Taenia solium

Common name, Pork tapeworm

The life cycle of Taenia solium is indirect and involves two hosts.

Humans are the definitive host, and pigs are the usual intermediate host.

Step 1. **Adult worm in human intestine.**

The adult worm resides in the small intestine of humans. Gravid proglottids release eggs that are passed in faeces.

Step 2. **Infection of pig**
Pigs ingest eggs from contaminated food or water. In the pig intestine, the oncosphere hatches, penetrates the intestinal wall, and enters the bloodstream.

Step 3. **Development of larval stage**
The embryo migrates to muscles and develops into a cysticercus, also called bladder worm.

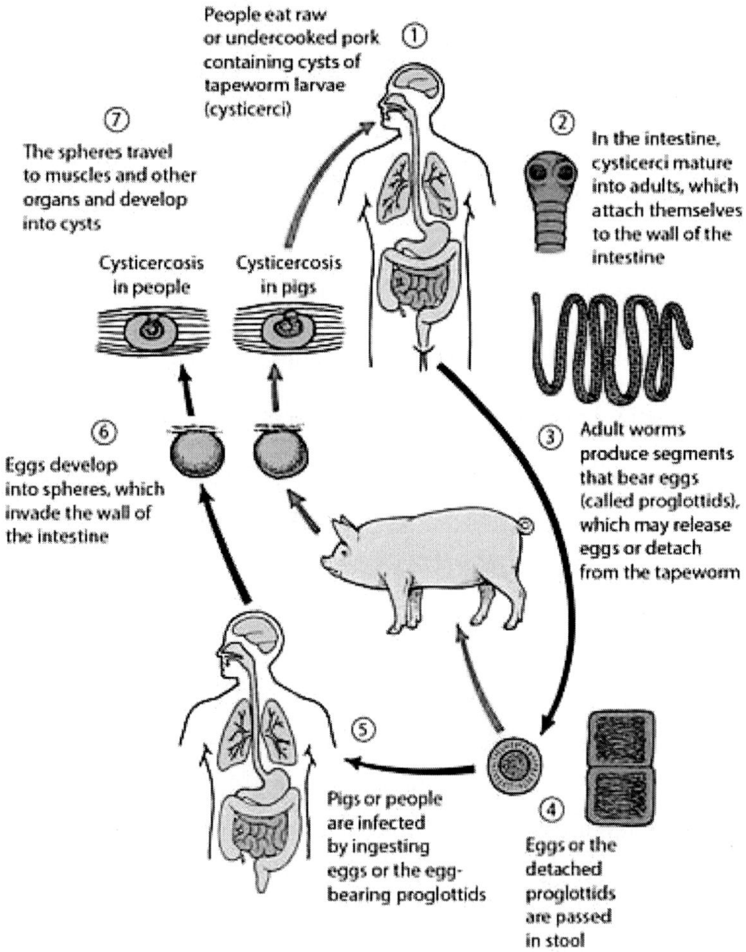

The cysticercus is the infective stage for humans in intestinal taeniasis.

Step 4. **Human infection by undercooked pork**
Humans acquire infection by consuming raw or undercooked pork containing cysticerci. In the small intestine, the cysticercus evaginates, attaches to the mucosa using its hooked scolex, and develops into an adult worm.

Important Clinical Concept

Humans may also ingest eggs directly through contaminated food or by autoinfection.

In this situation, humans act as the intermediate host instead of definitive host.

The oncosphere migrates to tissues and develops into cysticerci in organs such as:

- Brain
- Muscles
- Eyes
- Subcutaneous tissue

When humans ingest eggs, cysticercosis develops instead of simple intestinal taeniasis.Neurocysticercosis is one of the most serious complications and may cause seizures and raised intracranial pressure.

Terminology Related to Taenia solium Infection

Understanding the following terms is essential because **Taenia solium produces two different types of disease depending on the stage ingested.**

Cysticerci

Cysticerci are the larval forms of Taenia solium.

They develop when the oncosphere penetrates the intestinal wall and migrates through the bloodstream to tissues such as muscle, brain, or eye.

A cysticercus is a fluid filled bladder like structure containing an invaginated scolex.

The cysticercus is the infective stage for humans in intestinal taeniasis.

When present in tissues, cysticerci produce the disease known as cysticercosis.

Autoinfection

Autoinfection refers to self infection by ingestion of eggs produced by the adult worm already present in the intestine.

This may occur due to:

- Poor personal hygiene
- Reverse peristalsis carrying gravid proglottids into the stomach

In autoinfection, eggs hatch inside the same individual, and larvae migrate to tissues.

Autoinfection increases the risk of developing cysticercosis in a person already suffering from intestinal taeniasis.

Taeniasis

- Taeniasis is intestinal infection caused by the adult Taenia solium worm.
- It occurs when a person consumes undercooked pork containing cysticerci.

<u>The adult worm attaches to the small intestine and may cause:</u>

- Mild abdominal discomfort
- Nausea
- Altered appetite
- Passage of proglottids in stool

Taeniasis is usually less severe compared to cysticercosis.

Neurocysticercosis

Neurocysticercosis occurs when cysticerci develop in the brain.It results from ingestion of eggs, not cysticerci.

Larvae migrate to the central nervous system and form cysts within brain tissue.

Clinical manifestations may include:

- Seizures
- Headache
- Raised intracranial pressure
- Hydrocephalus
- Focal neurological deficits

Neurocysticercosis is the most serious complication of Taenia solium infection.

It is an important cause of acquired epilepsy in endemic regions.

Pathogenicity and Organ Localisation of Taenia solium

Type of Infection	Stage Ingested	Organ Localisation	Pathogenesis	Clinical Features	Severity
Taeniasis	Cysticercus in undercooked pork	Small intestine	Adult worm attaches to intestinal mucosa using suckers and hooks, causing mild mechanical irritation and nutrient absorption	Mild abdominal discomfort, nausea, altered appetite, passage of proglottids	**Usually mild and often asymptomatic**
Cysticercosis	Eggs from contaminated food, water, or autoinfection	Muscles, subcutaneous tissue, eyes	Oncosphere penetrates intestinal wall, enters bloodstream, and develops into cysticerci in tissues	Painless nodules, muscular discomfort, visual disturbances	**More serious than intestinal taeniasis**
Neurocysticercosis	Eggs	Brain parenchyma, ventricles, subarachnoid space	Larval cysts produce inflammation, oedema, and space occupying lesions	Seizures, headache, raised intracranial pressure, hydrocephalus, focal neurological deficits	**Most severe and potentially life threatening form**

The type of disease depends on the stage of the parasite ingested.

Cysticercus ingestion leads to intestinal infection.
Egg ingestion leads to tissue infection.

4. Laboratory Diagnosis of Taenia solium

The diagnosis depends on whether the infection is intestinal taeniasis or tissue cysticercosis.

Different clinical forms require different diagnostic approaches.

A. Diagnosis of Intestinal Taeniasis

- Specimen
- Stool sample

Methods

- Microscopic examination for eggs
- Identification of gravid proglottids
- Counting of uterine branches in expelled segments

Egg morphology

Eggs are spherical, thick walled, and contain a hexacanth embryo with six hooklets.

Eggs of Taenia solium and Taenia saginata are morphologically indistinguishable.

Therefore, species identification requires examination of the scolex or gravid proglottid.

Diagnostic differentiation

Taenia solium has 7 to 13 lateral uterine branches.
Taenia saginata has 15 to 30 lateral uterine branches.

Counting uterine branches is the most reliable method of differentiation in stool examination.

B. Diagnosis of Cysticercosis

Since cysticercosis is a tissue infection, stool examination is usually negative.

Diagnostic methods include:

- Imaging studies such as CT and MRI for neurocysticercosis
- Serological tests for detection of antibodies
- Biopsy of subcutaneous nodules in selected cases

Neuroimaging plays a crucial role in diagnosing neurocysticercosis.

Conceptual Summary

- Intestinal infection is diagnosed by stool examination.
- Tissue infection is diagnosed by imaging and serology.

The diagnostic approach depends on organ localisation of the parasite.

- Excellent. Now we complete Taenia solium with prevention and control.
- 5. Prevention and Control of Taenia solium
- Prevention is based on interrupting the life cycle at different stages.

Control measures must target both human and pig populations.

1. Proper Cooking of Pork

Consumption of raw or undercooked pork containing cysticerci is the main cause of intestinal taeniasis.

Pork should be thoroughly cooked to destroy larval cysts.

Proper cooking prevents intestinal infection.

2. Personal Hygiene

Egg ingestion occurs due to poor hand hygiene.

Regular hand washing before meals and after defecation is essential.

Good hygiene prevents cysticercosis and autoinfection.

3. Sanitation and Safe Disposal of Human Faeces

Open defecation contaminates soil and water with eggs.

Improved sanitation reduces transmission to pigs and humans.

Sanitation breaks the cycle between definitive and intermediate host.

4. Meat Inspection

Inspection of pork for cysticerci before sale is an important public health measure.

Infected meat should be condemned.

5. Treatment of Infected Individuals

Early detection and treatment of intestinal taeniasis reduces environmental contamination with eggs.

This indirectly prevents cysticercosis.

Conceptual Control Strategy

Prevent ingestion of cysticerci to stop taeniasis.
Prevent ingestion of eggs to stop cysticercosis.

Breaking the life cycle at any stage reduces disease transmission.

Taenia saginata

Common name, Beef tapeworm

Taenia saginata is an intestinal tapeworm of humans transmitted through consumption of undercooked beef.

Unlike Taenia solium, Taenia saginata does not cause cysticercosis in humans.

1. Morphology

Adult worm

The adult worm is long, flat, and segmented, measuring approximately 4 to 10 metres, and may be longer than Taenia solium.

Scolex

The scolex is quadrate and contains:

• Four well developed suckers
• No rostellum
• No hooks

Absence of hooks is the most important distinguishing feature from Taenia solium.

Neck

Short and narrow growth region.

Strobila

Composed of numerous proglottids arranged in immature, mature, and gravid stages.

Gravid proglottid

The uterus contains 15 to 30 lateral branches on each side.

Number of uterine branches is the key differentiating feature during laboratory examination.

Egg

Eggs are spherical, thick walled, and contain a hexacanth embryo.

Eggs are morphologically identical to those of Taenia solium.

2. Life Cycle of Taenia saginata

THE LIFE CYCLE of *Taenia saginata*

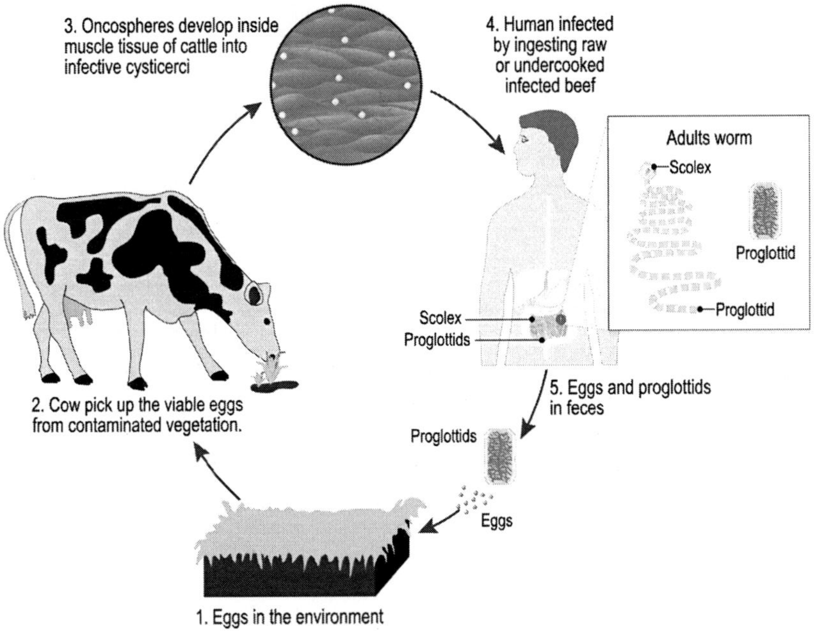

The life cycle of Taenia saginata is indirect and involves two hosts.

Humans are the definitive host, and cattle are the intermediate host.

Step 1. Adult worm in human intestine
The adult worm resides in the small intestine of humans. Gravid proglottids detach and pass out with faeces, releasing eggs into the environment.

Step 2. Infection of cattle
Cattle ingest eggs from contaminated grass or water. In the intestine of cattle, the oncosphere hatches, penetrates the intestinal wall, and enters the bloodstream.

Step 3. Development of larval stage
The embryo migrates to skeletal muscles of cattle and develops into cysticercus bovis.

Cysticercus bovis is the infective stage for humans.

Step 4. Human infection
Humans acquire infection by consuming raw or undercooked beef containing cysticercus bovis. In the small intestine, the larva evaginates, attaches to the mucosa using its four suckers, and develops into an adult worm.

Important Concept

Humans acquire infection only by ingestion of larval cysts in beef.

Ingestion of eggs does not produce cysticercosis in humans in Taenia saginata infection.

Therefore:

Taenia saginata causes only intestinal taeniasis.
It does not produce tissue infection in humans.

Very good. Now we proceed in structured format.

3. Pathogenicity and Organ Localisation of Taenia saginata

Type of Infection	Stage Ingested	Organ Localisation	Pathogenesis	Clinical Features	Severity
Taeniasis	Cysticercus bovis in undercooked beef	Small intestine	Adult worm attaches to intestinal mucosa using four suckers, causing mild mechanical irritation and nutrient absorption	Mild abdominal discomfort, nausea, increased appetite, passage of actively motile proglottids	**Usually mild and rarely produces serious complications**

Important Clinical Points

- The adult worm may grow longer than Taenia solium.
- Proglottids are more actively motile and may crawl out of the anus spontaneously.
- Nutritional deficiency is uncommon.
- Intestinal obstruction is rare but may occur in heavy infection.

Taenia saginata produces only intestinal infection and does not cause cysticercosis in humans.

Conceptual Comparison

Taenia solium
May cause intestinal and tissue infection

Taenia saginata
Causes only intestinal infection

This difference is one of the most important examination points in medical zoology.

4. Laboratory Diagnosis of Taenia saginata

Diagnosis is primarily based on stool examination.

Since Taenia saginata produces only intestinal infection, diagnosis depends on identification of eggs or proglottids in stool.

Specimen

Fresh stool sample
Passed proglottids

Methods

- Microscopic examination for eggs
- Macroscopic examination of expelled proglottids
- Counting uterine branches in gravid segments

Egg Morphology

Eggs are spherical, thick walled, and contain a hexacanth embryo with six hooklets.

Eggs of Taenia saginata and Taenia solium are morphologically identical.

Therefore, species identification cannot be done on the basis of eggs alone.

Differentiation from Taenia solium

The most reliable method is examination of gravid proglottids.

Taenia saginata
15 to 30 lateral uterine branches

Taenia solium
7 to 13 lateral uterine branches

Scolex examination also helps:

Taenia saginata
No hooks

Taenia solium
Hooks present

Counting uterine branches is the most practical method in routine laboratory diagnosis.

Very good observation. Laboratory diagnosis must include a brief procedural explanation. I will present it in concise academic format.

Laboratory Diagnosis of Taenia saginata

Procedural Overview

Diagnosis is made by microscopic examination of stool and by examination of proglottids.

Microscopy is the primary diagnostic method for confirming taeniasis.

A. Microscopic Examination of Stool

Specimen
Fresh stool sample collected in a clean, dry container.

Step 1. Direct smear preparation

A small portion of stool is placed on a clean glass slide.
A drop of normal saline is added.
The material is mixed gently using an applicator stick.
A coverslip is placed over the smear.

The slide is examined under low power and then high power of the microscope.

Purpose
To detect characteristic Taenia eggs.

Step 2. Iodine preparation

A second smear may be prepared using a drop of iodine solution instead of saline.

Iodine enhances internal structures of eggs and improves visibility.

Step 3. Concentration techniques

If eggs are scanty, stool concentration methods such as sedimentation technique may be used.

Concentration increases the chance of detecting eggs in light infections.

B. Examination of Proglottids

When segments are passed in stool, they are washed in saline.

The gravid proglottid is placed between two glass slides and gently pressed to spread the uterine branches.

The segment is examined macroscopically or under low power magnification.

The number of lateral uterine branches is counted.

Counting uterine branches differentiates Taenia saginata from Taenia solium.

Key Diagnostic Points

Egg morphology confirms taeniasis.
Proglottid examination confirms species.

Species identification cannot be done by egg morphology alone.

5. Prevention and Control of Taenia saginata

Prevention focuses on interrupting transmission between humans and cattle.

Control measures must break the cycle between definitive host and intermediate host.

1. Proper Cooking of Beef

Consumption of raw or undercooked beef containing cysticercus bovis is the main cause of infection.

Beef should be thoroughly cooked before consumption.

Proper cooking destroys cysticerci and prevents taeniasis.

2. Sanitation and Safe Disposal of Human Faeces

Open defecation contaminates pasture land with eggs.

Cattle become infected by grazing on contaminated grass.

Improved sanitation prevents transmission to cattle.

Sanitation prevents continuation of the life cycle.

3. Meat Inspection

Routine inspection of beef in slaughterhouses is essential.

Infected meat should be condemned or properly treated.

4. Health Education

Public awareness regarding safe meat consumption and hygiene practices is important in endemic areas.

5. Early Detection and Treatment

Identification and treatment of infected individuals reduce environmental contamination with eggs.

Treatment of Taenia solium and Taenia saginata

Infection	Causative Organism	Type of Disease	General Treatment Approach	Important Note
Intestinal taeniasis	Taenia solium	Adult worm in intestine	Treated with antihelminthic drugs such as praziquantel or niclosamide	**Usually simple and highly effective treatment**
Cysticercosis	Taenia solium	Tissue infection by larval cysticerci	Requires prolonged antihelminthic therapy under specialist supervision, often combined with anti inflammatory management	**Management depends on organ involvement, especially brain involvement**
Neurocysticercosis	Taenia solium	Brain involvement	Antihelminthic therapy with corticosteroid support and neuroimaging guided management	**Serious condition requiring specialist care**
Intestinal taeniasis	Taenia saginata	Adult worm in intestine	Treated with antihelminthic drugs such as praziquantel or niclosamide	**Does not cause cysticercosis in humans**

Key Academic Points

• Treatment of intestinal taeniasis is straightforward.
• Tissue infection in Taenia solium requires careful evaluation.
• Taenia saginata produces only intestinal disease.

The major therapeutic difference lies in the ability of Taenia solium **to produce cysticercosis.**

Academic Note

The above treatment information is provided **only for educational and academic understanding** of disease management principles in medical zoology.It is **not intended for clinical prescription, self medication, or therapeutic use.**Clinical management must always be performed by qualified medical professionals.

Echinococcus granulosus

Common name, Dog tapeworm

Echinococcus granulosus is a small tapeworm of dogs that produces hydatid disease in humans.

Humans act as accidental intermediate hosts in this infection.

Unlike Taenia species, the adult worm does not develop in humans.

1. Morphology

Adult worm

The adult worm is very small, measuring only 3 to 6 millimetres in length.

It consists of:

Scolex
Short neck
Only three proglottids

Immature segment
Mature segment
Gravid segment

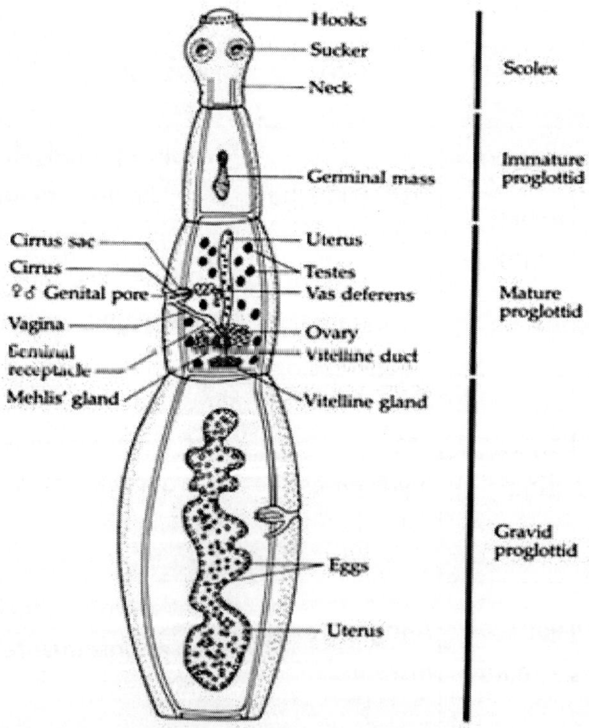

The presence of only three segments is a key identifying feature.

Scolex

The scolex contains:

- Four suckers
- A rostellum with hooks

Thus it resembles Taenia solium in having hooks, but is much smaller in size.

Egg

Eggs are spherical and morphologically identical to those of Taenia species.

Egg morphology alone cannot differentiate Echinococcus **from** Taenia**.**

Larval form

The larval stage is called the hydatid cyst.

This stage develops in intermediate hosts such as sheep, cattle, and humans.

The hydatid cyst is the pathogenic stage in humans.

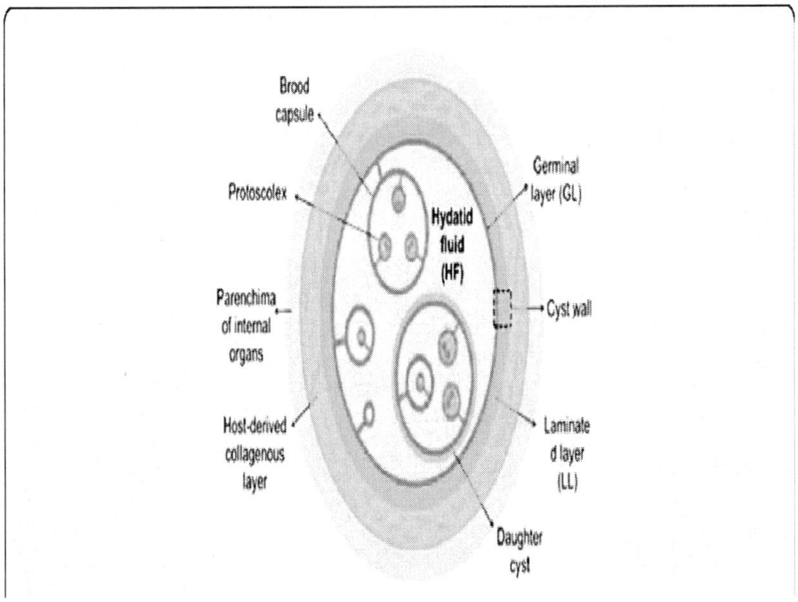

The life cycle of Echinococcus granulosus **is indirect and involves two hosts.**

Dogs are the definitive host, and sheep are the usual intermediate host.

Humans become accidental intermediate hosts.

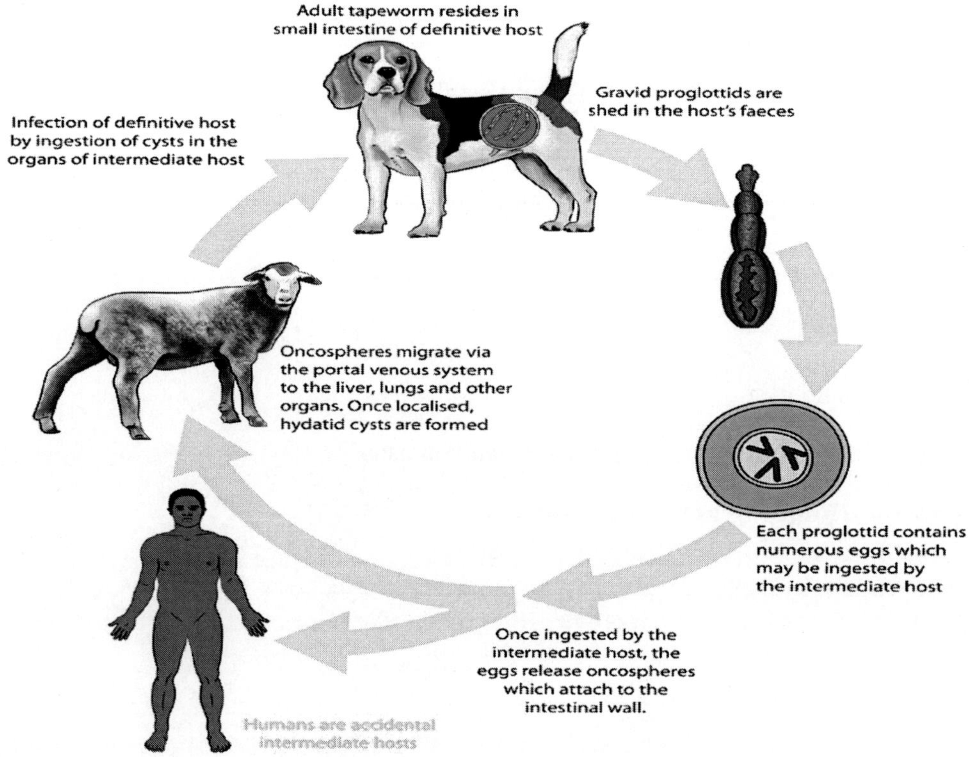

Step 1. Adult worm in dog intestine

The adult worm resides in the small intestine of dogs.

Gravid segments release eggs that are passed in dog faeces.

These eggs contaminate soil, water, vegetables, and animal feed.

Step 2. Infection of intermediate host

Sheep ingest eggs while grazing.

In the intestine, the oncosphere hatches, penetrates the intestinal wall, and enters the bloodstream.

It migrates mainly to:

- Liver
- Lungs

There it develops into a hydatid cyst.

The hydatid cyst is the larval and pathogenic stage.

Step 3. Completion of life cycle

- Dogs become infected by eating raw viscera of sheep containing hydatid cysts.
- Inside the dog intestine, the protoscolices develop into adult worms.

Human Infection

Humans acquire infection by:

• Ingestion of eggs from contaminated food or water
• Close contact with infected dogs

After ingestion, the embryo penetrates the intestinal wall and migrates to organs, most commonly:

- Liver
- Lungs
- Brain
- Other organs

Hydatid cysts slowly enlarge over months or years.

Humans do not develop adult worms.

Humans act as accidental intermediate hosts and the life cycle is not completed.

Conceptual Summary

- Dog to sheep cycle maintains transmission in nature.
- Human infection is incidental but clinically significant.

Hydatid disease is caused by the larval stage, not by the adult worm.

3. Pathogenicity and Organ Localisation of Echinococcus granulosus

Type of Infection	Stage Involved	Organ Localisation	Pathogenesis	Clinical Features	Severity
Hydatid disease	Hydatid cyst, larval stage	Liver, most common	Slow growing cyst causes pressure effect and compression of surrounding tissue	Hepatomegaly, abdominal pain, palpable mass	**Progressive but often asymptomatic for long period**
Pulmonary hydatid disease	Hydatid cyst	Lungs	Expanding cyst compresses lung tissue	Cough, chest pain, breathlessness	**May rupture into bronchial tree**
Cerebral hydatid disease	Hydatid cyst	Brain	Space occupying lesion with raised intracranial pressure	Headache, vomiting, neurological deficits	**Serious and potentially life threatening**
Ruptured hydatid cyst	Hydatid cyst	Any affected organ	Leakage of cyst fluid triggers hypersensitivity reaction	Sudden pain, allergic reaction, possible anaphylaxis	**Medical emergency**

Important Pathological Concepts

The hydatid cyst consists of:

- Outer laminated membrane
- Inner germinal layer
- Hydatid fluid
- Brood capsules
- Protoscolices

The cyst enlarges slowly and may remain undetected for years.

Disease manifestations are mainly due to pressure effect rather than direct tissue invasion.Hydatid disease is caused by the larval stage and not by the adult worm.

4. Laboratory Diagnosis of Echinococcus granulosus

Diagnosis of hydatid disease differs from intestinal cestodes because humans harbour only the larval stage.

Stool examination is not useful in human hydatid disease.

A. Imaging Studies

Imaging plays the primary role in diagnosis.

- Ultrasonography for liver cysts
- CT scan for detailed organ assessment
- MRI for brain involvement

Imaging reveals:

Well defined cystic lesion
Daughter cysts within main cyst
Hydatid sand in some cases

Imaging is the most important diagnostic tool for hydatid disease.

B. Serological Tests

Blood tests detect antibodies against hydatid antigens.

These tests support imaging findings.

Serology may be negative in early infection or intact cysts.

C. Microscopic Examination

Direct microscopic confirmation is usually obtained after surgical removal or aspiration of cyst fluid.

Cyst fluid may show:

Protoscolices
Hooklets
Hydatid sand

Demonstration of protoscolices confirms diagnosis.

D. Caution During Diagnostic Procedures

Aspiration of hydatid cyst carries risk of:

Cyst rupture
Anaphylactic reaction
Spread of infection

Therefore, diagnostic aspiration is performed under strict medical supervision.

Conceptual Summary

- Hydatid disease diagnosis depends mainly on imaging.
- Serology supports diagnosis.
- Stool examination has no role in human infection.

5. Treatment of Echinococcus granulosus

Management of hydatid disease depends on:

Size of cyst
Location of cyst
Presence of complications

Treatment strategy varies according to organ involvement and cyst characteristics.

General approaches include:

• Surgical removal of hydatid cyst in selected cases
• Image guided aspiration procedures in appropriate conditions
• Antihelminthic therapy such as albendazole as adjunct or primary therapy in selected patients

Large cysts producing pressure symptoms often require surgical management.

Small or inoperable cysts may be managed medically under specialist supervision.

Care must be taken to avoid cyst rupture during intervention, as leakage of cyst fluid may cause severe allergic reaction.

6. Prevention and Control of Echinococcus granulosus

Prevention focuses on breaking the dog sheep transmission cycle.

Control measures must target both definitive and intermediate hosts.

1. Regular Deworming of Dogs

Treatment of domestic dogs reduces shedding of eggs.

2. Proper Disposal of Animal Viscera

Dogs should not be allowed to consume raw offal from slaughtered animals.

3. Meat Inspection

Routine inspection of livestock organs helps detect hydatid cysts.

4. Personal Hygiene

Hand washing after handling dogs is essential.

Raw vegetables should be properly washed before consumption.

5. Public Health Education

Awareness programmes in endemic areas help reduce transmission.

Academic Note

The treatment information provided above is for educational understanding in medical zoology.

It is not intended for clinical prescription or therapeutic use.

Clinical management must always be performed by qualified medical professionals.

Hymenolepis nana

Common name, Dwarf tapeworm

Hymenolepis nana is a small intestinal cestode that infects humans worldwide. It is commonly known as the dwarf tapeworm because of its small size compared to other tapeworms.

It belongs to:

Kingdom Animalia
Phylum Platyhelminthes
Class Cestoda
Order Cyclophyllidea

Hymenolepis nana is the smallest tapeworm infecting humans.

Unlike most cestodes, Hymenolepis nana has a unique biological characteristic.

It can complete its life cycle in a single human host without requiring an intermediate host. Because of this feature, it may produce direct transmission from person to person.

It is more commonly seen in:

- Children
- Overcrowded communities
- Areas with poor sanitation

The infection caused by Hymenolepis nana is called hymenolepiasis.

Although often mild, heavy infections may produce gastrointestinal symptoms, especially in children.

Autoinfection is a distinctive feature of Hymenolepis nana infection.

Very good. Now we proceed in structured format.

- **Morphology of Hymenolepis nana**

The adult worm is small, measuring approximately 2 to 4 centimetres in length.

It is much smaller than Taenia species and hence called dwarf tapeworm.

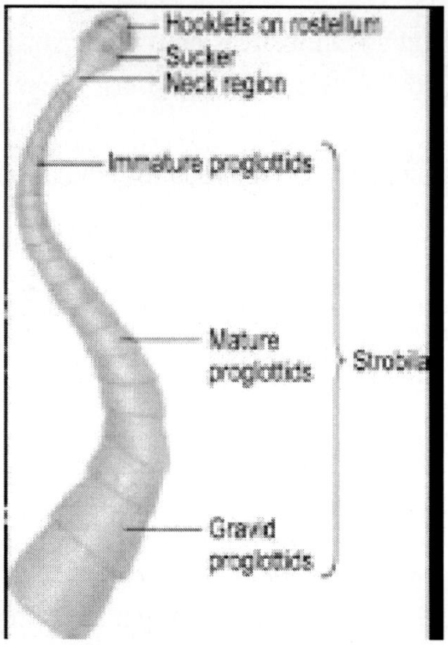

The body consists of:

Scolex
Neck
Strobila

Scolex

The scolex is small and globular.

It contains:

• Four suckers
• A retractile rostellum
• A single row of hooklets

Presence of a single row of hooks differentiates it from Taenia solium, which has a double row.

Neck

The neck is short and acts as the growth zone.

Strobila

The body is segmented and consists of numerous proglottids.

Each proglottid contains both male and female reproductive organs.

Thus, it is hermaphroditic.

Egg

The eggs are oval or spherical.

They contain:

- Hexacanth embryo with six hooklets
- Polar thickenings at each end
- Polar filaments arising from the inner membrane

Presence of polar filaments is the characteristic diagnostic feature of Hymenolepis nana eggs.

3. Life Cycle of Hymenolepis nana

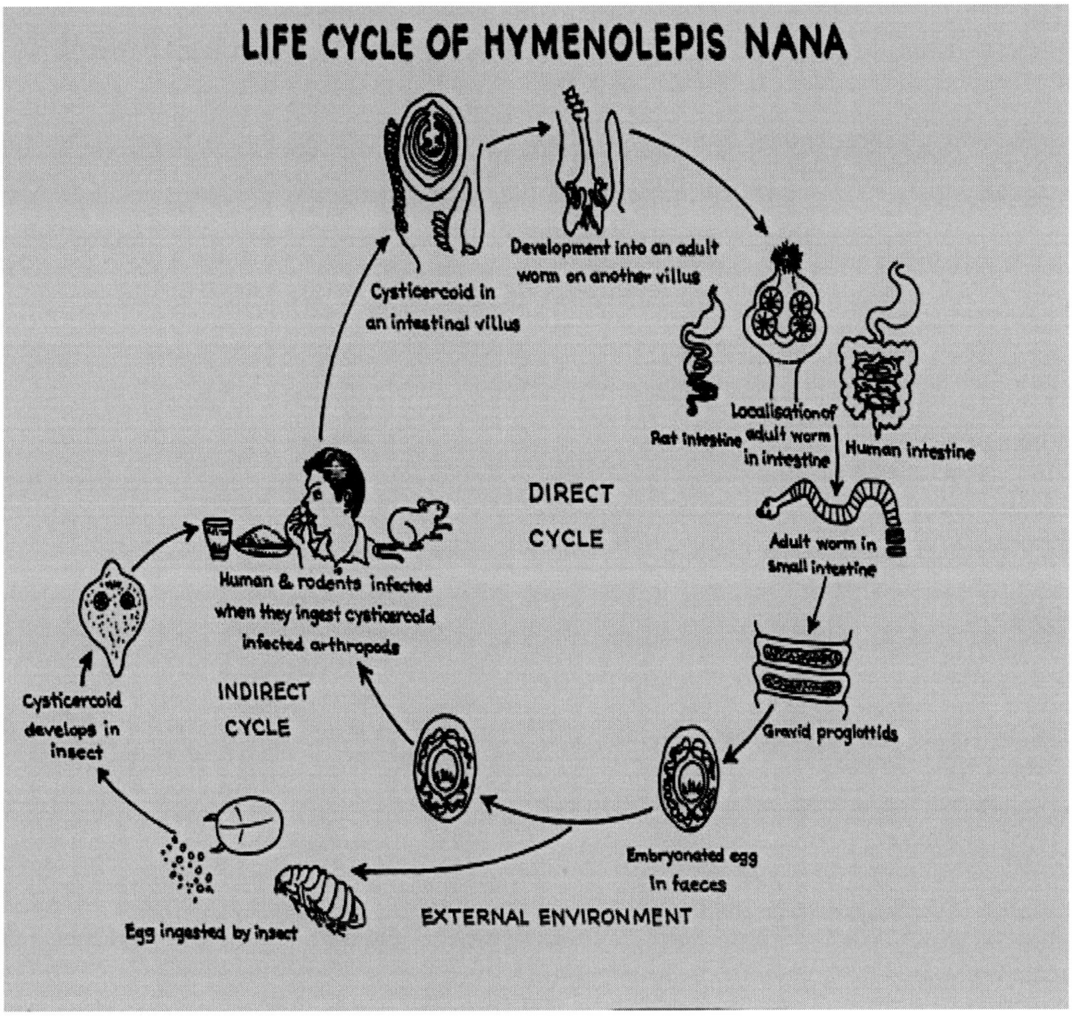

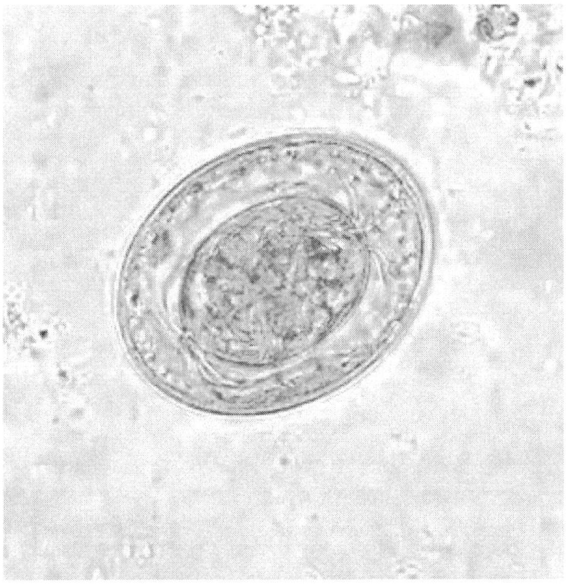

A. Direct Life Cycle

Step 1. Egg ingestion

Infective eggs are ingested through contaminated food, water, or hands.

Step 2. Oncosphere release

In the small intestine, the egg hatches and releases the oncosphere.

Step 3. Development in intestinal villi

The oncosphere penetrates the intestinal villi and develops into a cysticercoid larva.

Step 4. Return to intestinal lumen

After maturation, the cysticercoid re enters the intestinal lumen and develops into an adult worm.

No intermediate host is required in this cycle.

B. Indirect Life Cycle

Sometimes insects such as grain beetles may act as intermediate hosts.

Eggs are ingested by the insect and develop into cysticercoid larvae.

Humans become infected by accidental ingestion of infected insects in contaminated food.

Autoinfection

Autoinfection may occur when eggs hatch within the same intestine before leaving the body.

The released oncosphere reinvades intestinal villi and repeats the cycle.

Autoinfection can lead to heavy worm burden without external exposure.

Conceptual Importance

- Direct life cycle
- Autoinfection
- Person to person transmission

These features make Hymenolepis nana epidemiologically important, especially in children.

4. Pathogenicity and Organ Localisation of Hymenolepis nana

Type of Infection	Stage Involved	Organ Localisation	Pathogenesis	Clinical Features	Severity
Mild hymenolepiasis	Adult worm	Small intestine	Mechanical irritation of intestinal mucosa and mild inflammation	Mild abdominal pain, nausea, diarrhoea	**Usually mild and self limiting**
Heavy infection	Multiple adult worms due to autoinfection	Small intestine	Repeated invasion of intestinal villi by cysticercoid larvae leading to mucosal damage	Abdominal pain, diarrhoea, weakness, irritability in children	**More common in children and may cause nutritional impact**
Villous invasion stage	Cysticercoid larva	Intestinal villi	Larval development inside villi causes destruction and inflammatory response	Malabsorption, discomfort	**Damage mainly due to repeated autoinfection**

Important Pathological Concepts

- The adult worm resides in the small intestine.
- Larval development occurs temporarily within intestinal villi.
- Autoinfection increases worm burden and intensifies intestinal damage.
- Unlike Taenia solium, Hymenolepis nana does not produce tissue cysts in organs such as brain or liver.
- The infection remains confined to the intestine.

5. Laboratory Diagnosis of Hymenolepis nana

Diagnosis is based primarily on stool examination.

Microscopic identification of characteristic eggs confirms infection.

Specimen

Fresh stool sample collected in a clean, dry container.

A. Direct Microscopic Examination

Step 1. Saline wet mount

A small portion of stool is placed on a clean glass slide.
A drop of normal saline is added and mixed gently.
A coverslip is placed over the preparation.

The slide is examined under low power and then high power magnification.

Step 2. Iodine preparation

A second smear may be prepared using iodine solution.

Iodine enhances visibility of internal egg structures.

B. Egg Identification

Characteristic features of Hymenolepis nana eggs:

Oval or spherical shape
Hexacanth embryo with six hooklets
Polar thickenings at both ends
Polar filaments arising from inner membrane

Presence of polar filaments is the most important diagnostic feature.

C. Concentration Techniques

In light infections, stool concentration methods such as sedimentation may increase detection rate.

Conceptual Summary

Stool examination is sufficient for diagnosis.
No imaging studies are required because infection remains intestinal.

Egg morphology is diagnostic and differentiates it from other cestodes.

Excellent. Now we complete Hymenolepis nana.

6. Treatment of Hymenolepis nana

Intestinal hymenolepiasis is treated with antihelminthic drugs such as praziquantel.

Because autoinfection can occur, treatment may need careful follow up to ensure complete eradication.

Failure to treat properly may allow reinfection through internal autoinfection.

In heavy infections, management should include correction of nutritional deficiencies if present.

7. Prevention and Control of Hymenolepis nana

Prevention focuses on interrupting direct transmission and preventing autoinfection.

1. Personal Hygiene

Regular hand washing before meals and after defecation is essential.

Children should be educated regarding hygiene practices.

Good hygiene prevents person to person transmission.

2. Sanitation

Proper disposal of human faeces reduces environmental contamination with eggs.

3. Control of Insect Contamination

Food grains should be stored properly to prevent infestation by grain beetles and insects.

4. Early Detection and Treatment

Identification and treatment of infected individuals reduce spread in families and schools.

Academic Note

The treatment information provided above is for educational understanding in medical zoology.

It is not intended for clinical prescription or therapeutic use.

Clinical management must always be performed by qualified medical professionals.

Excellent. Now we complete the chapter academically by including the representative of Order Pseudophyllidea.

Diphyllobothrium latum

Common name, Fish tapeworm

1. Introduction

Diphyllobothrium latum is a large intestinal cestode transmitted through consumption of raw or undercooked freshwater fish.

It belongs to:

Kingdom Animalia
Phylum Platyhelminthes
Class Cestoda
Order Pseudophyllidea

It is the most important human tapeworm of Order Pseudophyllidea.

Unlike cyclophyllidean cestodes, this parasite has:

Operculated eggs
Two intermediate hosts in its life cycle

It is more common in regions where raw freshwater fish is consumed, such as parts of Europe, Russia, and East Asia.It is uncommon in India but remains important for academic completeness and global medical relevance.The infection caused is called diphyllobothriasis.

It is notable for causing vitamin B12 deficiency anaemia in some patients.

- **Morphology of Diphyllobothrium latum**

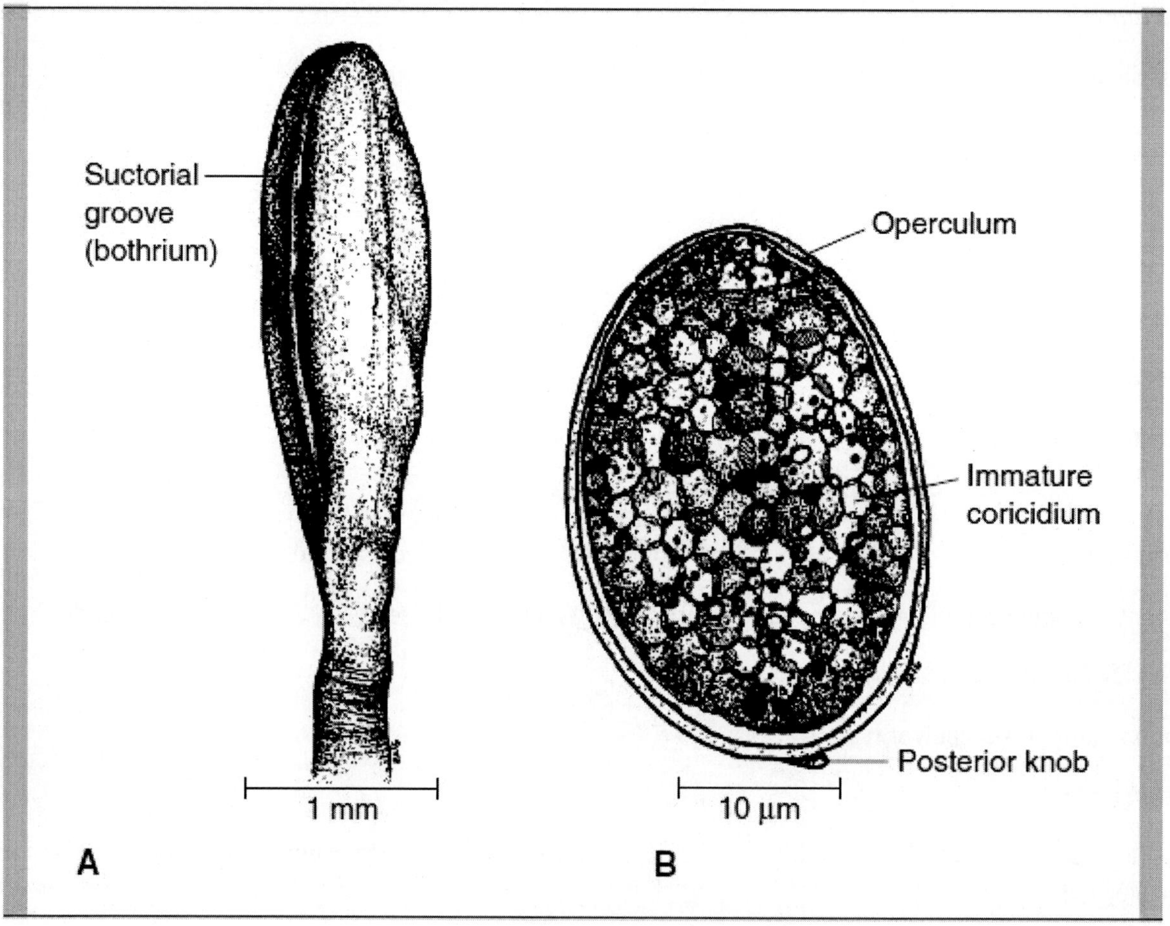

FIGURE 57–2
Diphyllobothrium latum.
A. Scolex. B. Ovum.

Diphyllobothrium latum is one of the largest tapeworms infecting humans.

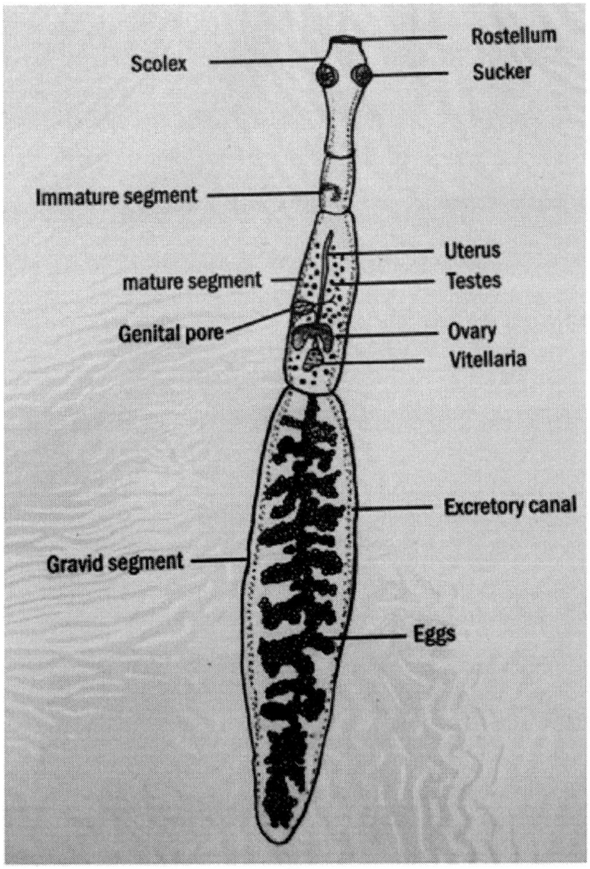

The adult worm may measure 5 to 10 metres in length and sometimes even longer.

It is larger than Taenia species.

The body consists of:

Scolex
Neck
Strobila

Scolex

The scolex is elongated and spoon shaped.

It does not have suckers or hooks.

Instead, it possesses:

Two longitudinal slit like grooves called bothria.

Presence of bothria instead of suckers is the distinguishing feature of Order Pseudophyllidea.

Neck

Short and narrow growth region.

Strobila

Composed of numerous proglottids.

Proglottids are broader than long.

Segments are wider than they are long, which differentiates them from Taenia species.

Uterus

The uterus forms a characteristic rosette shaped structure in gravid segments.

Egg

Eggs are:

Oval
Operculated at one end
Unembryonated when passed in stool

Presence of an operculum is the most important diagnostic feature.

Life Cycle of Diphyllobothrium latum

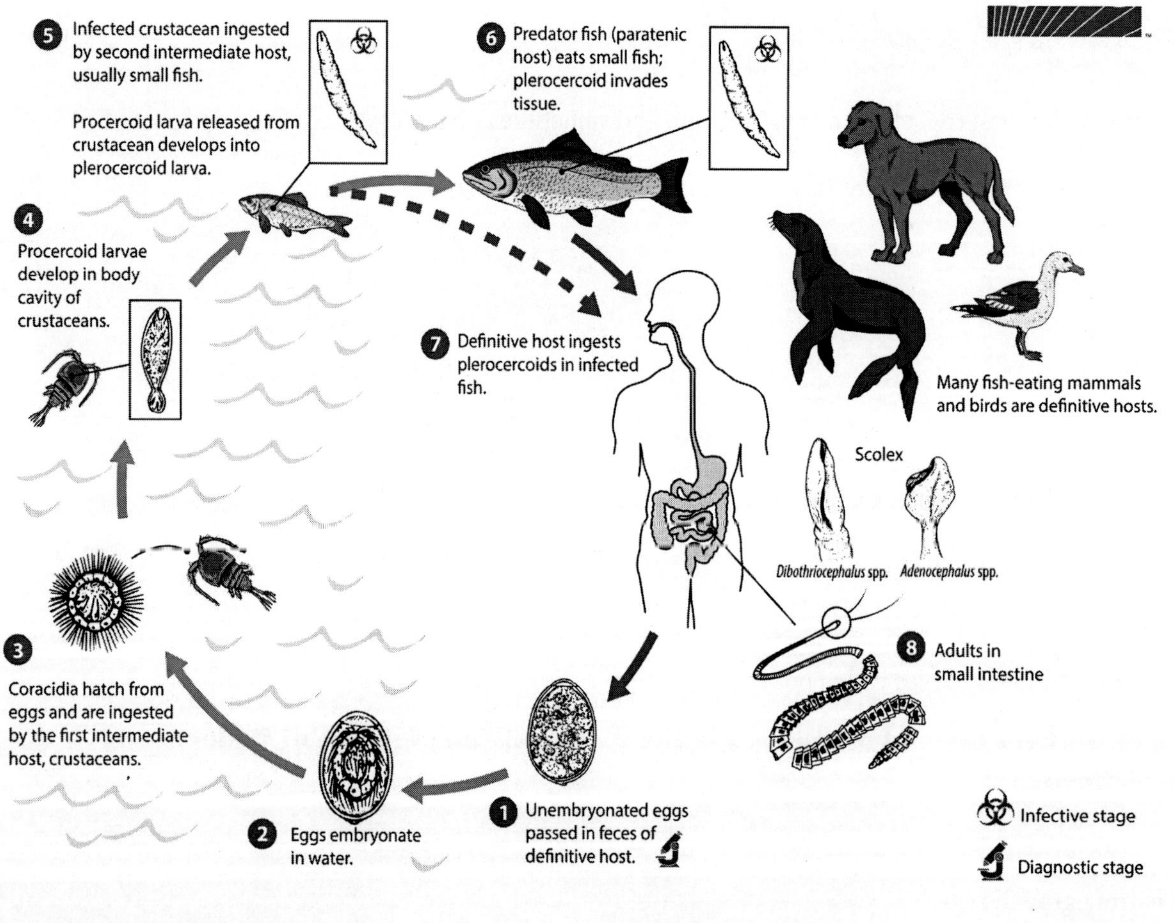

The life cycle of Diphyllobothrium latum is indirect and complex.

It requires two intermediate hosts.

Step 1. Egg release

Operculated eggs are passed in human faeces.When they reach freshwater, the eggs develop and release a ciliated larva called coracidium.

Step 2. First intermediate host

The coracidium is ingested by a small freshwater crustacean known as Cyclops.Inside Cyclops, it develops into a procercoid larva.

Step 3. Second intermediate host

Infected Cyclops is ingested by freshwater fish.In the fish muscle, the larva develops into a plerocercoid stage.

The plerocercoid is the infective stage for humans.

Step 4. Human infection

Humans acquire infection by consuming raw or undercooked freshwater fish containing plerocercoid larvae.

In the small intestine, the larva attaches to the mucosa using its bothria and develops into an adult worm.

Conceptual Summary

Two intermediate hosts are required.
Eggs are operculated.
Infective stage for humans is plerocercoid.

Pathogenicity and Organ Localisation of Diphyllobothrium latum

Type of Infection	Stage Involved	Organ Localisation	Pathogenesis	Clinical Features	Severity
Intestinal diphyllobothriasis	Adult worm	Small intestine	Mechanical irritation of intestinal mucosa and competition for nutrients	Mild abdominal discomfort, diarrhoea, passage of segments	**Usually mild and often asymptomatic**
Vitamin B12 deficiency anaemia	Adult worm	Small intestine	Parasite absorbs large amounts of vitamin B12, leading to deficiency	Weakness, pallor, glossitis, megaloblastic anaemia	**Most important clinical complication**
Heavy infection	Multiple worms	Small intestine	Large worm burden may cause intestinal obstruction	Abdominal pain, obstruction symptoms	**Rare but possible**

Important Pathological Concept

- Unlike other intestinal tapeworms, Diphyllobothrium latum competes with the host for vitamin B12.
- Vitamin B12 deficiency may lead to megaloblastic anaemia.

- The infection remains confined to the intestine.
- There is no tissue cyst formation in humans.

Laboratory Diagnosis of Diphyllobothrium latum

Diagnosis is based primarily on stool examination.

Identification of characteristic operculated eggs confirms infection.

Specimen

Fresh stool sample collected in a clean container.

A. Direct Microscopic Examination

Step 1. Saline wet mount

A small portion of stool is placed on a clean glass slide.
A drop of normal saline is added and mixed gently.
A coverslip is placed over the smear.

The preparation is examined under low power and then high power magnification.

B. Egg Identification

Characteristic features of Diphyllobothrium latum eggs:

Oval shape
Operculum at one end
Small knob at the opposite end
Unembryonated when passed

Presence of an operculum differentiates it from Taenia eggs.

C. Examination of Proglottids

Proglottids are broader than long.

The uterus shows a characteristic rosette shaped pattern.

D. Supportive Laboratory Findings

In cases with anaemia:

Peripheral blood smear may show megaloblastic anaemia.
Serum vitamin B12 levels may be reduced.

Conceptual Summary

Operculated egg is diagnostic.
No imaging required because infection is intestinal.

Egg morphology is the key laboratory feature distinguishing Order Pseudophyllidea from Cyclophyllidea.

Treatment of Diphyllobothrium latum

Intestinal diphyllobothriasis is treated with antihelminthic drugs such as praziquantel.

In cases associated with vitamin B12 deficiency, supplementation of vitamin B12 may be required.

Correction of anaemia is an important supportive measure.

Follow up stool examination is advisable to confirm eradication of the parasite.

Prevention and Control of Diphyllobothrium latum

Prevention focuses on interrupting transmission through freshwater fish.

1. Proper Cooking of Fish

Freshwater fish should be thoroughly cooked before consumption.

Raw or undercooked fish is the main source of infection.

2. Sanitary Disposal of Human Faeces

Preventing contamination of freshwater bodies with human faeces interrupts the life cycle.

3. Public Awareness

Education regarding risks of consuming raw freshwater fish reduces transmission.

Academic Note

The treatment information provided above is for educational understanding in medical zoology.

It is not intended for clinical prescription or therapeutic use.

Clinical management must always be performed by qualified medical professionals.

Key Conceptual Highlights

Taenia solium can cause both intestinal and tissue infection.

Taenia saginata causes only intestinal infection.

Echinococcus granulosus causes hydatid disease in humans who act as accidental intermediate host.

Hymenolepis nana is the only cestode capable of completing its life cycle in a single human host.

Diphyllobothrium latum belongs to Order Pseudophyllidea and has operculated eggs with two intermediate hosts.

Comparative Summary of Cestodes of Medical Importance

Feature	Taenia solium	Taenia saginata	Echinococcus granulosus	Hymenolepis nana	Diphyllobothrium latum
Common name	Pork tapeworm	Beef tapeworm	Dog tapeworm	Dwarf tapeworm	Fish tapeworm
Size of adult	2 to 7 m	4 to 10 m	3 to 6 mm	2 to 4 cm	5 to 10 m
Scolex	4 suckers, rostellum, double row of hooks	4 suckers, no hooks	4 suckers, hooks	4 suckers, single row of hooks	2 bothria, no suckers
Egg type	Non operculated	Non operculated	Non operculated	Polar filaments present	Operculated
Intermediate host	Pig	Cattle	Sheep	Not required, optional insect	2 hosts, Cyclops and fish
Infective stage for humans	Cysticercus or egg	Cysticercus bovis	Egg	Egg	Plerocercoid
Tissue infection in humans	Yes	No	Yes	No	No
Special feature	Causes cysticercosis	Only intestinal infection	Hydatid cyst formation	Direct life cycle, autoinfection	Causes vitamin B12 deficiency
Order	Cyclophyllidea	Cyclophyllidea	Cyclophyllidea	Cyclophyllidea	Pseudophyllidea

15. Trematodes of Medical Importance

Trematodes are parasitic flatworms commonly known as flukes. They belong to:

Kingdom Animalia
Phylum Platyhelminthes
Class Trematoda

They are dorsoventrally flattened, leaf shaped worms adapted for parasitic life.

Trematodes differ from cestodes in having an incomplete alimentary canal.

Unlike cestodes, trematodes are unsegmented and possess a digestive system, although it is incomplete.

Most trematodes are hermaphroditic, except one important genus.

Schistosoma species have separate sexes.

Trematodes require at least one intermediate host, usually a freshwater snail.

The infections caused by trematodes are collectively called trematodiasis.

They may involve:

Intestine
Liver
Lungs
Blood vessels

General Characteristics of Trematodes

- Body is leaf shaped and unsegmented
- Body cavity absent
- Alimentary canal incomplete
- Two suckers present, oral sucker and ventral sucker
- Mostly hermaphroditic
- Indirect life cycle
- Snail acts as intermediate host

Snail is an essential intermediate host in most trematode infections.

2. General Morphology of Trematodes

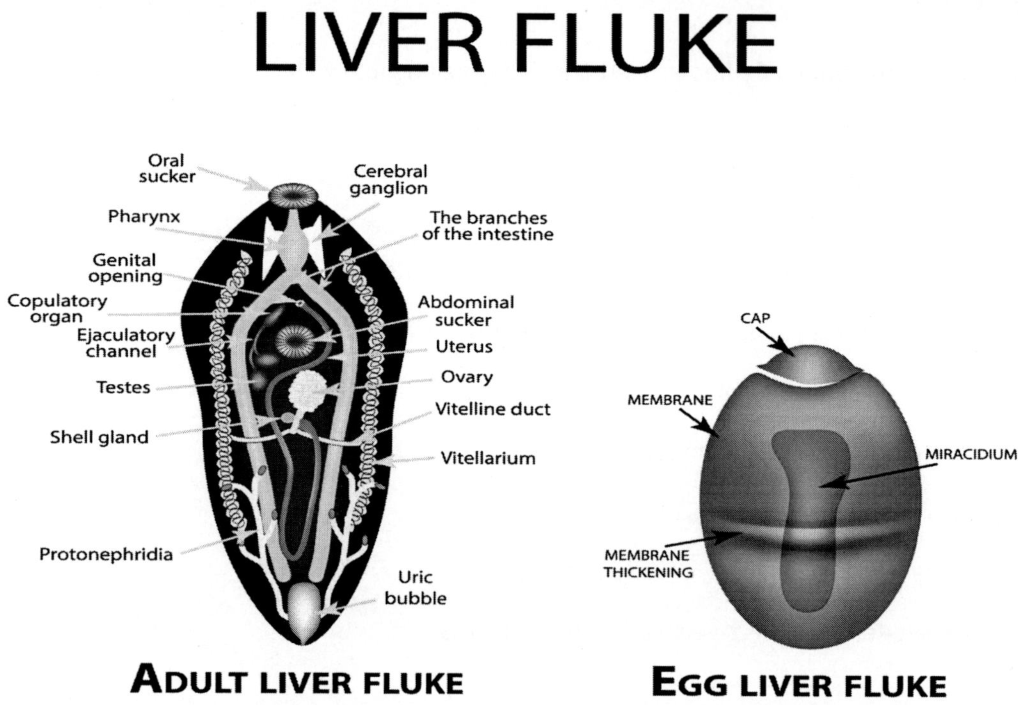

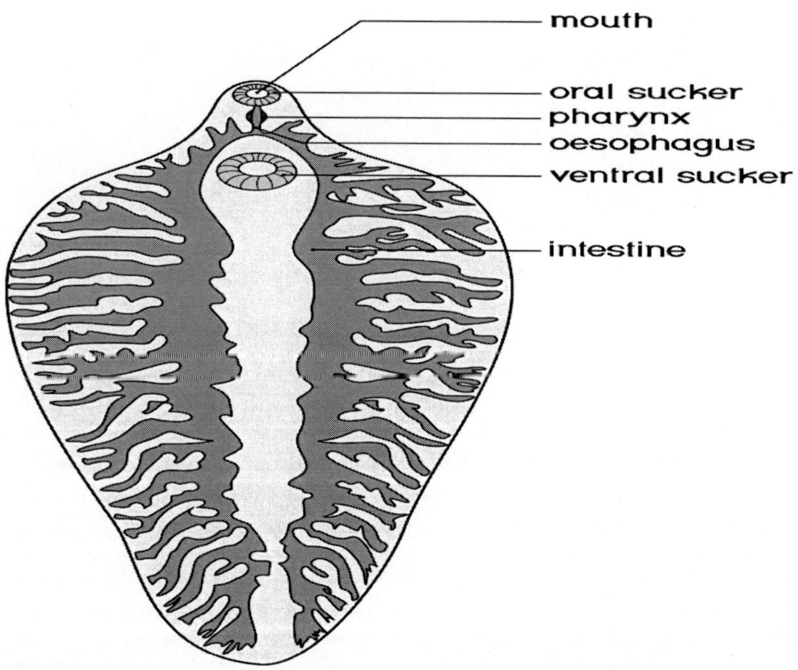

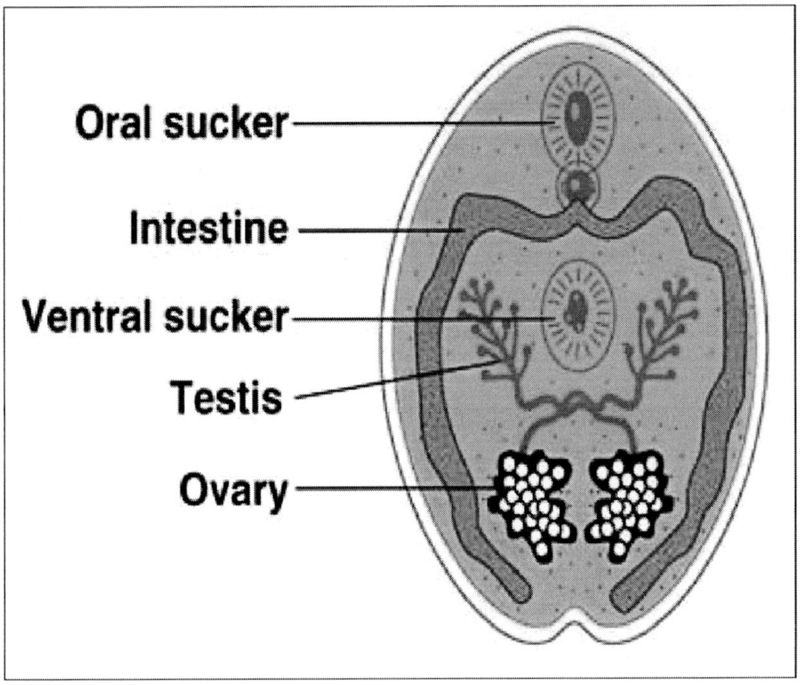

Trematodes are dorsoventrally flattened, leaf shaped, unsegmented worms.

Their body structure is compact and adapted for attachment and tissue invasion.

External Morphology

The body is covered by a tegument which protects the parasite from host enzymes and immune responses.

Two suckers are present:

Oral sucker located at the anterior end
Ventral sucker also called acetabulum located on the ventral surface

The two suckers are important attachment organs.

Digestive System

The mouth is located within the oral sucker.

Food passes into a muscular pharynx and then into a bifurcated intestine.

The intestine ends blindly.

Trematodes have an incomplete alimentary canal with no anus.

Reproductive System

Most trematodes are hermaphroditic.

They possess both male and female reproductive organs in the same individual.

Exception

Schistosoma species are dioecious and have separate male and female worms.

Body Cavity

True body cavity is absent.

They are acoelomate organisms.

Conceptual Difference from Cestodes

- **Trematodes**
  Unsegmented
  Have digestive system

- **Cestodes**
  Segmented
  No digestive system

Presence of digestive system differentiates trematodes from cestodes.

3. Classification of Trematodes of Medical Importance

Group	Primary Organ Localisation	Important Examples	Key Clinical Association
Liver flukes	Liver and bile ducts	Fasciola hepatica, Clonorchis sinensis	Hepatomegaly, biliary obstruction
Intestinal flukes	Small intestine	Fasciolopsis buski	Diarrhoea, intestinal irritation
Lung flukes	Lungs	Paragonimus westermani	Chronic cough, haemoptysis
Blood flukes	Blood vessels	Schistosoma haematobium, Schistosoma mansoni, Schistosoma japonicum	Schistosomiasis involving urinary or intestinal system

Important Conceptual Points

• **Organ localisation determines disease pattern.**
• **Schistosoma species are the only trematodes with separate sexes.**
• Snail acts as an essential intermediate host in most trematode infections.

Fasciola hepatica

Common name, Sheep liver fluke

Fasciola hepatica is a parasitic trematode that primarily infects the liver and biliary passages of herbivorous animals such as sheep and cattle. Humans become accidental hosts when they ingest the infective larval stage.

It belongs to:

Kingdom Animalia
Phylum Platyhelminthes
Class Trematoda

The disease caused by this parasite is called fascioliasis.

Fascioliasis is a hepatobiliary infection caused by a trematode parasite.

The infection occurs through consumption of raw aquatic vegetation, particularly watercress, contaminated with the infective stage known as metacercaria.

Fasciola hepatica is widely distributed in areas where livestock farming is common and where freshwater plants are consumed without proper washing.

After ingestion, the parasite migrates through the intestinal wall to the liver, where it causes tissue damage and inflammation before finally localising in the bile ducts.

The pathology is related both to migratory damage in the liver and obstruction of bile ducts.

Morphology of Fasciola hepatica

Fasciola hepatica is a large digenetic trematode exhibiting structural adaptations that enable survival within the hepatobiliary system of mammals. Its morphology reflects both parasitic specialisation and complex reproductive capacity, which are hallmarks of trematodes of medical importance.

General Body Form and Dimensions

The adult worm is dorsoventrally flattened and leaf shaped, a configuration that maximises surface area for nutrient absorption and facilitates movement within the bile ducts. The average length ranges from 25 to 30 millimetres, while the width varies between 4 and 12 millimetres. The body is elongated and oval, tapering towards both anterior and posterior ends.

A characteristic cephalic cone projects anteriorly from the main body mass. This conical anterior extension is an important taxonomic feature and assists in anchorage within the biliary passages. The flattened morphology allows the parasite to resist the flow of bile and maintain its position within narrow ducts.

The colour of the living worm is typically pale pink. However, due to ingestion of bile pigments and host material, the parasite often appears brownish when examined grossly.

FASCIOLA - LIVER FLUKE

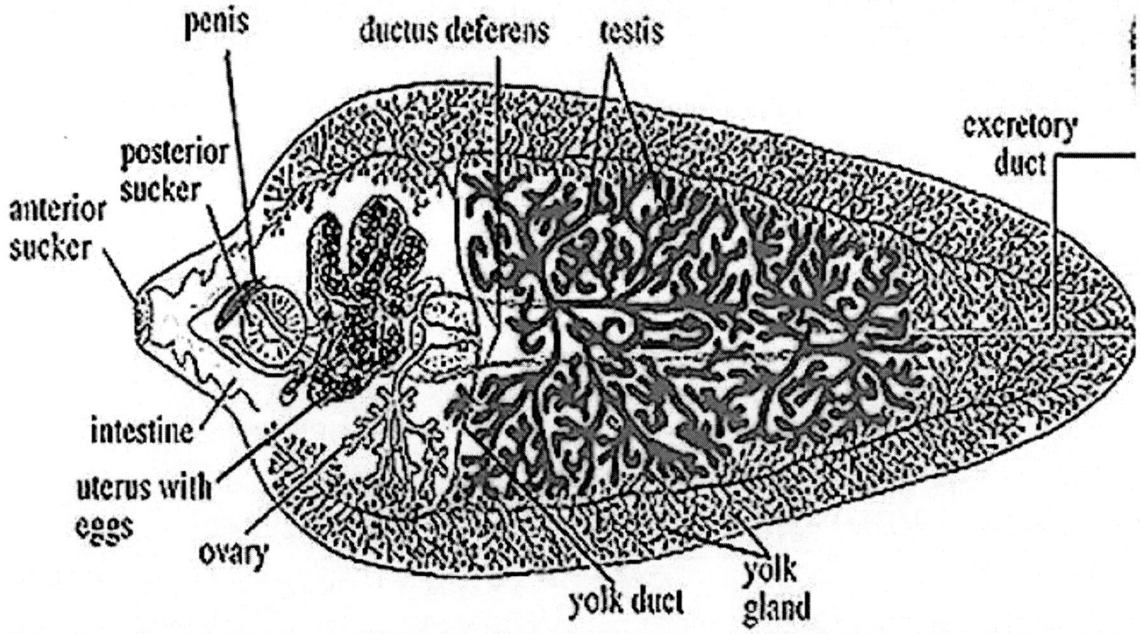

The leaf shaped flattened body is an adaptive feature for intraductal parasitism.

Tegument and External Covering

The entire body is covered by a thick, syncytial tegument. Unlike a simple epidermis, the tegument is metabolically active and multifunctional. It provides protection against bile salts, digestive enzymes, and host immune factors. Additionally, it participates in nutrient absorption and ion exchange.

The tegument may bear minute spines, particularly in the anterior region, which assist in attachment and migration through host tissues during early developmental stages. In adult worms, these spines are less prominent but contribute to mechanical anchorage.

The tegument is both protective and absorptive, representing a key adaptation to endoparasitic life.

Suckers and Attachment Mechanism

Two muscular suckers are present and serve as specialised attachment organs.The oral sucker is located at the anterior extremity and surrounds the mouth opening. It functions in both attachment and ingestion of host tissue and bile.The ventral sucker, also termed the acetabulum, is situated on the ventral surface slightly posterior to the oral sucker. It is typically larger and more powerful than the oral sucker.Together, these suckers provide firm attachment to the epithelial lining of bile ducts, preventing displacement by bile flow.

Dual sucker arrangement is characteristic of trematodes and essential for stable localisation within the host.

Digestive System

The digestive tract begins with the mouth located within the oral sucker. The mouth leads into a muscular pharynx, which generates suction for ingestion of host tissue fluids and bile.A short oesophagus extends posteriorly and bifurcates into two intestinal caeca. These caeca run longitudinally and exhibit extensive lateral branching. The branching pattern increases surface area for digestion and nutrient distribution.The digestive system is incomplete, as it lacks an anus. Undigested material is expelled through the mouth.This arrangement reflects a relatively simple but efficient feeding mechanism suited to a semi fluid nutrient environment.

The highly branched intestinal caeca maximise nutrient absorption within a confined body space.

Reproductive System

Fasciola hepatica is hermaphroditic, possessing both male and female reproductive organs within the same individual. This ensures reproductive success even when parasite density is low.The male reproductive system consists of two extensively branched testes located in the posterior region of the body. The vasa efferentia unite to form a vas deferens, which opens through the genital pore.The female reproductive system includes a single branched ovary situated anterior to the testes. The oviduct connects to the ootype, where fertilisation and shell formation occur. Vitelline glands are distributed laterally along the body and provide yolk cells and shell material for egg development.The common genital pore is located ventrally between the oral and ventral suckers.The extensive branching of reproductive organs reflects the high fecundity of the parasite, enabling production of thousands of eggs.

The complex and highly branched reproductive system is a major evolutionary adaptation for survival and transmission.

Excretory System

The excretory system consists of flame cells connected to collecting tubules, forming a protonephridial system typical of flatworms. These tubules converge into a median excretory bladder, which opens to the exterior through a posterior excretory pore.This system maintains osmotic balance and removes metabolic waste products.

Egg Morphology

The eggs of Fasciola hepatica are large, oval, and operculated. They measure approximately 130 to 150 micrometres in length. The shell is thin and yellowish brown.At one pole, a distinct operculum is present, which opens to allow release of the miracidium in freshwater.Eggs are unembryonated when passed in faeces and require development in water before hatching.

The large operculated egg is a key diagnostic feature in laboratory examination.

Life Cycle of Fasciola hepatica

The life cycle of Fasciola hepatica is indirect and complex, involving two hosts and multiple larval stages. It is a typical example of a digenetic trematode life cycle.

A freshwater snail acts as the essential intermediate host.

The life cycle includes the following stages:

- Egg
- Miracidium
- Sporocyst
- Redia
- Cercaria
- Metacercaria
- Adult worm

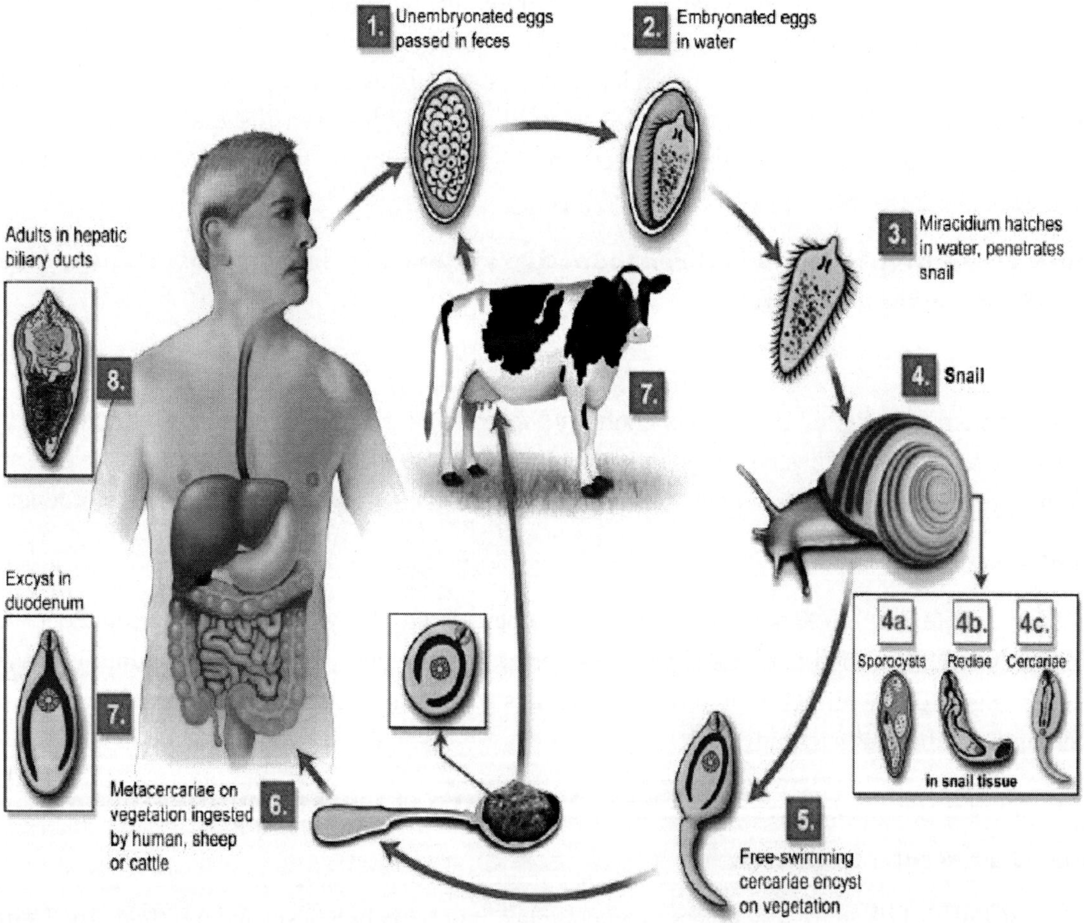

Life Cycle of **Fasciola hepatica**

1. Unembryonated Eggs Passed in Faeces

- Adult worms reside in the hepatic biliary ducts of cattle, sheep, or humans.
- Eggs are produced in the bile ducts and pass into the intestine with bile.
- They are excreted in faeces as unembryonated operculated eggs.

Eggs are not infective at the time of excretion.

2. Embryonation in Water

- When eggs reach freshwater, they undergo embryonation.
- Under suitable environmental conditions of temperature and oxygen, the miracidium develops inside the egg.
- This process may take 9 to 15 days depending on climate.

3. Miracidium Hatches and Penetrates Snail

- The operculum opens and releases a free swimming ciliated miracidium.
- The miracidium must find and penetrate a suitable freshwater snail within a short period.
- The snail acts as the intermediate host.

Snail penetration is essential for continuation of the life cycle.

4. Development within the Snail

- Inside the snail, the miracidium transforms into a sporocyst.
- The sporocyst produces rediae through asexual multiplication.
- Rediae further develop into cercariae.
- This stage amplifies the number of parasites.

One miracidium can give rise to numerous cercariae.

5. Free Swimming Cercariae

- Cercariae leave the snail and swim freely in water using their tail.
- They do not infect humans directly.

6. Encystment on Vegetation

- Cercariae attach to aquatic plants and lose their tails.
- They encyst to form metacercariae.
- Metacercariae are round, thick walled, and resistant to environmental stress.

Metacercaria is the infective stage for humans and cattle.

7. Ingestion and Excystation

- Humans, cattle, or sheep ingest aquatic vegetation contaminated with metacercariae.
- In the duodenum, the cyst wall dissolves.
- The larva is released and penetrates the intestinal wall.

8. Migration to Liver and Maturation

- The larva migrates through the peritoneal cavity to the liver.
- It penetrates the liver capsule and moves through hepatic parenchyma.
- After several weeks of migration and tissue destruction, it enters the bile ducts.
- In the bile ducts, it matures into an adult worm and begins egg production.

Host Roles According to Diagram

Snail
Intermediate host

Cow or Sheep
Definitive host and natural reservoir

Human
Accidental definitive host

Pathophysiological Insight

The life cycle contains two major pathogenic phases:

Migratory hepatic phase
Biliary obstructive phase

Liver migration causes acute tissue damage, while adult worms in bile ducts cause chronic biliary disease.

Pathogenicity and Organ Localisation of Fasciola hepatica

The disease produced by Fasciola hepatica occurs in two distinct phases:

1. Acute hepatic migratory phase
2. Chronic biliary obstructive phase

Clinical manifestations correspond to the stage of parasite migration and localisation.

Phase of Disease	Stage of Parasite	Organ Localisation	Pathogenesis	Clinical Features	Pathological Changes
Acute hepatic phase	Immature migrating larvae	Liver parenchyma	Larval penetration of intestinal wall followed by migration through liver tissue causing mechanical destruction and inflammation	Fever, right upper quadrant pain, hepatomegaly, eosinophilia	Hepatic necrosis, haemorrhagic tracts, inflammatory infiltration
Subacute phase	Developing flukes	Liver tissue	Continued migration and tissue irritation	Persistent abdominal discomfort, malaise	Progressive inflammatory changes
Chronic biliary phase	Adult worm	Bile ducts	Mechanical irritation and obstruction of bile ducts, epithelial hyperplasia	Biliary colic, jaundice, cholangitis in severe cases	Thickening of bile duct walls, fibrosis, biliary obstruction

Detailed Pathophysiological Explanation

During the acute phase, larvae mechanically disrupt hepatic tissue while migrating. The destruction of hepatocytes and small blood vessels leads to necrosis and haemorrhage. The immune response generates marked eosinophilia.

Acute symptoms are mainly due to tissue invasion and inflammatory reaction.

In the chronic phase, adult worms residing in bile ducts cause irritation and obstruction. Repeated mechanical trauma and metabolic products induce hyperplasia of biliary epithelium and fibrosis.

Long standing infection may lead to:

- Chronic cholangitis
- Biliary obstruction
- Secondary bacterial infection

Chronic pathology is primarily obstructive and inflammatory in nature.

Organ Localisation Summary

- Primary site
- Bile ducts

Secondary site during migration

- Liver parenchyma
- No systemic dissemination occurs beyond hepatobiliary system.

Laboratory Diagnosis of Fasciola hepatica

Diagnosis depends on the stage of infection. Since pathology occurs in two phases, laboratory findings differ in the acute migratory stage and the chronic biliary stage.

Stage of infection determines the diagnostic approach.

1. Diagnosis During Acute Hepatic Phase

During early infection, immature flukes are migrating through the liver and eggs are not yet produced.

Therefore:Stool examination is usually negative in early phase.

Laboratory findings may include:

- Marked peripheral eosinophilia
- Elevated liver enzymes
- Raised inflammatory markers

Serological tests detecting antibodies against Fasciola antigens are useful during this stage.

Serology is particularly valuable in the early migratory phase when eggs are absent in stool.

Imaging studies such as ultrasonography or CT scan may reveal hypoechoic lesions or migratory tracts in the liver.

2. Diagnosis During Chronic Biliary Phase

In the chronic phase, adult worms residing in bile ducts produce eggs.

A. Stool Examination

- Specimen
- Fresh stool sample.

Method

- Direct saline wet mount preparation.
- Sedimentation concentration technique improves detection.

Characteristic features of eggs:

- Large
- Oval
- Operculated
- Unembryonated when passed

Large operculated egg is the key diagnostic feature.

- Eggs may resemble those of other trematodes such as Clonorchis, but Fasciola eggs are significantly larger.

B. Bile Examination

- In selected cases, duodenal aspirate or bile samples may contain eggs.

C. Imaging Studies

- Ultrasound may show:
- Dilated bile ducts
- Mobile echogenic structures within ducts
- CT or MRI may demonstrate biliary obstruction.

3. Differential Diagnosis

- Important to differentiate from:
- Other liver flukes
- Biliary obstruction due to gallstones
- Viral hepatitis

Conceptual Summary

- Acute phase
- Serology and eosinophilia

- Chronic phase
- Stool examination for operculated eggs
- Egg detection confirms established biliary infection.

Treatment of Fasciola hepatica

Management depends on the stage of infection and severity of hepatobiliary involvement.

Therapeutic intervention aims to eliminate the parasite and prevent long term biliary damage.

The drug of choice for fascioliasis is triclabendazole, which is effective against both immature migrating larvae and adult worms.This property distinguishes it from many other antihelminthic agents.In the acute hepatic phase, treatment reduces inflammatory damage and prevents progression to chronic biliary disease.In the chronic phase, therapy eliminates adult flukes and reduces ongoing biliary irritation.

In complicated cases involving:

- Biliary obstruction
- Secondary bacterial cholangitis
- Severe fibrosis

Additional supportive or surgical management may be required under specialist care.

Academic Note

The treatment information provided here is for academic understanding in medical zoology.

It is not intended for clinical prescription or self medication.

Clinical management must be performed by qualified medical professionals.

Prevention and Control of Fasciola hepatica

Prevention focuses on interrupting transmission between definitive hosts and snail intermediate hosts.

1. Avoid Consumption of Raw Aquatic Vegetation

Raw watercress and other aquatic plants should be thoroughly washed and properly cooked.

Ingestion of metacercariae on vegetation is the main route of human infection.

2. Control of Snail Population

Reduction of freshwater snail habitats decreases transmission.

Environmental management and drainage of marshy areas are effective control strategies.

3. Veterinary Control Measures

Regular treatment of cattle and sheep reduces environmental contamination with eggs.

Livestock management plays a crucial role in endemic regions.

4. Safe Water Practices

Prevent contamination of water sources with animal faeces.

Epidemiological Insight

Sheep and cattle act as reservoir hosts.

Snail is essential intermediate host.

Humans are accidental hosts.

Breaking any one link in the cycle significantly reduces transmission.

Certainly. Below is the refined **Introduction** with detailed geographical distribution included in academically mature form.

Fasciolopsis buski

Common name, Giant intestinal fluke

1. Introduction

Fasciolopsis buski is a large intestinal trematode that parasitises the small intestine of humans and pigs. It is the largest intestinal fluke infecting humans and causes the disease known as fasciolopsiasis.

It belongs to:

Kingdom Animalia
Phylum Platyhelminthes
Class Trematoda

The parasite is predominantly distributed in South and Southeast Asia. Endemic regions include India, China, Bangladesh, Thailand, Vietnam, Taiwan, Indonesia, and parts of Malaysia. In India, cases are more frequently reported from eastern and northeastern states where pig farming and consumption of aquatic vegetation are common.The epidemiology of infection is closely linked to rural agricultural practices, freshwater bodies used for vegetable cultivation, and traditional dietary habits involving raw or inadequately washed aquatic plants.

The disease is geographically associated with regions where aquatic crops are cultivated in snail infested freshwater environments.

Pigs serve as the principal reservoir hosts and play a major role in maintaining transmission. Humans function as definitive hosts and acquire infection through ingestion of metacercariae encysted on aquatic plants such as water chestnut, lotus, and water bamboo.Unlike liver flukes, Fasciolopsis buski does not migrate through hepatic tissue. The parasite remains confined to the intestinal lumen throughout its adult life.

The absence of hepatic migration is a key biological distinction from Fasciola hepatica.

2. Morphology of Fasciolopsis buski

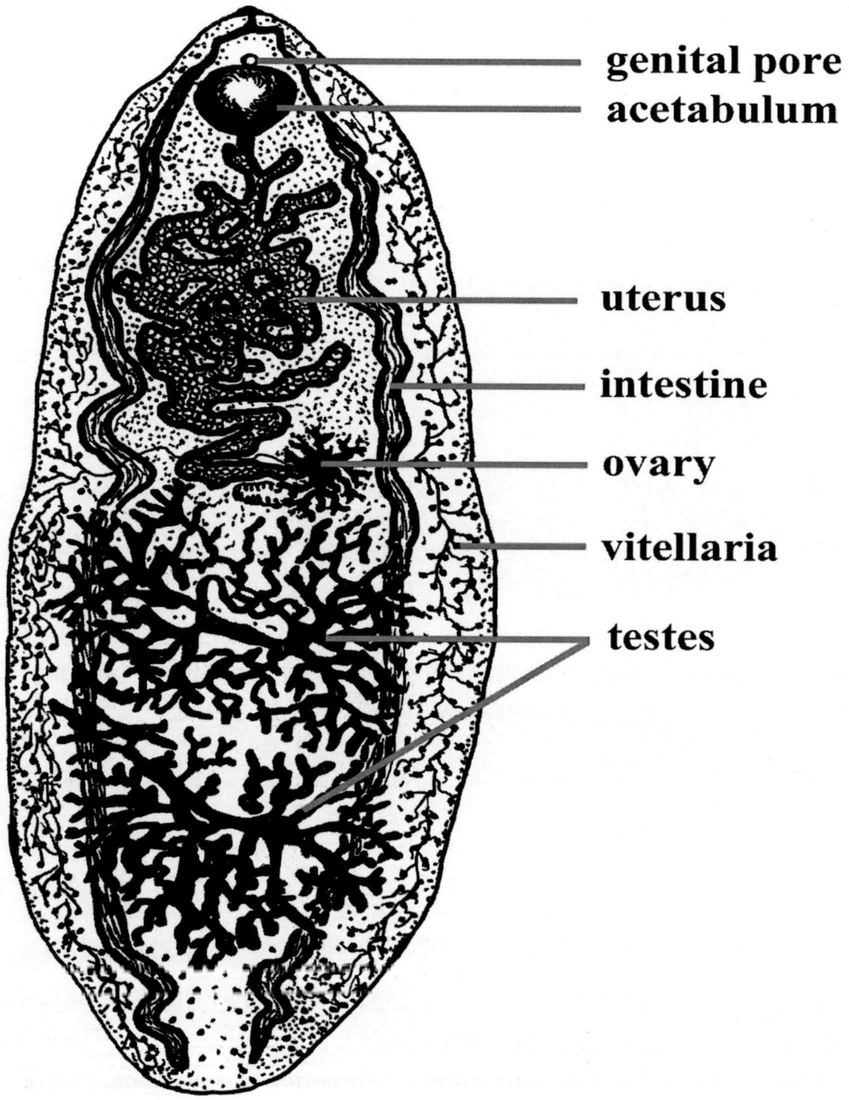

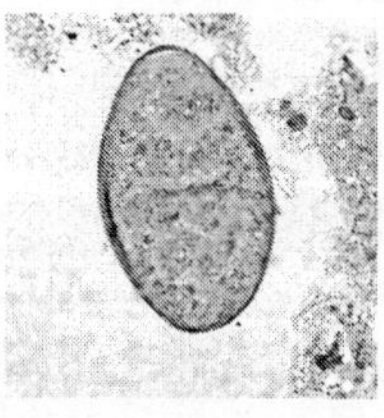

Fasciolopsis buski is structurally similar to Fasciola hepatica, yet exhibits important anatomical distinctions that correlate with its intestinal habitat.

It is the largest intestinal trematode infecting humans.

General Body Configuration

The adult worm is dorsoventrally flattened, fleshy, and leaf shaped. It measures approximately 20 to 75 millimetres in length and 8 to 20 millimetres in width, making it broader and thicker than many other trematodes.The anterior end is blunt and lacks the prominent cephalic cone seen in Fasciola hepatica. The body surface is smooth and covered by a thick tegument adapted to withstand digestive enzymes within the intestinal lumen.Its robust, muscular body allows firm attachment to the intestinal mucosa despite constant peristaltic movement.

Absence of a cephalic cone differentiates it morphologically from liver flukes.

Tegument

The tegument is syncytial and metabolically active. It serves multiple functions:

- Protection against digestive enzymes
- Absorption of nutrients
- Immune evasion

Unlike cestodes, trematodes retain a functional digestive tract; however, tegumental absorption supplements nutritional intake.The tegument may bear minute spines in early stages, though these are less prominent in adult forms.

Suckers and Attachment

Two muscular suckers are present:

- The oral sucker surrounds the mouth at the anterior end.
- The ventral sucker, also called the acetabulum, lies slightly posterior to the oral sucker and is usually larger.
- These suckers provide mechanical anchorage to the intestinal wall.

Because the parasite inhabits the small intestine rather than bile ducts, attachment is adapted to resist intestinal peristalsis rather than bile flow.

Dual sucker arrangement ensures stability within the dynamic intestinal environment.

Digestive System

The digestive system begins with the mouth within the oral sucker. The mouth leads to a muscular pharynx that generates suction for ingestion of intestinal contents.A short oesophagus bifurcates into two intestinal caeca that extend posteriorly without extensive branching.The digestive tract is incomplete and lacks an anus. Undigested material is expelled through the mouth.Compared with Fasciola hepatica, the intestinal branching is less elaborate, reflecting its luminal habitat rather than tissue invasive behaviour.

Reproductive System

Fasciolopsis buski is hermaphroditic and possesses highly developed reproductive organs.The male system consists of two large, branched testes located in the posterior region. The vas deferens opens through a genital pore situated anteriorly.The female reproductive system includes a single ovary, ootype, uterus, and extensive vitelline glands distributed laterally.The uterus is coiled and occupies a significant portion of the anterior body.The genital pore opens ventrally.

The extensive reproductive system reflects high fecundity and ensures transmission efficiency.

Excretory System

The excretory system consists of flame cells connected by tubules forming a protonephridial network. These tubules converge into a median excretory bladder opening posteriorly.This system maintains osmotic balance and removes metabolic waste.

Egg Morphology

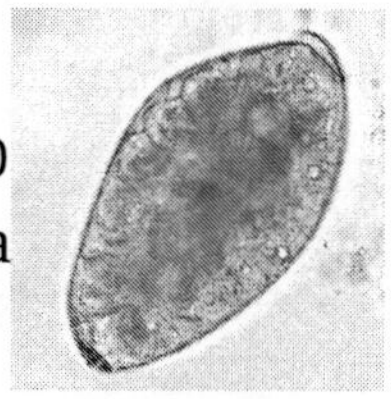

Eggs are large, oval, yellowish brown, and operculated. They measure approximately 130 to 150 micrometres in length.Eggs are morphologically similar to those of Fasciola hepatica and are unembryonated when passed in faeces.

Egg morphology alone cannot reliably distinguish Fasciolopsis buski **from** Fasciola hepatica.

Life Cycle of Fasciolopsis buski

First, remember that the adult worm lives in the small intestine of humans and pigs. The parasite produces large operculated eggs, and these eggs are passed out with faeces.Now, these eggs are not infective immediately. They must reach freshwater. In water, under suitable environmental conditions, a larva called the miracidium develops inside the egg.When fully developed, the miracidium hatches and swims actively. It must find a suitable freshwater snail within a limited time, otherwise it dies. The snail acts as the intermediate host.

Inside the snail, the miracidium undergoes transformation and multiplication. It first becomes a sporocyst, then rediae are formed, and finally cercariae are produced. This is an asexual multiplication phase, and one miracidium can produce many cercariae.The cercariae leave the snail and swim freely in water. However, they do not infect humans directly. Instead, they attach to aquatic plants and encyst, forming metacercariae.

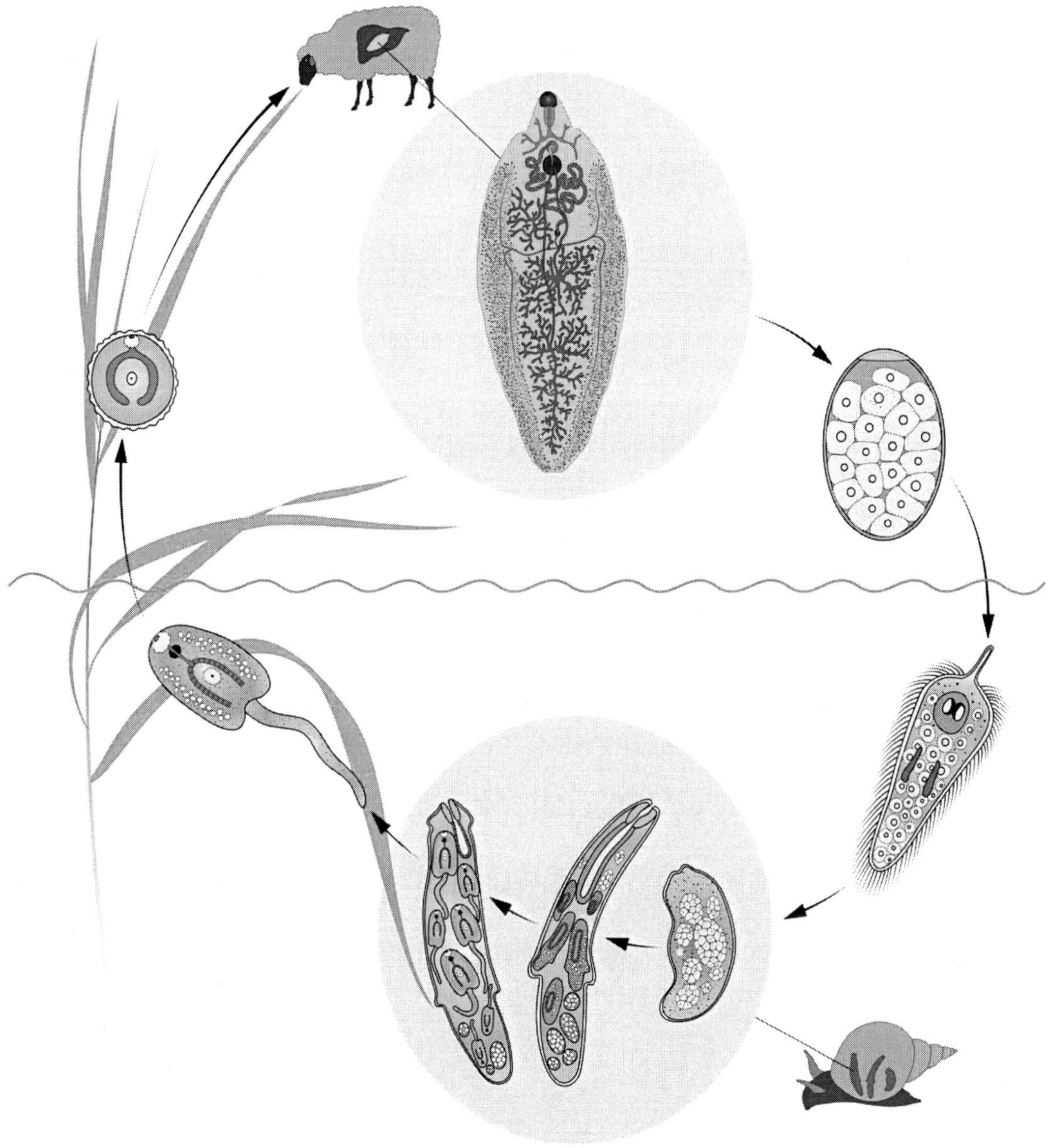

Now remember this carefully:

Metacercaria is the infective stage for humans.

When a person eats raw or inadequately washed aquatic plants such as water chestnut or lotus, they ingest the metacercariae.In the small intestine, the cyst wall dissolves, the juvenile fluke emerges, and it attaches to the intestinal mucosa. Unlike liver flukes, there is no migration through liver tissue.The worm matures in the intestine and starts producing eggs, completing the cycle.

So in summary:

- Egg in faeces
- Miracidium in water
- Snail as intermediate host
- Cercaria leaves snail
- Metacercaria on vegetation
- Human infection by ingestion

Pathogenicity and Organ Localisation of Fasciolopsis buski

The entire pathology is confined to the intestine.

Unlike liver flukes, this parasite does not migrate through tissues. It remains in the small intestine throughout its adult life.

Site of Localisation

The adult worm attaches to the mucosa of the small intestine, mainly the duodenum and jejunum.

Using its oral and ventral suckers, it firmly adheres to the intestinal wall.

When the worm burden is small, the damage is usually minimal.

But when multiple worms are present, the situation changes significantly.

Mechanism of Disease Production

The parasite produces disease mainly by:

- Mechanical irritation
- Inflammation of intestinal mucosa
- Nutritional interference
- Toxic metabolic products

Let us break this down.

Mechanical Irritation

The suckers attach to the intestinal mucosa, causing local trauma.

This repeated attachment and movement lead to:

- Mucosal erosion
- Ulceration
- Inflammatory reaction

Inflammatory Response

The presence of worms stimulates inflammatory cell infiltration.

This may result in:

- Oedema of intestinal wall
- Increased mucus secretion
- Hyperemia

In heavy infections, this can impair intestinal absorption.

Clinical Manifestations

In mild infection:

The patient may be asymptomatic or have mild abdominal discomfort.

In moderate infection:

- Abdominal pain
- Diarrhoea
- Nausea
- Loss of appetite

In heavy infection, especially in children:

- Severe diarrhoea
- Malabsorption
- Weakness
- Oedema due to protein loss
- Even intestinal obstruction in rare cases

Severity depends largely on worm burden.

Complications

In heavy infestation, the large size of worms may lead to:

- Mechanical intestinal obstruction
- Protein losing enteropathy
- Marked nutritional deficiency

Severe cases may produce generalised oedema due to hypoproteinaemia.

Pathophysiological Summary

There are two important principles to remember:

- First, pathology is luminal, not migratory.
- Second, disease severity is proportional to worm load.

No hepatic phase exists in this infection.

Laboratory Diagnosis of Fasciolopsis buski

Now let us understand how we confirm the diagnosis.

First, remember one principle:

Since the parasite remains in the intestine, stool examination is the primary diagnostic method.

There is no need for liver imaging or tissue biopsy, because there is no tissue migration phase.

Specimen Collection

- A fresh stool sample is collected in a clean container.
- Since eggs are passed in faeces, repeated stool examinations may improve detection.

Microscopic Examination

- A direct saline wet mount is prepared.
- A small portion of stool is placed on a glass slide.
- A drop of normal saline is added.
- The sample is mixed and covered with a coverslip.

- It is examined under low power and then high power magnification.
- If egg count is low, sedimentation concentration technique is preferred because trematode eggs are heavy.

Egg Identification

The eggs are:

- Large
- Oval
- Yellowish brown
- Operculated
- Unembryonated when passed

The egg morphology is similar to Fasciola hepatica.

Therefore, clinical correlation is important. In Fasciolopsis buski, the infection is intestinal. In Fasciola hepatica, there is hepatic involvement.Size measurement may assist differentiation, but practically they are very similar.

Additional Findings

In heavy infections, stool may show:

- Large number of eggs
- Occasionally adult worms passed spontaneously
- Peripheral eosinophilia may be present, but it is not specific.

Diagnostic Summary

- Stool examination confirms infection.
- Operculated eggs establish trematode diagnosis.
- Clinical history and organ involvement differentiate species.

Egg detection in stool confirms established intestinal infection.

The goal of treatment is complete elimination of adult worms from the intestine.

- The drug of choice for fasciolopsiasis is praziquantel.
- It is effective against adult intestinal flukes and produces rapid clearance of infection.

- Since the parasite does not migrate into tissues, treatment is generally straightforward compared with liver flukes.
- In heavy infections, especially in children, supportive care may be required.

This may include:

- Correction of dehydration
- Nutritional supplementation
- Management of protein deficiency

In rare cases of intestinal obstruction due to massive worm load, surgical intervention may be necessary.

Academic Note

The treatment information provided here is for educational understanding in medical zoology.It is not intended for clinical prescription or self medication.Clinical management must be performed by qualified medical professionals.

Prevention and Control of Fasciolopsis buski

Remember:

Human infection occurs by ingestion of metacercariae on aquatic vegetation.

Therefore prevention strategies are directed at interrupting this route.

1. Avoid Raw Aquatic Plants

Aquatic vegetables such as water chestnut and lotus should be thoroughly washed and properly cooked before consumption.Cooking destroys metacercariae.

2. Sanitation

Proper disposal of human and pig faeces prevents contamination of freshwater bodies with eggs.This reduces infection of snail intermediate hosts.

3. Control of Snail Population

Environmental management and reduction of snail habitats decrease transmission.

4. Veterinary Control

Regular deworming of pigs reduces environmental egg contamination.Since pigs are reservoir hosts, control in animals is essential.

Epidemiological Insight

- Snail-Intermediate host

- Pig-Reservoir and definitive host
- Human-Definitive host

Breaking any one link in this cycle significantly reduces disease transmission.

Paragonimus westermani

Common name, Oriental Lung Fluke

Introduction

Paragonimus westermani is a tissue invading digenetic trematode of major medical importance and the principal causative agent of pulmonary paragonimiasis. It is commonly referred to as the Oriental lung fluke because of its historical association with East and Southeast Asia, where the disease remains endemic.Unlike intestinal and hepatobiliary trematodes, Paragonimus westermani localises primarily in the lungs after undergoing extensive tissue migration. The infection is acquired through ingestion of raw or undercooked freshwater crabs or crayfish containing the encysted metacercarial stage.Clinically, pulmonary paragonimiasis frequently mimics tuberculosis because of chronic cough, haemoptysis, and radiological cavitary lesions. This resemblance has significant diagnostic implications in endemic regions.

Paragonimiasis is fundamentally a pulmonary tissue infection caused by a migrating trematode.

Taxonomic Position

Kingdom Animalia
Phylum Platyhelminthes
Class Trematoda
Order Plagiorchiida
Family Paragonimidae
Genus Paragonimus
Species Paragonimus westermani

Geographical Distribution

Paragonimus westermani is predominantly distributed in East and Southeast Asia. Endemic zones include:China, Japan,South Korea, Taiwan,Philippines,Thailand,Vietnam,Laos,Cambodia and IndonesiaIn South Asia, focal endemicity has been documented in northeastern India, particularly in Manipur, Nagaland, Arunachal Pradesh, and Assam, where consumption of freshwater crustaceans is culturally prevalent.Related Paragonimus species occur in parts of Africa and South America, but P. westermani remains the most significant Asian species.The epidemiological distribution is strongly associated with:

- Freshwater ecosystems
- Presence of suitable snail hosts
- Traditional dietary practices involving raw crustaceans

Geographical distribution is determined by ecological suitability and cultural food habits.

Morphology of Adult *Paragonimus westermani*

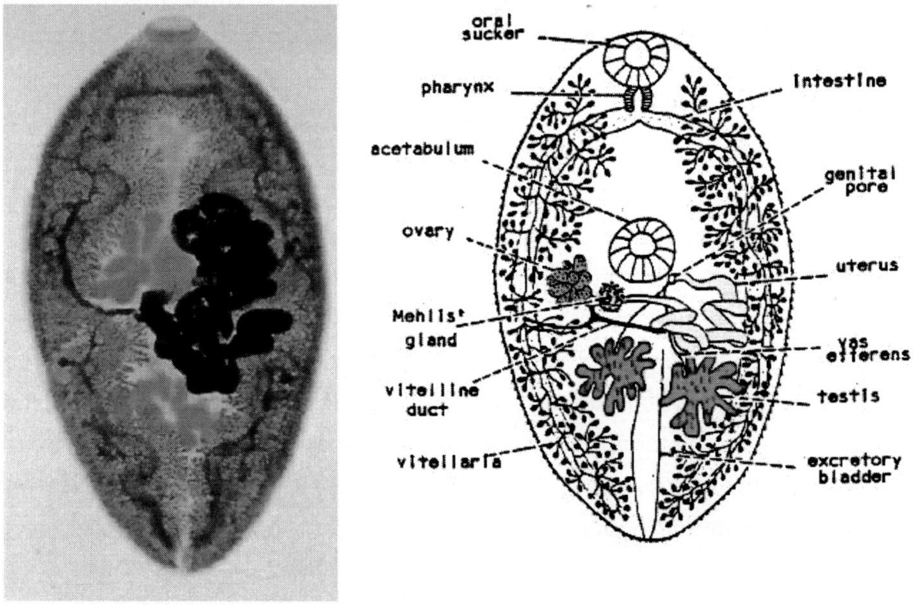

Morphology

Adult Worm

The adult fluke is thick, fleshy, and reddish brown in colour. Its shape resembles a coffee bean due to a slightly convex dorsal surface and flattened ventral surface.The average size ranges from 7.5 to 12 millimetres in length and 4 to 6 millimetres in width.

Two muscular suckers are present:

- The oral sucker surrounds the mouth at the anterior end.
- The ventral sucker is slightly posterior and aids in firm attachment within pulmonary tissue.

The tegument is thick and resistant, enabling survival within cystic cavities in lung parenchyma.Internally, the parasite possesses a branched digestive tract and well developed reproductive organs, as it is hermaphroditic.

Its compact, robust body reflects adaptation to a cystic pulmonary environment.

Egg

- Eggs are golden brown, oval, and operculated.
- They measure approximately 80 to 120 micrometres in length.
- A characteristic opercular shoulder is often visible, which aids microscopic identification.

- Eggs are unembryonated when released and require freshwater for further development.

Egg morphology is diagnostic when identified in sputum.

Life Cycle

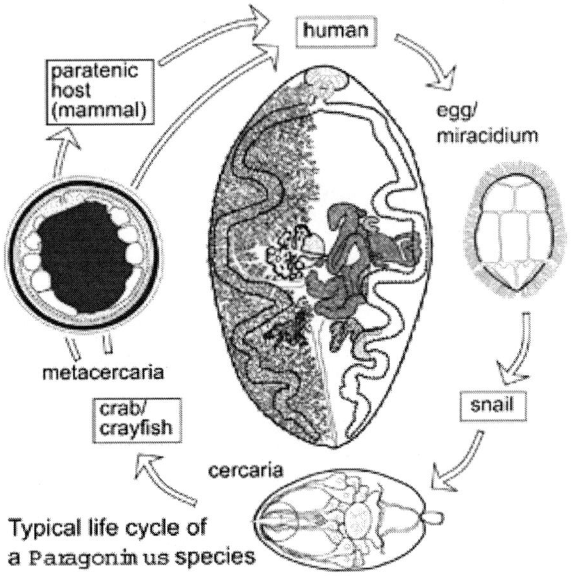

Typical life cycle of a Paragonimus species

The life cycle is indirect and requires two intermediate hosts.

Egg Release

- Eggs are discharged in sputum when pulmonary cysts communicate with bronchi. They may also be swallowed and passed in faeces.
- In freshwater, embryonation occurs and a miracidium develops within the egg.

First Intermediate Host

- The miracidium hatches and penetrates a suitable freshwater snail.
- Within the snail, the parasite undergoes asexual multiplication through sporocyst and redial stages, eventually producing cercariae.

Second Intermediate Host

- Cercariae leave the snail and penetrate freshwater crabs or crayfish.
- Within the musculature or viscera of the crustacean, they encyst as metacercariae.

Metacercaria is the infective stage for humans.

Human Infection and Migration

- Humans acquire infection by consuming raw or inadequately cooked crustaceans.
- After ingestion, metacercariae excyst in the duodenum.
- Juvenile flukes penetrate the intestinal wall, enter the peritoneal cavity, migrate through the diaphragm, and finally reach the lungs.

- This migratory phase may take several weeks.
- In the lungs, the parasites form fibrous cyst like cavities, usually in pairs, where they mature and begin egg production.

Tissue migration distinguishes lung flukes from intestinal trematodes.

Pathogenesis

- Disease manifestations occur in two phases:

1. Migratory phase
2. Pulmonary phase

During migration, larvae may cause abdominal pain, fever, and eosinophilia.

In the pulmonary phase, adult worms induce chronic inflammation, cyst formation, and fibrosis.

Clinical features include:

- Chronic cough
- Chest pain
- Rusty or blood stained sputum
- Haemoptysis

Cyst rupture into bronchi results in egg expectoration.

Extrapulmonary Paragonimiasis

Occasionally, parasites may lodge in ectopic sites such as:

- Brain
- Subcutaneous tissue
- Liver
- Cerebral involvement may produce seizures and focal neurological deficits.

Cerebral paragonimiasis is a serious complication.

Diagnosis

- Definitive diagnosis is established by identification of characteristic operculated eggs in sputum.
- Eggs may also be detected in stool if sputum is swallowed.
- Radiological imaging may reveal cystic lesions or cavitary shadows in lungs.

Serological tests assist in early or ectopic infection.

Differential diagnosis includes:

- Pulmonary tuberculosis
- Lung abscess
- Bronchiectasis

Treatment

- Praziquantel is the drug of choice and is highly effective.
- Supportive management is required in complicated pulmonary or cerebral disease.
- This information is provided for academic purposes only and not for clinical prescription.

Prevention and Control

- Avoid consumption of raw or undercooked freshwater crabs and crayfish.
- Health education in endemic regions is essential.
- Proper disposal of sputum and faeces reduces contamination of freshwater bodies.
- Control of snail intermediate hosts contributes to reduction in transmission.

Conceptual Summary

- Two intermediate hosts required
- Infective stage is metacercaria
- Primary site is lung
- Mimics tuberculosis
- Egg detected in sputum

Paragonimiasis is a pulmonary trematode infection acquired through dietary exposure.

Schistosoma Species

Common name, Blood flukes

Introduction

The genus Schistosoma comprises digenetic trematodes of major medical and epidemiological importance. Unlike other trematodes, these parasites inhabit the venous circulation of the human host and exhibit sexual dimorphism, with separate male and female worms.Schistosomiasis is one of the most prevalent parasitic diseases worldwide and is considered a major neglected tropical disease. It affects millions of individuals, particularly in tropical and subtropical regions.

The most important human species are:

- Schistosoma haematobium
- Schistosoma mansoni
- Schistosoma japonicum

Schistosoma species are the only trematodes with separate sexes and blood dwelling habitat.

Geographical Distribution

Schistosoma haematobium

Primarily distributed in Africa and parts of the Middle East. It is the principal cause of urinary schistosomiasis.

Schistosoma mansoni

Found in Africa, the Middle East, parts of South America, and the Caribbean. It causes intestinal and hepatosplenic schistosomiasis.

Schistosoma japonicum

Endemic in East Asia, particularly China, the Philippines, and Indonesia. It is associated with more severe hepatosplenic disease due to higher egg production.

In India, classical endemicity is limited, but sporadic cases have been reported in certain regions.

Distribution depends on presence of specific freshwater snail intermediate hosts.

Morphology

Adult Worms

Unlike other trematodes, Schistosoma species are elongated and cylindrical rather than leaf shaped.

The male worm is shorter and broader, possessing a ventral groove called the gynecophoral canal in which the slender female resides.

This permanent pairing is characteristic.

The tegument is thick and adapted to resist host immune mechanisms within blood vessels.

Sexual dimorphism is a defining feature of blood flukes.

Eggs

Egg morphology differs among species and is essential for identification.

- Schistosoma haematobium
  Terminal spine

- Schistosoma mansoni
  Large lateral spine

- Schistosoma japonicum
  Small rudimentary lateral spine

Eggs are non operculated.

Spine position is the key diagnostic feature for species differentiation.

Life Cycle

The life cycle differs fundamentally from other trematodes.

- Only one intermediate host is required.

- Egg Release
- Eggs are deposited in venules of the host and migrate into lumen of bladder or intestine.
- They are passed in urine in S. haematobium and in faeces in S. mansoni and S. japonicum.

Miracidium and Snail Infection

- In freshwater, eggs hatch and release miracidia.
- Miracidia penetrate specific freshwater snails.
- Within the snail, development proceeds through sporocyst stages to produce cercariae.
- There is no redial stage in schistosomes.

Cercarial Stage

- Cercariae are fork tailed and free swimming.
- They actively penetrate intact human skin during contact with contaminated water.
- **Skin penetration is the mode of human infection.**

Migration in Human Host

- After penetration, cercariae lose their tails and become schistosomula.
- They enter circulation, migrate through lungs, and eventually reach the portal venous system.
- Mature worms settle in specific venous plexuses:

S. haematobium

- Venous plexus of urinary bladder

S. mansoni

- Mesenteric veins of large intestine

S. japonicum

- Mesenteric veins of small intestine

Pathogenesis

- Disease is primarily due to host immune reaction against deposited eggs rather than adult worms.
- Granuloma formation occurs around trapped eggs in tissues.

This leads to:

- Fibrosis
- Portal hypertension
- Haematuria
- Bladder wall thickening
- Chronic infection may result in severe organ damage.

Egg induced granulomatous inflammation is the central mechanism of disease.

Clinical Manifestations

Acute Stage

- Dermatitis at penetration site
- Fever
- Eosinophilia

Chronic Stage

- Urinary schistosomiasis
- Haematuria
- Bladder fibrosis

Intestinal schistosomiasis

- Abdominal pain
- Hepatosplenomegaly
- Portal hypertension
- Chronic S. haematobium infection is associated with increased risk of bladder carcinoma.

Diagnosis

- Egg detection in urine or stool is confirmatory.
- Urine examination for terminal spine eggs in S. haematobium.
- Stool examination for lateral spine eggs in S. mansoni.
- Serology and imaging assist in complicated cases.

Treatment

- Praziquantel is effective against adult worms.
- Control programmes involve mass drug administration in endemic areas.
- This information is presented for academic understanding and not for clinical prescription.

Comparative Study of Medically Important Schistosoma Species

Feature	**Schistosoma haematobium**	**Schistosoma mansoni**	**Schistosoma japonicum**
Common name	Urinary blood fluke	Intestinal blood fluke	Oriental blood fluke
Geographical distribution	Africa, Middle East	Africa, Middle East, South America, Caribbean	China, Philippines, Indonesia
Habitat in human host	Vesical and pelvic venous plexus	Inferior mesenteric veins	Superior mesenteric veins
Eggs passed in	Urine	Stool	Stool
Egg morphology	Oval with terminal spine	Oval with large lateral spine	Rounded with small rudimentary lateral spine
Egg production rate	Moderate	Moderate	High
Intermediate host snail	Bulinus species	Biomphalaria species	Oncomelania species
Major organ involvement	Urinary bladder	Colon and liver	Small intestine and liver
Major complication	Haematuria, bladder fibrosis, carcinoma risk	Portal hypertension, hepatosplenomegaly	Severe hepatosplenic disease
Association with malignancy	Strong association with squamous cell carcinoma of bladder	No strong direct association	No strong direct association
Severity of hepatosplenic disease	Mild to moderate	Moderate	Often severe due to high egg burden

Key Conceptual Distinctions

Spine position is the most important diagnostic feature in microscopy.

Disease manifestations are primarily due to egg induced granulomatous inflammation.

- S. haematobium
  Primarily urinary disease
- S. mansoni
  Intestinal and hepatic disease
- S. japonicum
  More aggressive hepatosplenic involvement

Pathophysiological Insight

The adult worms themselves cause minimal direct damage.

The principal pathology results from:

- Immune mediated granuloma formation
- Chronic inflammation
- Progressive fibrosis

In long standing infection:

- Portal hypertension may develop in intestinal species.
- Bladder wall calcification and malignancy risk occur in urinary species.

T

16.Laboratory Diagnosis of Parasitic Infections

Introduction

Accurate laboratory diagnosis forms the cornerstone of clinical parasitology. Unlike many bacterial and viral infections, parasitic diseases often present with non specific clinical manifestations that may mimic other systemic disorders. Therefore, definitive identification of the parasite, its developmental stage, or host immune response is essential for correct diagnosis, therapeutic decision making, epidemiological surveillance, and control strategies.

Parasitic infections may involve the gastrointestinal tract, blood, tissues, or multiple organ systems. The diversity of parasites, including protozoa, helminths, and ectoparasites, necessitates a broad range of diagnostic approaches. No single laboratory method is sufficient for all parasitic diseases.

Laboratory confirmation is critical because clinical features alone are often misleading in parasitic infections.

Diagnostic methods in parasitology are traditionally categorised into:

- Microscopic methods
- Concentration techniques
- Staining procedures
- Culture methods
- Serological tests
- Molecular diagnostic techniques
- Imaging and supportive investigations

The choice of diagnostic technique depends upon:

- Type of parasite suspected
- Stage of infection
- Site of localisation
- Available laboratory facilities

Modern parasitology integrates conventional microscopy with advanced immunological and molecular tools to enhance sensitivity and specificity.

Importance of Laboratory Diagnosis

Laboratory diagnosis serves multiple purposes:

- Confirmation of clinical suspicion
- Identification of species for appropriate therapy
- Assessment of parasite burden
- Monitoring response to treatment
- Epidemiological mapping and control programmes

In endemic regions, laboratory detection is essential for surveillance and implementation of public health interventions.

In immunocompromised patients, early and accurate detection becomes even more crucial due to atypical presentations.

Species level identification directly influences therapeutic strategy in many parasitic infections.

Specimen Collection and Handling

Accurate laboratory diagnosis of parasitic infections begins with proper specimen collection. Errors at the pre analytical stage may lead to false negative results, misidentification, or degradation of diagnostic structures.

Correct specimen collection is as important as the diagnostic technique itself.

The type of specimen required depends on the suspected parasite and its site of localisation.

1. Stool Examination

Stool is the most commonly examined specimen in parasitology, particularly for intestinal protozoa and helminths.

Collection

The specimen should be freshly passed and collected in a clean, dry, wide mouthed container. It must not be contaminated with urine, water, or disinfectants.

If immediate examination is not possible, appropriate preservatives such as formalin may be used.

Indications

Detection of:

- Protozoan trophozoites and cysts
- Helminth eggs
- Larvae
- Proglottids

For certain parasites, multiple stool samples collected on consecutive days increase sensitivity.

Intermittent shedding of eggs or cysts necessitates repeated sampling.

2. Blood Examination

Blood is essential for diagnosis of haemoparasites.

Indications

- Malaria parasites
- Microfilariae
- Trypanosomes
- Babesia

Collection

- Peripheral blood is obtained by finger prick or venipuncture.
- Timing may be important in certain infections. For example, microfilariae may show nocturnal periodicity.
- Thick and thin blood smears are prepared for microscopic examination.

Proper smear preparation and staining are critical for accurate identification.

3. Urine Examination

- Urine is examined primarily for detection of Schistosoma haematobium eggs.
- Midday urine samples are preferred, as egg excretion peaks during this period.
- Centrifugation may enhance detection.

4. Sputum Examination

- Sputum is important in pulmonary parasitic infections such as paragonimiasis.
- Early morning sputum is preferable for egg detection.
- Care must be taken to differentiate sputum from saliva.

5. Tissue Biopsy and Aspirates

Certain tissue dwelling parasites require biopsy specimens.

Examples include:

- Hydatid cyst fluid
- Muscle biopsy in trichinellosis
- Lymph node aspirates in leishmaniasis

Specimens must be handled aseptically and processed promptly.

6. Cerebrospinal Fluid

- CSF examination may be required in suspected cerebral parasitic infections such as neurocysticercosis or cerebral malaria.
- Strict aseptic technique is essential.

Preservation and Transport

- If delay in examination is expected, preservation methods must be applied.
- Temperature control, use of fixatives, and proper labeling are essential.
- All specimens should include complete patient details and clinical history.
- Accurate labeling and documentation prevent diagnostic errors.

Excellent. We now proceed to the core of diagnostic parasitology.

Microscopic Techniques

Microscopy remains the fundamental and most widely used method for diagnosis of parasitic infections. Despite advances in molecular and immunological assays, direct visualisation of the parasite or its developmental stages continues to be the gold standard in many settings.

Microscopy provides direct evidence of infection by demonstrating the parasite itself.

The sensitivity of microscopic diagnosis depends upon:

- Quality of specimen
- Skill of the observer
- Appropriate preparation technique
- Parasite load

Microscopic techniques in parasitology may be broadly classified into:

1. Direct examination methods
2. Concentration techniques
3. Staining procedures
4. Blood smear examination

1. Direct Wet Mount Examination

This is the simplest and most rapid method, particularly for stool specimens.

A small amount of specimen is placed on a glass slide and mixed with normal saline. A coverslip is applied, and the preparation is examined under low and high power magnification.

Saline preparation allows detection of:

- Motile protozoan trophozoites
- Helminth eggs

- Larvae

An iodine preparation may also be used. Iodine enhances visibility of internal structures of cysts but kills motile organisms.

Wet mount examination is essential for detecting motility in protozoa.

2. Concentration Techniques

In light infections, parasite numbers may be low. Concentration methods increase the probability of detection by separating parasites from debris.

Two major types are used:

1. Sedimentation techniques
2. Flotation techniques

Sedimentation methods rely on gravity or centrifugation to concentrate heavier eggs and cysts.

Flotation techniques use solutions of higher specific gravity, causing lighter eggs to float to the surface.

Sedimentation is particularly useful for trematode eggs, which are heavy and may not float efficiently.

Choice of concentration method depends on the type of parasite suspected.

3. Staining Techniques

Certain parasites require special stains for identification.

Permanent stained smears provide better morphological detail compared with wet mounts.

Commonly used stains include:

- Iodine stain
- Giemsa stain
- Trichrome stain
- Modified acid fast stain

Giemsa stain is widely used for blood parasites such as malaria and leishmania.

Modified acid fast staining is useful for coccidian parasites.

Staining enhances structural detail and improves diagnostic accuracy.

4. Blood Smear Examination

Blood smear microscopy is critical for haemoparasites.

Two types of smears are prepared:

1. Thick smear
2. Thin smear

Thick smear concentrates blood elements and increases sensitivity for parasite detection.

Thin smear preserves morphology and is useful for species identification.

Proper staining and controlled examination under oil immersion are essential.

Thick smear for detection, thin smear for species identification.

Limitations of Microscopy

- Operator dependent
- Requires experience
- May miss low level infections
- Time consuming in heavy workloads

Despite limitations, microscopy remains indispensable, especially in resource limited settings.

Culture Methods

Culture techniques are used for certain protozoan parasites where direct microscopy may be insufficient or when parasite multiplication is required for confirmation.

Culture improves sensitivity and allows further characterisation of organisms.

Culture is mainly useful for protozoal parasites rather than helminths.

Indications for Culture

- Amoebiasis in doubtful cases
- Leishmaniasis from tissue aspirates
- Free living amoebae
- Certain intestinal protozoa

General Principles

- Specimens must be collected aseptically and processed promptly.
- Specific culture media are required depending on the parasite.

For example:

- Novy MacNeal Nicolle medium for Leishmania .Specialised media for intestinal amoebae
- Culture requires controlled temperature and sterile conditions.
- While useful, culture is time consuming and not routinely required in most helminthic infections.

Serological Methods

Serology detects host antibodies or circulating parasite antigens.

These methods are particularly useful when:

- Parasite burden is low
- Parasite is located in deep tissues
- Eggs or larvae are not easily detectable

Serological tests are valuable in tissue parasitic infections.

Common Serological Techniques

Enzyme linked immunosorbent assay
Indirect haemagglutination test
Indirect immunofluorescence
Rapid immunochromatographic tests

ELISA is widely used because of its high sensitivity and specificity.

Serology is especially useful in:

Hydatid disease
Cysticercosis
Toxoplasmosis
Visceral leishmaniasis

Limitations of Serology

Cannot always distinguish past from active infection
Cross reactivity may occur
Antibody levels may persist after treatment

Therefore, serology must be interpreted in clinical context.

Molecular Diagnostic Techniques

Molecular methods represent a major advancement in parasitology.

Polymerase chain reaction based assays allow detection of parasite DNA or RNA with high sensitivity.

Molecular diagnostics provide high specificity and are useful in low level infections.

Applications

- Species differentiation
- Drug resistance detection
- Early diagnosis
- Detection in immunocompromised patients
- Real time PCR allows quantitative estimation of parasite load.

These techniques are particularly useful in:

- Malaria species differentiation
- Leishmaniasis
- Toxoplasmosis
- Intestinal protozoa

Limitations

- High cost
- Need for specialised laboratory infrastructure
- Technical expertise required

Molecular techniques complement but do not replace microscopy in many endemic settings.

Imaging in Parasitic Infections

Imaging studies support diagnosis in tissue infections.

Examples include:

- Ultrasonography in hydatid disease
- CT scan in neurocysticercosis
- Chest radiography in paragonimiasis

Imaging provides structural evidence but does not identify species.

Quality Control and Biosafety

Accurate laboratory diagnosis requires:

- Standardised procedures
- Internal quality control
- Proper staining protocols
- Regular calibration of equipment

Biosafety measures must be observed to prevent laboratory acquired infections.

Specimens should be handled with gloves and proper waste disposal methods followed.

Quality assurance ensures reliability of parasitological diagnosis.

Integrated Diagnostic Approach in Parasitology

Laboratory diagnosis of parasitic infections should follow a systematic and rational approach rather than isolated testing.

Diagnosis must be guided by clinical suspicion, epidemiological history, and organ involvement.

The diagnostic strategy can be conceptualised in stepwise form.

Step 1. Clinical and Epidemiological Assessment

Before laboratory testing, important factors must be evaluated:

1. Travel history
2. Residence in endemic area

3. Dietary habits
4. Water exposure
5. Animal contact
6. Immune status

These factors help narrow the list of probable parasites.

Step 2. Selection of Appropriate Specimen

- Intestinal symptoms
  Stool examination

- Fever with chills
  Blood smear

- Haematuria
  Urine examination

- Chronic cough with haemoptysis
  Sputum examination

- Neurological symptoms
  Imaging and serology

Correct specimen selection improves diagnostic yield.

Step 3. Initial Microscopy

Microscopy should be the first line investigation in most parasitic infections.

- Direct wet mount
- Concentration techniques
- Blood smear

Microscopy confirms presence of parasite structures.

Step 4. Supplementary Tests

If microscopy is negative but suspicion remains high:

- Serological testing
- Molecular assays
- Imaging studies

These are particularly useful for tissue parasites.

Step 5. Species Identification

Accurate species identification is critical because treatment protocols may differ.

For example:

Different malaria species require different management strategies.
Schistosoma species differ in clinical complications.

Practical Diagnostic Algorithm

- Suspected intestinal parasite
  Stool microscopy
  If negative and symptoms persist, repeat sampling and apply concentration method

- Suspected blood parasite
  Prepare thick and thin smear
  If negative but clinically suspected, repeat during fever spike

- Suspected tissue parasite
  Imaging plus serology
  Confirm with biopsy or molecular test if required

Challenges in Laboratory Diagnosis

- Low parasite burden
- Intermittent shedding
- Morphological similarity between species
- Operator dependency
- Limited resources in endemic regions

No single method is universally sufficient.

An integrated approach ensures accuracy.

Concluding Perspective

Laboratory diagnosis is not merely detection of parasites, but a structured process combining:

Clinical reasoning
Microscopy
Immunology
Molecular biology
Public health awareness

The modern parasitology laboratory integrates classical techniques with advanced diagnostics to achieve precision.

Accurate laboratory diagnosis is essential for effective treatment, epidemiological surveillance, and disease control.

17.Zoonotic Parasitic Diseases

Introduction

Zoonotic parasitic diseases are infections naturally transmitted between vertebrate animals and humans. These infections occupy a critical intersection between zoology, veterinary science, and human medicine.Unlike strictly human parasites, zoonotic parasites maintain their life cycle primarily in animal hosts, with humans serving as accidental or incidental hosts in many cases.

Zoonotic parasitism reflects the biological continuity between animal and human ecosystems.

The epidemiology of zoonotic parasitic diseases is influenced by:

- Animal reservoirs
- Environmental exposure
- Occupational practices
- Dietary habits
- Human encroachment into wildlife habitats

In recent decades, increasing urbanisation, deforestation, livestock expansion, and global travel have amplified the transmission potential of zoonotic infections.

Concept and Classification of Zoonosis

- The term zoonosis refers to diseases and infections that are naturally transmitted between vertebrate animals and humans.
- Zoonotic parasitic diseases may be classified based on transmission pattern.
- Direct Zoonosis
- Transmission occurs directly from infected animal to human without intermediate hosts.

Example
Toxocariasis from dogs

Cyclozoonosis

- The life cycle requires more than one vertebrate host but no invertebrate host.

Example
Echinococcosis involving dog and sheep

Metazoonosis

- Transmission requires both vertebrate and invertebrate hosts.

Example
Leishmaniasis involving sandfly vector

Saprozoonosis

- Infection involves environmental stages such as soil or water.

Example
Toxoplasmosis via contaminated soil

Understanding transmission pattern is essential for designing control strategies

Importance of Zoonotic Parasitic Diseases

Zoonotic parasites contribute significantly to global disease burden.

They may produce:

- Chronic disability
- Organ damage
- Neurological complications
- Economic loss in livestock

Many zoonotic parasitic diseases are neglected tropical diseases and disproportionately affect rural and economically disadvantaged populations.

In addition, zoonotic parasites have emerged in new geographical regions due to climate change and ecological disturbance.

The One Health concept recognises that human health is inseparable from animal and environmental health.

Major Zoonotic Protozoal Diseases

Zoonotic protozoa represent an important group of pathogens that maintain natural reservoirs in animals while occasionally infecting humans. These infections may range from asymptomatic carriage to severe systemic disease.

1. Toxoplasmosis

Toxoplasma gondii is an obligate intracellular protozoan parasite of global distribution. It is one of the most successful zoonotic parasites worldwide.

Reservoir and Transmission

The definitive host is the domestic cat and other felids, in which sexual reproduction occurs. Oocysts are shed in cat faeces and contaminate soil, water, and food.

Humans acquire infection through:

Ingestion of oocysts from contaminated soil or vegetables
Consumption of undercooked meat containing tissue cysts
Congenital transmission from mother to fetus

Cats play a central role in environmental dissemination of oocysts.

Clinical Significance

In immunocompetent individuals, infection is often asymptomatic.

In immunocompromised individuals, particularly those with impaired cellular immunity, severe disease may occur, including encephalitis.

Congenital toxoplasmosis may result in:

- Hydrocephalus
- Chorioretinitis
- Intracranial calcifications

Toxoplasmosis exemplifies environmental and food borne zoonotic transmission.

2. Leishmaniasis

Leishmaniasis is caused by protozoa of the genus Leishmania and transmitted by sandflies.

Dogs and wild mammals serve as reservoir hosts in many endemic regions.

Transmission

Infected female sandflies transmit promastigotes during blood feeding.

The disease manifests in different clinical forms:

Visceral leishmaniasis
Cutaneous leishmaniasis
Mucocutaneous leishmaniasis

In visceral leishmaniasis, parasites multiply within macrophages and affect spleen, liver, and bone marrow.

Reservoir animals sustain transmission cycles in endemic areas.

3. Cryptosporidiosis

Cryptosporidium species infect both humans and domestic animals.

Transmission occurs through ingestion of oocysts in contaminated water.

Cattle are important reservoirs.

The disease is particularly severe in immunocompromised individuals.

Waterborne zoonotic transmission is a significant public health concern.

Major Zoonotic Helminthic Diseases

Disease	Causative Parasite	Animal Reservoir	Mode of Human Infection	Role of Humans	Major Clinical Manifestation	Key Concept
Echinococcosis	Echinococcus granulosus	Dog definitive host, sheep intermediate host	Ingestion of eggs from dog contaminated environment	Accidental intermediate host	Hydatid cyst in liver and lungs	Humans interrupt natural cycle
Taeniasis and Cysticercosis	Taenia solium	Pig intermediate host	Ingestion of cysticerci in pork or eggs from contaminated food	Definitive host in taeniasis, intermediate host in cysticercosis	Intestinal infection, neurocysticercosis	Dual role of humans
Trichinellosis	Trichinella spiralis	Pig and wild carnivores	Consumption of raw or undercooked meat	Definitive and intermediate host	Muscle pain, fever	Entire life cycle in one host
Toxocariasis	Toxocara canis, Toxocara cati	Dog and cat	Ingestion of embryonated eggs from soil	Dead end host	Visceral and ocular larva migrans	Larvae migrate but do not mature
Fascioliasis	Fasciola hepatica	Sheep and cattle	Ingestion of metacercariae on aquatic plants	Accidental definitive host	Hepatic and biliary disease	Overlap of veterinary and human infection

Conceptual Interpretation

This table highlights key biological patterns:

Accidental intermediate host
Dead end host
Dual host role
Food borne transmission
Environmental contamination

Zoonotic helminths demonstrate diverse host parasite relationships requiring integrated control strategies.

Emerging and Re Emerging Zoonotic Parasites

Emerging zoonotic parasitic diseases are those that have recently appeared in a population or are increasing in incidence or geographic range. Re emerging infections are previously controlled diseases that are again becoming significant public health problems.The emergence of zoonotic parasites is closely linked to ecological, environmental, and socio economic changes.

Human encroachment into wildlife habitats has increased zoonotic transmission.

Factors Contributing to Emergence

a) Environmental changes

b) Deforestation and urban expansion

c) Intensive livestock farming

d) Climate change affecting vector distribution

e) Global travel and migration

f) Changing dietary habits

Climate change has altered the geographical range of vector borne parasites, allowing transmission in previously non endemic regions.

Examples of Emerging Zoonotic Parasites

1. Leishmaniasis Expansion

Urbanisation and adaptation of sandflies to peri urban environments have increased transmission.

2. Echinococcosis in Urban Areas

Increased dog populations in cities have expanded environmental contamination.

3. Cryptosporidiosis

Waterborne outbreaks linked to livestock contamination highlight environmental transmission.

4. Angiostrongyliasis

Rat lungworm infections have expanded geographically due to global trade and movement of intermediate hosts.

Wildlife Reservoirs and Spillover

Wildlife species serve as reservoirs for numerous parasites. When ecological balance is disturbed, spillover to humans becomes more likely.

Agricultural intensification and wildlife trade increase the risk of cross species transmission.

Spillover events are often linked to ecological imbalance.

The One Health Concept

The One Health approach recognises that human health, animal health, and environmental health are interconnected.

This concept emphasises:

a) Integrated surveillance
b) Veterinary and medical collaboration
c) Environmental monitoring
d) Vector control
e) Public education

In zoonotic parasitic diseases, effective control cannot be achieved by treating humans alone. Animal reservoirs and environmental contamination must be addressed simultaneously.

Application of One Health in Parasitology

Control of echinococcosis requires:

- Deworming of dogs
- Meat inspection
- Public education

Control of leishmaniasis requires:

- Vector control
- Management of reservoir hosts
- Community level surveillance

Control of toxoplasmosis requires:

- Safe meat practices
- Proper disposal of cat faeces
- Food hygiene

One Health is a preventive philosophy rather than a reactive strategy.

Concluding Perspective

Zoonotic parasitic diseases illustrate the dynamic relationship between humans and the animal world.

Emerging infections underscore the need for:

- Interdisciplinary collaboration
- Sustainable environmental practices
- Continuous epidemiological monitoring

Future parasitology must integrate zoology, veterinary science, ecology, and public health.

18.Prevention and Control of Parasitic Diseases

Parasitic diseases remain a major cause of morbidity and socioeconomic burden in many parts of the world, particularly in tropical and subtropical regions. Effective prevention and control require a comprehensive understanding of parasite biology, transmission dynamics, environmental factors, and human behaviour. Unlike many bacterial infections that can be controlled primarily through antimicrobial therapy, parasitic diseases often demand multifaceted strategies targeting multiple stages of the life cycle. Sustainable control depends not only on medical intervention but also on environmental management, health education, and socioeconomic development.

Prevention of parasitic diseases fundamentally relies on interrupting the life cycle of the parasite. Each parasite possesses critical stages that are vulnerable to intervention. These may include elimination of intermediate hosts, protection against infective stages, reduction of environmental contamination, or treatment of reservoir hosts. By identifying weak links within the transmission cycle, targeted control measures can significantly reduce disease incidence.

Improvement of sanitation is one of the most powerful preventive tools in parasitology. Many intestinal helminths and protozoa are transmitted through faecal contamination of soil, water, or food. Proper disposal of human and animal waste, access to safe drinking water, and hygienic food handling practices greatly reduce transmission. In communities where open defecation persists, soil transmitted helminths continue to thrive. Construction of sanitary latrines and implementation of community led sanitation programmes have demonstrated measurable reductions in parasitic burden.

Personal protective measures also play a crucial role. Regular hand washing, proper washing and cooking of food, use of footwear in endemic areas of soil transmitted helminths, and avoidance of raw or undercooked meat and fish reduce exposure to infective stages. In regions where schistosomiasis is endemic, avoidance of contact with contaminated freshwater can significantly lower infection rates. Public awareness and behavioural modification remain essential components of prevention.

Vector control is central to the management of vector borne parasitic diseases such as malaria, leishmaniasis, and lymphatic filariasis. Reduction of mosquito breeding sites, use of insecticide treated bed nets, indoor residual spraying, and environmental management disrupt parasite transmission. Climate change and ecological alteration have expanded vector habitats in certain regions, making integrated vector management increasingly important.

Control of zoonotic parasitic diseases requires coordinated veterinary and public health interventions. Deworming of dogs to prevent echinococcosis, inspection of meat to reduce taeniasis and trichinellosis, vaccination of livestock where applicable, and management of stray animal populations contribute significantly to transmission reduction. The One Health framework emphasises collaboration between medical and veterinary sectors to address shared health threats.

Chemotherapeutic control strategies, including mass drug administration programmes, have been implemented for several parasitic diseases. Periodic administration of antihelminthic drugs in endemic communities reduces worm burden and transmission potential. Such programmes have been particularly effective in controlling lymphatic filariasis and soil transmitted helminths. However, reliance solely on chemotherapy without environmental improvement may result in reinfection. Sustainable control must therefore integrate pharmacological intervention with long term preventive measures.

Health education forms the foundation of all preventive efforts. Communities must understand how parasitic diseases are transmitted and how simple behavioural changes can reduce risk. Educational campaigns in schools and rural settings enhance awareness regarding hygiene, safe food practices, and environmental cleanliness. Empowering communities promotes active participation in control programmes rather than passive dependence on medical services.

Surveillance and epidemiological monitoring are essential for assessing the effectiveness of control strategies. Laboratory diagnosis, case reporting, and mapping of endemic zones enable public health authorities to identify high risk populations and allocate resources efficiently. Emerging and re emerging parasitic diseases necessitate continuous vigilance and adaptive response mechanisms.

Socioeconomic development plays an indirect yet powerful role in parasitic disease control. Improved housing, access to clean water, better nutrition, and enhanced healthcare infrastructure reduce vulnerability to infection. Parasitic diseases are often diseases of poverty, and long term reduction depends on addressing underlying social determinants.

Global initiatives led by international health organisations have prioritised the elimination or control of several parasitic diseases. Integrated approaches combining mass treatment, vector control, sanitation improvement, and public education have demonstrated success in reducing disease prevalence in many regions. Continued political commitment, funding, and interdisciplinary collaboration remain essential to sustain progress.

In conclusion, prevention and control of parasitic diseases require a holistic and integrated approach that encompasses biological understanding, environmental management, public health policy, and community participation. No single intervention is sufficient in isolation. Sustainable control is achieved when medical treatment, sanitation, vector management, veterinary collaboration, and health education function together as complementary strategies. The future of parasitology lies not only in accurate diagnosis and effective therapy but also in preventive foresight and coordinated global action.

INDEX

References

1. Chatterjee KD. Parasitology: Protozoology and Helminthology. 13th ed. Kolkata: CBS Publishers and Distributors; 2019.
2. Paniker CKJ, Ghosh S. Paniker's Textbook of Medical Parasitology. 8th ed. New Delhi: Jaypee Brothers Medical Publishers; 2018.
3. Arora DR, Arora B. Medical Parasitology. 4th ed. New Delhi: CBS Publishers; 2021.
4. Garcia LS. Diagnostic Medical Parasitology. 6th ed. Washington DC: ASM Press; 2016.
5. Roberts LS, Janovy J, Nadler SA. Foundations of Parasitology. 10th ed. New York: McGraw Hill Education; 2019.
6. Markell EK, John DT, Krotoski WA. Markell and Voge's Medical Parasitology. 9th ed. Philadelphia: Saunders Elsevier; 2006.
7. Cox FEG. Modern Parasitology: A Textbook of Parasitology. 2nd ed. Oxford: Wiley Blackwell; 2009.
8. Soulsby EJL. Helminths, Arthropods and Protozoa of Domesticated Animals. 7th ed. London: Baillière Tindall; 1982.
9. World Health Organization. Basic Laboratory Methods in Medical Parasitology. Geneva: WHO; 1991.
10. World Health Organization. Control of Neglected Tropical Diseases: Strategic and Technical Advisory Group Reports. Geneva: WHO; latest edition.
11. Centers for Disease Control and Prevention. Parasites and Health Information. Atlanta: CDC; updated periodically.
12. Murray PR, Rosenthal KS, Pfaller MA. Medical Microbiology. 9th ed. Philadelphia: Elsevier; 2020.
13. Cook GC, Zumla A. Manson's Tropical Diseases. 23rd ed. London: Elsevier; 2014.
14. Bogitsh BJ, Carter CE, Oeltmann TN. Human Parasitology. 5th ed. London: Academic Press; 2018.
15. Garcia HH, Del Brutto OH. Neurocysticercosis. Lancet Neurology. 2005;4:653 to 661.
16. McManus DP, Gray DJ, Li Y, Feng Z, Williams GM. Schistosomiasis. Lancet. 2018;391:2393 to 2406.
17. White NJ, Pukrittayakamee S, Hien TT, Faiz MA, Mokuolu OA, Dondorp AM. Malaria. Lancet. 2014;383:723 to 735.

Further references were consulted from peer reviewed journals, WHO publications, and updated parasitology guidelines during preparation of this manuscript.
